Universal Design as a
Rehabilitation Strategy

Jon A. Sanford, MArch, is the Director of the Center for Assistive Technology and Environmental Access (CATEA) and an Associate Professor of Industrial Design in the College of Architecture at Georgia Tech, where he teaches courses on universal design and design for healthy aging. At CATEA, he is the Co-Director of the Rehabilitation Engineering Research Center on Workplace Accommodations, which is a 5-year grant supported by the National Institute on Disability and Rehabilitation Research (NIDRR). Mr. Sanford is also a research architect at the Rehabilitation Research and Development Center of Excellence at the Atlanta Veterans Affairs Medical Center.

Mr. Sanford is one of the few architecturally trained researchers engaged in accessible and universal design and has been well recognized for his expertise in home modifications, workplace accommodations, and design for aging for over 25 years. He is one of the authors of the *Principles of Universal Design,* and his research spans all scales of design from toilet and bathing facilities, to community barriers to mobility.

He has contributed over 250 articles, book chapters and professional presentations to the field, and he is a member of several editorial boards, including *Housing for the Elderly, Journal of Applied Gerontology, Australian Journal of Rehab Counseling,* and *Journal of Physical and Occupational Therapy in Geriatrics.* In addition, Mr. Sanford is an active member of several professional associations, including Gerontological Society of America (where he was the Chair of the Physical Environments and Aging Informal Interest Group from 2005 to 2008), American Society on Aging, where he was the Chair of the Network on Environments Services and Technologies from 2006 to 2009, and the Rehabilitation Engineering Society of North America.

Universal Design as a Rehabilitation Strategy

Design for the Ages

Jon A. Sanford, MArch

SPRINGER PUBLISHING COMPANY
NEW YORK

Springer Publishing Company, LLC
11 West 42nd Street
New York, NY 10036
www.springerpub.com

Acquisitions Editor: Sheri W. Sussman
Composition: The Manila Typesetting Company

ISBN: 978-0-8261-2552-1
E-book ISBN: 978-0-8261-2553-8

12 13 14 15/ 5 4 3 2 1

The author and the publisher of this Work have made every effort to use sources believed to be reliable to provide information that is accurate and compatible with the standards generally accepted at the time of publication. The author and publisher shall not be liable for any special, consequential, or exemplary damages resulting, in whole or in part, from the readers' use of, or reliance on, the information contained in this book. The publisher has no responsibility for the persistence or accuracy of URLs for external or third-party Internet Web sites referred to in this publication and does not guarantee that any content on such Web sites is, or will remain, accurate or appropriate.

Library of Congress Cataloging-in-Publication Data

Sanford, Jon A.
  Universal design as a rehabilitation strategy : design for ages / Jon A. Sanford.
     p. cm.
  Includes bibliographical references and index.
  ISBN 978-0-8261-2552-1
  1.   Universal design. 2.   Barrier-free design. 3.   Architecture and society.
4. Architecture–Human factors.   I. Title.
   TH4816.15.S26 2012
   720.1'08–dc23
                                                          2011050894

Printed in the United States of America by Bang Printing

This book is dedicated to Bettye Rose Connell, friend, colleague, and general pain in the ass without whom much of the content in this book would still be just random thoughts and who will forever be known as the first author of the Principles of Universal Design just because her last name happened to come alphabetically before the other nine of us.

Contents

PART III. BREAKING DOWN BARRIERS: ADOPTION OF UNIVERSAL DESIGN AS A REHABILITATION INTERVENTION   *265*

Preface

Much has been written about the use of environmental intervention as a rehabilitation strategy, including both assistive devices/technologies and accessible design. Similarly, much has been written about universal design, but rarely as a rehabilitation strategy. The reason is simple, universal design is typically viewed as incompatible with the fundamental goals of rehabilitation itself. Rehabilitation, by its very nature, is about the individual, specifically an individual with impaired function. As such, rehabilitation interventions such as assistive technologies and accessible designs are specialized designs that are tailored to the needs of individuals or groups of individuals with specific types of functional limitations. In contrast, universal design is not about specific individuals or about impaired function. It is not specialized, accessible design. Universal design is about design for all people with all types and levels of abilities. As Steinfeld (1994) pointed out, these differences are not simply semantic. Specialized design typically results in separate facilities for people with disabilities (e.g., "handicapped parking," "handicapped entrance," "handicapped bathroom"), whereas universal design provides one design solution that can accommodate people with disabilities and everyone else.

In fact, because impaired function is a universal human experience, universal design is about people with (dis)abilities. Although this approach is inclusive of those with and without rehabilitation needs, it promotes interventions that are not individualized and are useful in the absence of a health condition. As a result, it is, by its very nature, antithetical to traditional paradigms that guide not only current rehabilitation practice but also U.S. health care policy that drives reimbursement for that practice.

Why should universal design be considered as a rehabilitation strategy? The most basic reason is that rehabilitation professionals should use every possible tool available to improve the lives of their clients and people with disabilities in general. If universal design happens to help others along the way, then society as a whole will benefit as well. In addition, disability is rarely static. Not only are many limitations progressive but also, as people age, their abilities typically decline. Universal design accommodates change over time. It can enable people to continue to engage in activities and participate in society with as little disruption in their lives as possible. From a market standpoint, design for everyone makes good sense because it creates economies of scale that are considerably more cost-effective than niche-marketed specialized assistive technologies and accessible designs. This is not to say that universal design is a panacea that will forever obviate the need for specialized design. Rather, it creates a higher, more inclusive baseline from which rehabilitation can operate. As a result, it may eliminate the need for specialized design for some or reduce the need for others. In either case, it not only enhances function and participation but also facilitates rehabilitation practice and reduces health care costs.

This text is intended for rehabilitation, design, and building professionals. It is not a treatise on disability, a coffee-table book of best-practice universal design exemplars, or a how-to-book on the Americans with Disabilities Act Accessibility Guidelines (ADAAG) in disguise. It is a book about awareness and understanding of human function, physical form, and design functionality. For rehabilitation professionals who do not design for the general population, it is awareness about form and understanding of how to apply their knowledge of function to everyday design. For designers and builders who do not design for special populations, it is awareness about function and understanding of how to apply their knowledge of form to specialized design. For each, it is awareness of why the form of everyday design achieves neither function nor functionality for most users and understanding why universal design transcends traditional disciplinary design problem solving to produce form that achieves both.

Universal design is a term originally articulated by Ron Mace, an architect who had a disability, a leading advocate of legislation promoting accessible design, a designer of assistive devices, and the founding director of the Center for Universal Design at NC State University (originally the Center for Accessible Housing). Despite his staunch support for traditional rehabilitation strategies, Mace developed the concept of universal design to describe design of everyday physical form, including objects; controls, hardware, and other user interfaces; buildings; and public spaces that would overcome the stigma, segregation, and other social shortcomings of the specialized designs that characterized traditional rehabilitation practices. Universal design is intended to engender both positive activity and participation outcomes by focusing on all abilities of all individuals rather than on people with disabilities alone. As a result, universal design is not just about access for some, but it is about usability and inclusion for all.

Whereas these concepts may be conceptually appealing, this book recognizes that universal design is a utopian design theory that may not always be technically achievable. It imagines what a world should be, not necessarily what the world will be. As a result, the contribution of this text is in providing rehabilitation professionals with a new way of thinking about rehabilitation interventions rather than a cookbook of the interventions themselves.

This is not an easy task because adopting universal design as a viable rehabilitation strategy requires discarding current, yet outdated 20th century paradigms that favor activity- and function-based interventions over those that also promote participation and functionality. Despite the technical success of traditional specialized design strategies in increasing function for individuals, they have, on the one hand, created signalizing, stigmatizing, and segregating environments while, on the other, failed to live up to their expectation that being able to engage in activity would lead to societal integration of people with disabilities. Such experiments in the "activity-begets-participation" paradigm have demonstrated that even if we build it, not everyone will come. In contrast, universal design is rooted in a more integrative rehabilitation paradigm that makes function and functionality (i.e., usability and inclusivity) the design norm rather than the exception. By integrating specialized design into everyday design, universal design is not just hard to see, it is invisible.

This idea of intervention invisibility is clearly not an outcome with which rehabilitation practice is familiar. Therefore, to familiarize rehabilitation professionals with universal design, this text not only describes what universal is but also contrasts it with what it is not—disability-specific specialized designs with which rehabilitation professionals are very familiar. More specifically, it makes the case that specialized design, as embodied by the technical specifications in the ADAAG, defines a set of *prescriptive rules* of "what to do," whereas universal design, as articulated by a set of *performance guidelines* (i.e., *Principles of Universal Design*), defines "why it should be done." As such, specialized design is an application approach to improve function that requires little expert problem solving (i.e., anyone can do it), whereas universal design is a problem-solving approach that requires rehabilitation and design expertise to achieve both function and functionality.

When the reader reaches the end of this book, there should be no big "duh moment." There will be no silver bullet that will define what to do and for whom. In fact, it is just the opposite. This book is about how to think about rehabilitation problems in a broader more universal way. Then again, perhaps the big duh is why universal design is not a rehabilitation strategy already.

Acknowledgments

Most importantly, I want to thank Carolyn Kaplan for her patience with the process and with me, which caused her to not only endure many weekends alone when I was at my office writing but also withstand my curt, aggravated responses to her innocent inquiries about my daily progress.

I wish to acknowledge the other nine authors of the *Principles of Universal Design*, which have forever changed the way I view and think about the world around us and without which this book would not have been possible.

I also want to acknowledge the contributions of Carrie Bruce, who not only provided a sounding board over the years for many of the ideas expressed in the book but also had an uncanny knack of finding the most interesting examples of inaccessible accessible design wherever she went.

Finally, I want express my gratitude to the many colleagues who contributed photographs for the book and to my editor, Sheri W. Sussman, not just for sticking with me as deadlines and promises came and went, but, more importantly, for not killing me (it was not her style) when they did.

Prologue

FIVE MYTHS ABOUT UNIVERSAL DESIGN THAT HAS LIMITED ITS USE AS A REHABILITATION STRATEGY

Myth 1: *Universal design* **is just another term for assistive technology, accessible design, and design for aging.** Universal design is not a euphemism for either accessibility or assistive technology for people with disabilities or older adults. Although the origin of universal design comes from the disability rights movement and has been widely adopted by the aging community, universal is not about design solely for people who have *disabilities or limited abilities.* On the contrary, it is about design for people of *all abilities.*

Myth 2. *Universal design* **is just another term for the Americans with Disabilities Act–Architectural Barriers Act Accessibility guidelines/ standards.** Universal design is not about compliance with legal minimum legal guidelines and standards. It does not prescribe rules of what must be done or demand compliance with existing codes and standards. It is a performance-based approach that describes why and how to do it. In fact, there are times when universal design may not even meet the Americans with Disabilities Act–Architectural Barriers Act Accessibility (ADA-ABA) guidelines, but that is a problem of ADA myopia, not universal design.

Myth 3. Universal design is just about improving performance in daily activities. Universal design is about improving performance in daily activities. However, the inspiration for universal design is rooted in the ideas of social equity and inclusivity. Although facilitating engagement in activity can create opportunities for inclusion, activity performance by itself is not sufficient to guarantee it. As such, universal design equally addresses activity and inclusivity through participation in community and societal roles.

Myth 4. Universal design is ugly and institutional. Universal design is not a prescribed set of design features or attributes. It could, just like the design of any object, space, product, or system, be ugly. However, ugly is not intrinsic to universal design, just like it is not intrinsic to any other design. Aesthetics reside in the design, not the design process, although universal design, which integrates functionality from the beginning and throughout the design process, is more likely to be aesthetically pleasing than a design paradigm that does not. Neither is universal design institutional looking. Universal design is contextual, that is, the aesthetics are appropriate for the context regardless of the setting. In the end, universal design is invisible.

Myth 5. Universal design costs more. It could, and sometimes it does; but it does not have to. Higher cost is not inherent in universal design. Cost is an artifact of the free market system, and things that are of good design often command a greater price. Universal design is, simply, good design.

PART 1

FORM, FUNCTION, AND FUNCTIONALITY

*U*niversal design is the design of all products and environments to be usable by all people to the greatest extent possible without the need for adaptation or specialized design (Mace, Hardie, & Place, 1991). Unlike traditional rehabilitation strategies that use specialized assistive technologies and accessible designs to increase function (of individuals) by minimizing demands of physical form of everyday design on individuals with specific disabilities, universal design increases function and functionality (of design) by using physical form itself to minimize demands on individuals with all types and levels of abilities. As a result, the extent to which any physical form is universal is dependent on the degree to which its attributes minimize demands on the widest array of users (Sanford, 2010).

FORM

Physical *form* (n) is the design of an object. It is the outward appearance, proportions, shape, and structure of something as distinguished from its substance (American Heritage Dictionary, 1985). Physical form can be two- or three-dimensional, thus encompassing design at all scales from interfaces, products, and spaces to digital and graphical information. Its features and the attributes of those features make any form distinguishable from other forms.

A design *feature* (n) is any identifiable design element at any scale of design, from spaces and places (e.g., door, window, toilet, ramp, walkway, park, lake) to products, devices, and technologies to hardware and interfaces. Design features are merely categories of identifiable objects (i.e., they have a name). As such, they cannot be measured; they can only be described as being either present or absent. Environmental features can be described at three scales of design: spaces, products, and user interfaces (e.g., controls/hardware). Spaces include interior building spaces, such as rooms and corridors, and exterior spaces, such as playgrounds, parks, streets, pedestrian walks, or parking areas. Products are located in rooms or other spaces and include appliances, such as stoves, refrigerators, and microwave ovens; plumbing fixtures, such as toilets and sinks; vending and fare machines; and building elements, such as doors and windows. Controls and hardware interfaces are either operable or inoperable. Operable controls and hardware, such as handles, knobs, and locks on doors; levers and faucets on toilets or tubs; and electronic or mechanical controls on appliances or building elements are generally components of a product. In contrast, inoperable hardware, such as handrails and grab bars, are fixed and are generally installed as part of a space.

Although features are categorical, not all features of a specific type (e.g., ramp) look or act alike. They can be made of different material and have different shapes, sizes, configurations, and colors. Even standard ramps, which have specific requirements mandated by the ADAAG, do not all look alike. In fact, it is difficult to find two that do look alike (Figure I.1). What differentiates one feature from other features of a specific type are its design attributes.

FIGURE I.1

Just like the homes they are added on to, design features such as ramps can look completely different from each other.

A design *attribute* (adj.) is a measurable (i.e., quantifiable or describable) characteristic of a feature, such as height, length, width, color, texture, and condition that define the proportions, appearance, and other qualities (e.g., acoustic) of a feature (Figure I.2). Not only are attributes themselves variable, but they also vary by type of feature (see also Sanford & Bruce, 2010; Sanford & Jones, 2001; Stark & Sanford, 2005). For example, common attributes of spaces include configuration/layout (e.g., size of space/ subspaces, orientation of structures, and arrangement of key elements); entry (e.g., location, width, entryway height, threshold height); circulation routes/level changes (e.g., location of routine and emergency egress/ ingress, visibility, width, length, slope); orientation cues (e.g., location of signage, landmarks); location of products, devices, and technologies (e.g., clear floor space for approach and use, mounting height); location of environmental controls (e.g., mounting height and clear floor space at switches and outlets); ground/floor and wall materials/finishes (e.g., color, type, texture, reflectivity, slip resistance); and ambient conditions (e.g., light levels, temperature, shade, acoustic properties, and noise levels). In contrast, attributes of products, devices, and technologies include type, dimensions (e.g., height, shape, width), weight, location of user interfaces (mounting height and location, space between controls), and materials/finishes (type, texture, and color contrast).

Finally, user interfaces include a variety of controls and hardware. They can be either operable (e.g., doorknob or thermostat) or fixed (such as a drawer pull or grab bar). Generally, their purpose is to operate products, although occasionally inoperable hardware, such as grab bars, operates independently of a product or device. In addition, although many operable interfaces are located on products or devices, environmental controls,

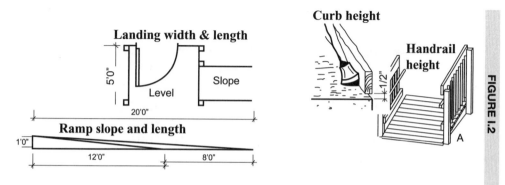

FIGURE I.2

Typical attributes that can be varied to make each ramp different.

whether wired or remote, including light switches, elevator call buttons, thermostats, and alarm systems, are typically located in the surrounding spatial environment rather than attached directly to the product. Specific attributes of user interfaces that affect performance include type of interface (dispenser, toilet handle, lock, assist, receptacle, and control); minimum approach distance and angle (space needed to use the device); size (diameter, length, and width); activation method (voice and grip required); operational characteristics (direction and distance interfaces need to be moved, calibration, type of sensory feedback, force required, and voice sensitivity); and materials/finish (type, texture, and color contrast).

FUNCTION AND FUNCTIONALITY

Function refers to the types of intrinsic human abilities, such as learning, ambulating, seeing, communicating, and hearing. *Functionality* is usability and inclusivity of physical form that enable engagement in activities/tasks and participation in society and societal roles. Functionality is a product of the interaction between demands exerted by physical form and human function. Features, being only categorical descriptions of the environment, do not exert demands directly on individuals. As such, they do not, in and of themselves, determine functionality of form.

Basic assumptions can be made about the functionality of form based on the inherent properties of a feature. For example, steps are vertical, whereas a ramp is inclined, disabling a wheelchair user from rolling up steps but enabling the same user to roll up a ramp. However, these assumptions may not always be true. The same individual with the same abilities may not be able to roll up every ramp even though all ramps, by definition, have the same property of inclination. Therefore, although properties of features have a propensity to exert a certain type of demand, their lack of variability from feature to feature suggests that their demand strength is constant.

Attributes, on the other hand, vary among features of the same type. As a result, they have different demand strengths. Demand strength interacts with abilities to determine functionality. A ramp, for example, can have different angles of inclination or slopes. Inclination is a property of the ramp; degree of inclination is an attribute. Therefore, a wheelchair user will not be able to roll up a ramp when the slope of the ramp exceeds his or her abilities.

To affect functionality, the relevant demand-producing attributes of any feature must be identified and the potential interactions between those attributes and human function must be clearly understood. For example, spatial attributes, such as the layout of a space, will influence way finding given a person's cognitive and visual abilities; configuration of rooms along corridors will affect an individual's ability to access spaces given their ability to ambulate and maneuver; light levels can determine if an individual can read a sign or see a door handle given his or her visual ability; and the height of a towel dispenser will affect whether a person can reach it given a person's stature and reaching ability. Similarly, product level attributes, such as the location of controls at the front or rear of an appliance given an individual's reach and stature, will affect operation, or the weight of a door interacting with strength will determine if an individual can open it. Finally, user interface attributes, such as the size and shape of a door handle given an individual's gripping ability, the color of a digital display given and the individual's acuity and contrast sensitivity, or the audibility of a doorbell given one's hearing ability, all impact usability.

The magnitude of demand-producing attributes interacting with the level of an individual's ability determine the influence that the environment has on functionality (i.e., demand strength). The goal of universal design is to minimize demand strength across all levels of ability.

ONE

The Functionality of Form:
The Link Between Design and Rehabilitation

*A*lthough the physical environment has long been associated with individual functioning and disability (Iwarsson, 2004, 2005; Rubenstein, 1999; Scheidt & Windley, 2006; Wahl, 2001), there has been a disconnect between rehabilitation practice, on the one hand, and rehabilitation theory, on the other. Practice has been driven by federal health care policies in which disability is the result of an impairment or medical condition intrinsic in the individual, whereas theory has consistently espoused social models in which disability is a result of intrinsic and extrinsic contextual factors. As a result, rehabilitation practice has focused on fixing the individual, whereas theory suggests that fixing both the person and the environment are equally important strategies.

Traditional medical models do not differentiate pathology from disability, attributing disability primarily to intrinsic health conditions that resulted in deficits in the individual. As a result, any impairment of a given severity is sufficient to result in disability (Brandt & Pope, 1997). In 1980, this paradigm was clearly articulated by the World Health Organization in its *International Classification of Impairment Disability and Health* as "any restriction or inability resulting from a disturbance or loss of bodily or mental function associated with disease, disorder, injury, or trauma or other health-related state" (WHO, 1980, p. 143).

Toward the end of the 20th century, however, the emergence of social construction models represented a paradigm shift that moved the focus of disability from the individual to the society. Embracing Nagi's (1965, 1976) earlier work that defined *disability* as the outcome of an interaction between impairment and environmental factors, social construction models associated restrictions in activity and participation with a societal-imposed human disadvantage (Samaha, 2007). As a result, disability is an outcome of the interaction of intrinsic and extrinsic factors.

SOCIAL CONSTRUCTION MODELS

A key tenet of social construction models is that disability is situational—the result of complex interactions between an individual's abilities (as opposed to limitations) and the demands of the physical, social, economic, and political environments. More specifically, physiological factors set the threshold on ability, whereas environmental factors set the threshold on when limitations in ability become a disability (Stineman, Ross, Masilin, & Gray, 2007). As a result, engagement in activity is expressed as the fit or misfit between an individual's abilities and the design of relevant environmental attributes. Design that fits an individual (i.e., low demands) will facilitate engagement in activities when, where, and with whom he or she desires. In contrast, an environment that does not fit an individual (i.e., high demands) will result in low levels of functionality that may make it difficult or even prevent an individual from engaging in an activity altogether.

Social construction models represent a critical shift in attitudes and approaches to disability that have wide-ranging implications for rehabilitation practice. In moving away from intrinsic causes of disability to include extrinsic influences, social models suggest that rehabilitation is both individual and societal. Although rehabilitation strategies can often promote function regardless of form at the individual level, at the unit (e.g., family/home, work/workplace) or societal level, where others are exposed to individualized rehabilitation interventions, the fit between form and function for everyone in the unit is essential. Universal design is a rehabilitation strategy that promotes that fit.

Over the past three decades, a number of ecological–social construction models have been proposed. Although the models differ slightly on the relationship among medical conditions, impairments, functional limitations, and effects of the interaction of the person with the environment (Brandt & Pope, 1997), the relationship between the person and the environment is always dynamic, complex, and interdependent (Rigby & Letts, 2003). Among the various models, four models of person–environment (P-E) interaction contribute to a fundamental understanding of the link between design and rehabilitation that is relevant to universal design as a rehabilitation strategy. These include the environmental press model, person–environment–occupation model (PEO), enabling–disabling process model, and the *International Classification of Functioning, Disability, and Health (ICF)*. The first three are rehabilitation models, albeit from different rehabilitation disciplines (psychology, occupational therapy, and rehabilitation engineering, respectively); the latter is a public health paradigm that encompasses rehabilitation.

Environmental Press Model. The environmental press model (Lawton & Nahemow, 1973) provides the first rehabilitation conceptualization of the P-E fit. It is based on Lewin's field theory, a psychological model that described behavior as the outcome of a transactional relationship between an individual and the environment (Lewin, 1951). Building on Lewin's work, the model describes an individual's behavior as the outcome of a transactional relationship between an individual's competence (e.g., cognitive, social, and behavioral skills and abilities) and the level of demands posed by the environment, referred to as press. As a result, functionality of design and therefore engagement in activity is an expression of the fit or *mis*fit between an individual and his or her environment.

Because the environmental press model has its origins in gerontological psychology, much of the language used is behavioral rehabilitation rather than physical rehabilitation. Nonetheless, the concepts (Figure 1.1) are equally applicable to rehabilitation in general. The level of an individual's competencies is conceptually represented on the vertical axis, and the strength of environmental demands is represented on the horizontal axis. The outcome of a transaction is depicted on the graph at the intersection of an individual's skill level and demand strength.

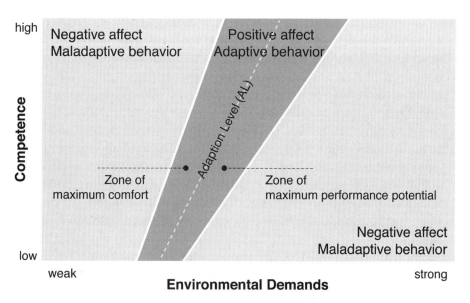

FIGURE 1.1

Environmental press model (Adapted from Lawton & Nahemow, 1973)

As indicated by the zone of maximum comfort to maximum performance, optimal P-E fit occurs when an individual's abilities and the environmental demands are compatible. In other words, when the strength of the demand is commensurate with one's ability, the environment acts as a facilitator of function, and hence, the form has functionality. Conversely, when the strength of demands either exceeds (i.e., the environment is too challenging) or falls short of ability (i.e., environment is not challenging enough), form is not functional, and there is a P-E misfit. Therefore, as an individual moves farther to the right or to the left of his or her baseline adaptation level, negative behavioral outcomes occur, defined by either negative affect (i.e., emotion) or maladaptive behavior.

The environmental press model has generated several hypotheses that are relevant to understanding the impact of the environment on people with reduced abilities. First, following the transactional nature of disability, Lawton and Nahemow (1973) postulated that *excess disability*, defined by an individual's level of dependency, will be greater than expected given the level of impairment alone. Second, the environmental docility hypothesis (Lawton, 1990; Lawton & Simon, 1968) suggests that the demand strength (i.e., the amount of influence that the environment has on functionality) is a result of the interaction between the physical form and an individual's ability. In other words, although all physical form has demand-producing potential, actual demands are only exerted when the environment comes into contact with human ability. Further, the strength of actual demands will be greater on individuals with less ability than individuals with greater levels of ability. As a result, individuals with less ability will be more challenged by the same environmental demands than individuals with greater levels of ability.

The environmental press model has played a major role not only in geriatric rehabilitation but also in establishing a theoretical basis for using design intervention as a rehabilitation strategy. However, the model only conceptualizes the relationship between design and rehabilitation. It does not provide a basis for measuring either an individual's competence level or the demands of a particular physical form. As a result, the model only provides a rationale for design as a rehabilitation intervention; it does not provide a mechanism that will translate that knowledge into rehabilitation practice.

Person–Environment–Occupation Model. The relationship between person and environment has been an important component of occupational therapy practice for some time. Nonetheless, in the decade between the publication of the *Americans with Disabilities Act Accessibility Guidelines* in 1991 and the ICF in 2001 (discussed later in this chapter), a number of occupational therapy-specific models emerged (Letts, Rigby, & Stewart, 2003) that shared common elements of person, environment, and occupation factors, although how these factors were defined and interacted varied considerably. These models include the following: the ecology of human performance model (Dunn, Brown, & McGuigan, 1994), the model of human occupation (Kielhofner, 1995), the PEO (Law et al., 1996), the Canadian model of occupational performance (Canadian Association of Occupational Therapists, 1997), the person–environment–occupation–performance model (Christianson & Baum, 1997), the competent occupational performance in the environment (Hagedorn, 2000), and the occupational adaptation model (Schkade & McClung, 2001).

Among these models, the PEO is most relevant as an adaptation of the environmental press model for the field of occupational therapy (Law et al., 1996). As an adaptation, the PEO model tends to be more of an elucidation of assumptions made by and about the environmental press model than a unique model itself. Nonetheless, because there were two key changes that added an activity and function rehabilitation emphasis to the existing model, the PEO model (Figure 1.2) warrants discussion.

First, whereas Lawton's model focused on behavior and affect as outcomes of P-E transactions, the PEO model specifically articulates occupational performance as an outcome of person–environment interactions. This adaptation clearly makes the model more function friendly, although the focus on behavior in the original model is an artifact of its psychology origins and is, as discussed above, conceptually generalizable to other rehabilitation outcomes. Second, whereas the environmental press model does not

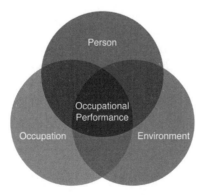

FIGURE 1.2

Person–environment–occupation model (Adapted from Law et al., 1996)

specifically identify engagement in activity as a component of P-E transactions, such interaction is implicit, as it is clear that the environment does not exert demands in the absence of activity. Nonetheless, the PEO model makes that relationship explicit by defining occupational performance as the outcome of transactions among person, occupation, and environment within which the occupations are performed. Further, in the PEO model, occupations are viewed as self-directed tasks and activities in which the person engages to meet intrinsic needs for self-maintenance, expression, and fulfillment, within a variety of roles throughout the life span (Rigby & Letts, 2003). Thus, the model suggests, although never explicitly states, that occupations, like the environment, also exert demands on the individual.

Enabling–Disabling Process Model. In 1997, the Institute of Medicine (IOM), complying with a request from Congress, convened a panel to assess the state of rehabilitation science, engineering, and practice. Among the tasks was an evaluation of existing rehabilitation models. Based on their analysis, the committee proposed the enabling–disabling process model (Brandt & Pope, 1997), which clearly identified the environment as a pathway for rehabilitation intervention. Unlike the earlier IOM and other models, the enabling–disabling process model defined both a pathway to disability as well as a pathway to restore function. The model (Figure 1.3) suggests that due to increasing needs relative to the environment, the *disabling process* is the dislocation of an individual from his or her prior

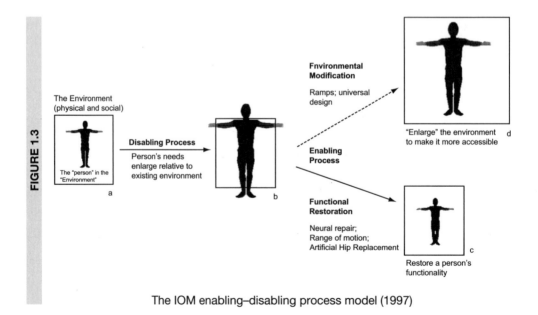

FIGURE 1.3

The Environment
(physical and social)

The "person" in the "Environment"

a

Disabling Process

Person's needs
enlarge relative to
existing environment

b

**Fnvironmental
Modification**

Ramps; universal
design

"Enlarge" the environment   d
to make it more accessible

**Enabling
Process**

**Functional
Restoration**

Neural repair;
Range of motion;
Artificial Hip Replacement

c

Restore a person's
functionality

The IOM enabling–disabling process model (1997)

integration in the environment. In contrast, the *enabling process* is either the restoration of the individual's function or environmental modification to remove barriers to improve design functionality.

Although the model explicitly identifies these two potential pathways to rehabilitation, it offers little insight into how to identify or measure the environmental demands that account for the misfit among form, function, and functionality. Unlike the environmental press model, which suggests that P-E misfit is the result of the interaction between measurable competencies and potentially measurable demands, only the person side (i.e., impairment) of the P-E misfit equation is measurable in the enabling–disabling process model. The environment, on the hand, is a black box, with no acknowledgment that there are specific measurable factors that contribute to the misfit. As a result, the model provides no explicit guidance for using design as a rehabilitation strategy.

International Classification of Functioning, Disability, and Health. Two decades after the WHO (1980) published its *International Classification of Impairment Disability and Health* medical model, it developed a new model based on a more robust social construction paradigm. Although a health-based model, the revised ICF described human function and disability as important components of health (WHO, 2001). The new framework (Figure 1.4) not only defines disability as the interaction of body function and structure with contextual (i.e., environmental and personal)

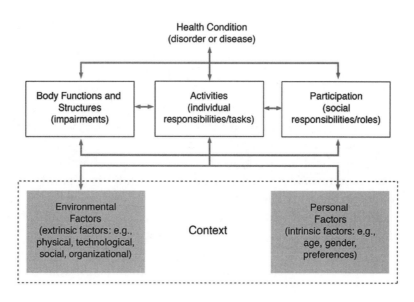

ICF Model (Adapted from WHO, 2001)

FIGURE 1.4

factors but also extends that interaction to include health, as well as activity and participation outcomes. Specifically, the ICF attributes differences between what individuals can do (capacity to engage in activities and participation based on body function and structure) and what they actually do (performance of activities) to the influence of personal and environmental (both social and physical) factors. As a result, the environment is viewed as either a barrier or a facilitator to activities and participation in social roles.

In addition, the ICF not only includes but also distinguishes between activity and participation as equally important rehabilitation goals. *Activity*, defined as "the execution of specific tasks or actions by an individual," is clearly in the domain of the individual without the connection to others. In contrast, participation, which is "involvement in a life situation" lies in the social context, including involvement in valued occupations (e.g., employment), social roles, social relationships, independence/interdependence, and assimilation (i.e., sense of inclusion; Dijkers, 2006; Rochette, Korner-Bitensky, & Levasseur, 2006; Winkler, Unsworth, & Sloan, 2006).

Although the ICF has a theoretical framework, its primary purpose is to serve as a classification system. As a result, it includes several components. First, it considers changes in functional states associated with health conditions and the body (i.e., body function and structure), including anatomical and physiological functions of the human body. Second, it outlines the range of activities performed by an individual and describes areas of life in which an individual participates. Finally, unlike the other models, the ICF provides a fairly complete taxonomy of environmental features at all scales of design, organized in sequence from the individual's most immediate environment to the general environment. The classification system not only associates environmental factors with positive or negative outcomes but also provides a mechanism for measuring the level of P-E fit/misfit by rating the strength of a particular factor as a facilitator (from 0 to positive 4) or a barrier (from 0 to negative 4).

The ICF, as a health model, in contrast to basic rehabilitation models that are based on impairment and associated limitations in ability, assumes a continuum of degrees of ability in all people. By assuming that individuals have differential abilities to begin with, the ICF recognizes that a health condition does not have to be a prerequisite for functional deficits and design intervention. Moreover, the environmental classification index is the most comprehensive description of environmental factors that contribute to activity and participation deficits, and it represents the first attempt to identify and measure salient environmental factors that contribute to the P-E misfit.

Unfortunately, the ICF reflects little understanding of the interaction between form, function, and functionality that would enable design to be useful in rehabilitation practice. First, it lacks an understanding of the environment that would provide a taxonomic structure that is familiar to designers and engineers (e.g., features are organized by products and technology and natural and human-made changes to the environment). Second, the taxonomy is primarily based on design features rather than the demand-producing attributes that are necessary to identify specific P-E misfits and subsequently appropriate design interventions.

Interestingly, the environment classification system is the only ICF construct, including body structure/function and personal contextual factors that is defined by features rather than by demand-producing attributes. For example, personal factors are characterized by a variety of individual attributes, such as age, gender, education, coping style, and social background. However, the taxonomy's focus on environmental features (e.g., a ramp), even though other constructs clearly focus on specific attributes, limits measurement of environmental factors to that of categorical descriptions of what exists (e.g., a ramp that is provided or not provided) rather than measurable demand-producing attributes (i.e., a ramp has a 1:12 slope). Without a framework for quantifying environmental demands, the ICF, like other models, lacks a mechanism to implement environmental intervention as a rehabilitation strategy.

THEORETICAL IMPLICATIONS FOR UNIVERSAL DESIGN AS A REHABILITATION STRATEGY

Although social models of disability have facilitated a shift from focusing on individual deficits to examining the interaction between design and rehabilitation practices, they are not a panacea. In particular, social models have a tendency to ignore how impairment in and of itself has the potential to debilitate regardless of the environmental and social conditions (Shakespeare & Watson, 2001).

In addition, although all models are based on press mediating between what an individual can and cannot do, none account for the range of contextual factors that place demands on the individual and contribute to differences between capacity and actual performance. Implicit in the environmental press model are the physical and social environments. The PEO model goes one step further and includes occupation as exerting demands. Nonetheless, a number of other factors lie outside of, yet interact with, the ability to create press (Bruce & Sanford, 2009), including physical environmental factors, social environmental factors (e.g., attitudes of others), individual factors (e.g., preferences, cultural or spiritual beliefs, values, financial limitations), organizational factors (e.g., policies, employer support), external factors (e.g., legal restrictions, cost, and availability of assistive technologies), and occupational/task factors (e.g., lifting, pulling, and bending). Whereas the demands exerted by physical environmental factors are clearly of greatest concern for universal design, the demands placed by all of the factors are themselves transactional, interacting with the physical environmental to determine overall demand. As such, these interactions are important in understanding the impact of design on functionality and, more specifically, in determining what is universal within any context.

Finally, from a design perspective, all of the models fail to provide a mechanism to quantify environmental demands that impact functionality. Even the ICF, which quantifies the overall strength of demands exerted by environmental features, does not specifically quantify the demands themselves. As a result, none of the existing ecological models provide a framework that enables us to specify which environmental attributes create demands during the performance of specific activities. If we want to identify environmental attributes that create demands during the performance of specific activities, we need a framework that links attributes to ability. The next chapter will begin to lay out that framework.

TWO

The Fiasco of Form: Disabling Design

Social construction ecological models suggest a framework that links disability to the interaction of form and ability. However, the models are noticeably conceptual, offering no definitions or measures of either ability or disability that can be used to determine the extent to which any design is enabling or disabling. An early attempt to define and associate ability/disability was the Enabler (Figure 2.1) model proposed by Steinfeld et al. (1979) as part of the development of the 1980 American National Standards Institute A117.1 Accessibility Standards. The Enabler attempts to address the interaction between environment and disability by assessing the strength of relevant environmental demands on specific impairments (e.g., loss of sight, loss of hearing), functional limitations (e.g., difficulty reaching, difficulty bending), and mobility aids (e.g., reliance on wheelchair or walking aid).

Unlike the Enabler, which uses three nonmutually exclusive methods of defining disability, other sources tend to focus on one of the three approaches. Although conventional definitions of disability are of less interest to universal design than delineating the types and levels of ability, a discussion of disability is nonetheless crucial to understanding the driving forces behind specialized assistive technologies/accessible designs and universal design. Ultimately, functionality is defined by the interaction between form (design) and function (ability). As a result, understanding the continuum from ability and disability is critical for appreciating the impact of form on function, beginning with the disabling nature of everyday design to the enabling nature of specialized and universal designs.

DISABILITY, ABILITY, AND (DIS)ABILITY
Disability

Most disability-related legislation uses definitions of disability that are rooted in medical model notions of impairment and chronic conditions.

19

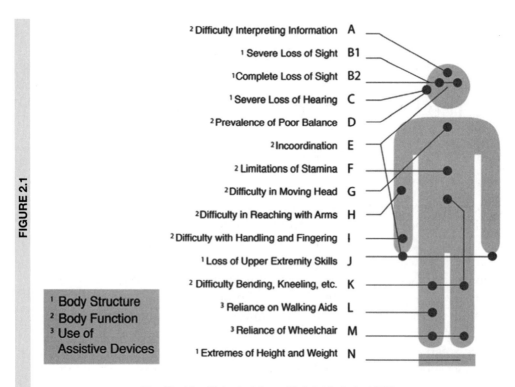

FIGURE 2.1

[2] Difficulty Interpreting Information	A
[1] Severe Loss of Sight	B1
[1] Complete Loss of Sight	B2
[1] Severe Loss of Hearing	C
[2] Prevalence of Poor Balance	D
[2] Incoordination	E
[2] Limitations of Stamina	F
[2] Difficulty in Moving Head	G
[2] Difficulty in Reaching with Arms	H
[2] Difficulty with Handling and Fingering	I
[1] Loss of Upper Extremity Skills	J
[2] Difficulty Bending, Kneeling, etc.	K
[3] Reliance on Walking Aids	L
[3] Reliance of Wheelchair	M
[1] Extremes of Height and Weight	N

[1] Body Structure
[2] Body Function
[3] Use of Assistive Devices

The Enabler (Adapted from Steinfeld et al., 1979).

Even the Americans with Disabilities Act, a pseudosocial construction model that incorporates removal of environmental barriers that restrict activity, defines disability in terms of a physical or mental impairment that substantially limits one or more major life activities (ADA, 1990). This is not surprising, for in the regulatory arena, it is clearly more expedient to include someone with an identifiable impairment than someone who is limited by a nebulous transaction between the person and the environment. Although definitions that are based on medical models are the narrowest conceptualizations of disability, clearly social model definitions open the door for almost anyone to experience disability given sufficiently high levels of environmental barriers.

Despite the narrow definition adopted by the disability legislation, definitions adopted by various public health agencies (including the U.S. Census Bureau) are somewhat broader because they are based on actual ability and activity, rather than impairment alone. The broadest definition of disability is the concept of activity limitation. The National Center for Health Statistics, which is part of the Centers for Disease Control, defines activity limitation as any long-term reduction in activity resulting from chronic disease or impairment. In other words, activity limitations describe what activities an individual actually does/does not do or has difficulty doing, not necessarily what activities the individual is able to do. Activity limitations are a key component of the National Health Interview Survey (NHIS) conducted annually by the National Center for Health Statistics. In the NHIS, activity limitations are defined by difficulty engaging in a range of activities (e.g., reading, watching TV, sewing, listening to music, visiting friends, attending clubs and meetings, going to parties, shopping, watching movies, or going to sporting events) by oneself and without using any special equipment because of a health problem (i.e., any physical, mental, or emotional problem or illness). Activity limitations are also included in the Survey of Income and Program Participation (SIPP), which is conducted by the U.S. Census Bureau. In contrast to the NHIS, the SIPP includes a more limited battery of questions that includes standard activities of daily living (ADLs), such as dressing, walking, eating, and bathing, and instrumental activities of daily living (IADLs), such as preparing meals, doing light housework, and managing medication.

Functional limitation, which is somewhat narrower in scope than activity limitation, is a second way of conceptualizing disability. The SIPP measures functional limitation by reductions in an individual's capacity (i.e., ability) to perform a range of sensory and physical tasks under standardized conditions. Therefore, unlike activity limitation, functional limitation is a measure of what body functions an individual is capable of doing irrespective of environment, rather than what he or she actually does. For example, the SIPP is composed of questions that assess difficulty with a number of abilities including the following: seeing the words and letters in ordinary newspaper print even when wearing glasses or contact lenses; hearing what is said in a normal conversation with another person even when wearing a hearing aid; lifting and carrying something as heavy as 10 pounds, such as a bag of groceries; sitting for 1 hour; stooping, crouching, and kneeling; walking up a flight of 10 stairs. Although the NHIS also includes capacity reduction questions, they are more limited than the SIPP, and they are mistakenly included as activity rather than functional limitations.

A third and still more focused mechanism for defining disability is dependence on equipment or others to overcome activity limitations. One source of prevalence of assistance use is derived from the National Long Term Care Survey (NLTCS) funded by National Institute on Aging. Like the SIPP, the NLTCS is focused on what an individual can do in terms of ADLs and IADLs, but unlike the SIPP, it defines disability in terms of use of help, use of disability-related of equipment, or reported need for help with ADLs and IADLs.

Among the four definitions of disability, activity limitation and dependence come closest to applying the person–environment (P-E) fit paradigms set out in the ecological models. Both measure what activities one does or does not do, but do so in the absence of knowing what one is capable of doing or even if the limitation is the result of a health condition (i.e., impairment of body structure or function) that might cause the activity limitation. Moreover, the environment is not explicitly addressed in the definition, although contextual bias is implicit in defining activity outcomes. Of the two definitions, dependence is perhaps conceptually closer to measuring disability as it assumes that a given activity would not be possible without assistance. Nonetheless, this may tend to overestimate disability, as it fails to account for devices, such as eyeglasses or hearing aids, that might eliminate activity limitation altogether. On the other hand, activity limitation may be too broad, as it may include individuals who have activity limitations solely due to environmental demands in the absence of impairment or functional limitation.

In contrast, only the functional limitation approach directly addresses actual reduction in levels of abilities. Unfortunately, functional limitation may also overestimate disability. First, it may or may not result from a health condition. Second, it may include people who have reductions in abilities that are sufficiently large to affect function, but are not sufficient to result in disability when they interact with the environment. As such, functional limitation may be a better measure of (dis)ability than it is of disability.

Finally, the impairment-based definition does not explicitly measure any construct related to ability or disability. Rather, it operationally defines disability based on a health condition. Specifically, it presumes that a change in body structure resulting from impairment is a precursor to loss of ability. However, the same impairment does not always result in disability, nor is it even associated with the same types and levels of ability/(dis)ability in different individuals.

Separately, the four definitions each represent a piece of the disability puzzle. Together, they present a series of events that can potentially result in either (dis)ability (functional limitation) or disability (activity limitation) given the context in which activity occurs (Figure 2.2). For example, pupil constriction, which is associated with aging, is a change in body structure in which a decrease in pupil size causes one third as much light to reach the photoreceptor cells in the retina compared with a 20-year-old. The change in body function decreases ability to use peripheral vision and requires a longer adjustment period when moving between different lighting levels. Thus, an individual can be temporarily blinded when

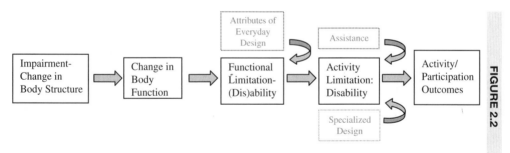

The relationship between impairment, functional limitation, activity limitation, and the effects of design and traditional rehabilitation interventions.

moving from a well-lit room to one that is poorly lit. Similarly, arthritis is an age-related degenerative joint inflammation condition that causes pain, stiffness, and damage to joint cartilage and surrounding structures. The damage can lead to joint weakness, instability, loss of tactile sensation, and limited joint movement. These functional changes can cause corresponding limitations in reaching, changing positions, ambulating, lifting, carrying, pushing, pulling, gripping, pinching, turning, fingering, and pressing. The interaction of these functional limitations with a physical form, such as a drawer handle, a doorknob, a jar, or a lamp switch, will result in activity limitations if the demands produced by their attributes exceed *functional* abilities.

Ability and (Dis)Ability

Whereas impairment, activity limitation, functional limitation, and dependence may inform specialized design, information about disability (at whatever threshold it is defined) is only one portion of the information required to inform universal design. Universal design, in contrast to specialized design, requires an understanding about the entire range of ability (i.e., function) from no ability to full ability.

Ability is the quality of being able to do something. It includes capacity, competence, talent, skill, and aptitude. Therefore, regardless of the terminology used (e.g., competence, capacity), each of the ecological models reference human ability as the interactive agent with the environment as if ability is a single attribute. However, human ability is not a single quality. Human abilities can be distinguished by both type and magnitude.

Types of Ability. As depicted in the Enabler (Steinfeld et al., 1979), types of abilities encompass the entire individual from head to toe, covering domains of motor function, mental function, sensation and perception, and communication. Although several taxonomies of functional ability have been developed, none were specific to P-E interactions. To create a taxonomy that was useful for understanding the relationship between form and function, two robust taxonomies developed for occupational assessment (Department of Labor, 1991; Gaudin, Matheson, & Mael, 2001) were adapted. In doing so, some abilities that were not environmentally relevant were omitted, whereas others were combined to reflect relevant P-E interactions. The result was a taxonomy (Figure 2.3 and Table 2.1) that includes four domains of ability: motor, mental, sensation and perception, and communication. Within each domain, there are numerous types of abilities. For example, within the domain of motor abilities, types of abilities include moving the head, maintaining posture, and changing position. Similarly, each type of ability is composed of a number of function-specific abilities. For example, moving the body includes specific abilities of moving the head and the neck, moving the upper extremity, moving the hand, and moving the lower extremities.

Levels of (Dis)Ability. In the absence of an identifiable threshold at which ability becomes disability, the range of abilities is better conceived of as a continuum from "no ability" to "maximum ability" (Figure 2.4). Moreover, given the variability in ability among individuals without impairments in body structure as well as among those with impairments, that continuum might be more appropriately characterized as a continuum of abilities/(dis)abilities than one of simply abilities.

Whereas the level of no ability is easily understood, *maximum ability* is a relative term. Many individuals have full, unimpaired ability, although they can have different levels of that ability (e.g., ability to reach 30 in. over head vs. ability to reach 33 in. over head). As a result, maximum ability must be defined by human anthropometry as a threshold of human potential. It represents an ideal that few, if any individuals, actually attain. As such, an individual can have full ability, yet fall somewhere below maximum ability on the continuum. This suggests that regardless of etiology (e.g., a short arm with 30-in. reach or a long arm with an impairment that causes a 30-in. reach), individuals with and without impairments may fall at similar points along the continuum.

Level of ability also varies across types of abilities both within and across individuals. Although deficits in some abilities are often associated with deficits in others (e.g., older adults typically have lower levels of several motor abilities as well as seeing and hearing abilities), for all

MOTOR ABILITIES

Moving Body Parts	Maintaining Posture	Changing Position	Moving Body in Space	Manipulating Objects	Coordinating Movements		
Moving muscles and joints to complete tasks	Initiating & sustaining body positions to perform tasks	Transitioning from lying, standing or sitting positions to other positions	Moving oneself across space	Reaching, lifting, handling and transporting objects	Performing movements in a purposeful, orderly combination		
❑ Head & Neck Movement ❑ Upper Extremity ❑ Hand ❑ Lower Extremity ❑ Trunk	❑ Balancing ❑ Standing ❑ Sitting	❑ Whole Body Positioning ❑ Lying ❑ Sit to Stand ❑ Whole Body Transfer	❑ Ambulation ❑ Device-aided Mobility ❑ Climbing ❑ Crawling	❑ Reaching ❑ Grasping ❑ Lifting/ Lowering ❑ Pushing/ Pulling ❑ Carrying ❑ Releasing ❑ Turning	❑ Hand Coordination ❑ Eye-Hand-Foot Coordination ❑ Lower Body Coordination ❑ Upper Body Coordination ❑ Foot-Hand Coordination		

MENTAL ABILITIES

Perceiving Space	Attending to Task	Understanding and Interpreting Numbers	Remembering	Learning	Reasoning	Executive Functioning	Reacting to Stimuli
Identifying oneself in relation to location and time	Initiating and sustaining focus on tasks	Understanding & applying numerical concepts	Using memory to complete tasks	Understanding instructions, reasoning and making judgments	Developing concepts & processing abstract information	Engaging in complex goal directed behaviors to complete tasks	Ability to react quickly to stimuli
❑ Orientation ❑ Way finding ❑ Spatial Relations	❑ Selective Attention ❑ Sustained Concentration ❑ Divided Attention	❑ Numeracy ❑ Telling Time ❑ Calculation ❑ Mathematical Reasoning	❑ Short-term Memory ❑ Long-term Memory ❑ Prospective Memory ❑ Procedural Memory	❑ Learning	❑ Abstract ❑ Logical ❑ Sequencing	❑ Organization and Planning ❑ Time Management ❑ Cognitive Flexibility ❑ Insight ❑ Judgment ❑ Problem Solving	❑ Auditory Speed ❑ Visual Speed ❑ Haptic Speed ❑ Olfactory Speed ❑ Multi-modal Speed

SENSATION AND PERCEPTION ABILITIES / COMMUNICATION ABILITIES

Seeing	Hearing	Sensing Odors and Flavors	Sensing and Feeling by Touch	Producing Communication	Receiving Communication	Conversing	Interpersonal Skills
Sensing the presence of light and form, size, shape and color of visual stimuli	Sensing presence of and discriminating location, pitch, loudness and quality of sounds	Sensing the presence of and discriminating differences in odors/flavors	Feeling and sensing variations in touch and texture	Expressing meaningful messages using forms of language	Decoding messages in different forms of language to obtain their meaning	Engaging in a purposeful exchange of language with one or more people	Interacting with people in a contextually and socially appropriate manner
❑ Near Vision ❑ Far Vision ❑ Central Visual Acuity ❑ Visual Field ❑ Color Discrimination ❑ Visual Accommodation ❑ Light Sensitivity ❑ Visual Scanning	❑ Noise Sensitivity ❑ Localization of Sound ❑ Sound Detection ❑ Speech Discrimination ❑ Auditory Discrimination	❑ Smell ❑ Taste ❑ Odor Sensitivity ❑ Flavor Sensitivity	❑ Cutaneous Discrimination ❑ Material Sensitivity ❑ Environment Sensitivity	❑ Speaking ❑ Writing ❑ Signing ❑ Gesturing ❑ Drawing	❑ Reading ❑ Listening ❑ Understanding Sign ❑ Understanding Gestures ❑ Understanding Drawing	❑ Conversing ❑ Discussing	❑ Social Cueing ❑ Regulating Emotion

FIGURE 2.3

Taxonomy of types of abilities.

TABLE 2.1
Description of Abilities

MOTOR ABILITIES

Moving body: moving muscles and joints to complete tasks
    Moving head and neck: ability to move head and neck to complete tasks
    Moving upper extremity: ability to move arm and forearm to complete tasks
    Moving hand: ability to move hand and fingers to complete tasks
    Moving lower extremity: ability to move leg and foot to complete tasks
    Moving trunk: ability to move waist and trunk to complete tasks

Maintaining posture: initiating and sustaining body positions to perform tasks
    Balancing: ability to maintain equilibrium while body is in motion or at rest
    Standing: ability to perform tasks in a standing position
    Sitting: ability to perform tasks in a sitting position

Changing position: transitioning from lying, standing, or sitting positions to other positions
    Positioning whole body: ability to stoop, crouch, kneel, or otherwise position the body to
      perform tasks beyond arm's reach
    Lying: ability to lie down and get up from a lying position to perform tasks
    Sitting to standing: ability to sit down and stand up to perform tasks
    Transferring whole body: ability to move from one surface to another without standing or
      walking

Moving around: moving oneself across space
    Ambulating: ability to move oneself across space by walking
    Wheeling: ability to move one's body across space using a wheeled mobility aid
    Climbing: ability to walk up or down stairs or ladders
    Crawling: ability to move on hands and knees

Manipulating objects: reaching, lifting, handling, and transporting objects
    Reaching: ability to stretch arms and trunk in a coordinated manner to grasp or manipulate
      objects
    Grasping: ability to seize, hold, objects with hands or fingers
    Lifting and lowering: ability to lift and lower objects
    Pushing and pulling: ability to push and pull objects
    Carrying objects: ability to hold objects while moving
    Releasing: ability to let go of objects with hands or fingers
    Turning: ability to turn or twist objects with hands or fingers

Coordinating movements: performing movements in a purposeful, orderly combination
    Coordinating hand movements: ability to use the hands in a coordinated manner
    Coordinating eye–hand–foot movements: ability to coordinate fine movements using visual
      information
    Coordinating lower body movements: ability to use the lower extremities in a coordinated
      manner
    Coordinating upper body movements: ability to use the upper extremities in a coordinated
      manner
    Coordinating foot–hand movements: ability to move the feet in coordination with hands

(continued)

TABLE 2.1
Description of Abilities (*continued*)

MENTAL ABILITIES

Orienting: knowing or ascertaining ones relation to self, to others, to time, and to one's surroundings
  Orienting to place: awareness of one's location
  Orienting to time: awareness of day, date, month, and year
  Orienting to person: awareness of one's identity and the identity of individuals in the immediate environment

Perceiving space: identifying oneself in relation to location and time
  Wayfinding: ability to find one's way
  Perceiving spatial relationships: ability to understand and manipulate the physical relationship between both static and dynamic objects in an environment including one's body

Attending to task: initiating and sustaining focus on tasks
  Using selective attention: ability to suppress external distraction while focusing on relevant tasks
  Using sustained concentration: ability to mentally focus on a task for an extended period
  Using divided attention: ability to focus attention on several stimuli at the same time

Understanding and interpreting numbers: understanding and applying numerical concepts
  Using numbers (numeracy): ability to demonstrate a basic understanding of numbers and their application such as numbering system in a building or facility
  Telling time: ability to accurately determine the time of day
  Calculating: ability to perform arithmetic tasks
  Mathematical reasoning: ability to use mathematical computation and comparisons to solve problems

Remembering: using memory to complete tasks
  Using short-term memory: ability to remember and use information acquired in the past minutes
  Using long-term memory: ability to remember information acquired in past hours, days, weeks, months, or years
  Using prospective memory: ability to access and use memory when needed
  Using procedural memory: ability to perform tasks without requiring conscious awareness

Learning ability: ability to understand instructions, reason, and make judgments
  Learning: ability to acquire new knowledge and skills

Reasoning: developing concepts and processing abstract information
  Abstract reasoning: ability to detect commonalities and differences across members of a group
  Logical reasoning: ability to identify and use logical relations
  Sequencing: ability to organize and perform the steps of an individual task in a logical and efficient order

Executive functioning: engaging in complex goal directed behaviors to complete tasks
  Organizing and planning: ability to coordinate parts into a whole and to develop a method of proceeding
  Managing time: ability to complete tasks in an allocated amount of time
  Using cognitive flexibility: ability to change strategies or shift mental sets during problem solving
  Using insight: accurate mental awareness and understanding of oneself and one's functional abilities
  Using judgment: ability to prospectively identify and evaluate different options in order to make decisions or form opinions

(continued)

TABLE 2.1
Description of Abilities (*continued*)

Solving problems: ability to identify, analyze, and integrate incongruent or conflicting information into a solution

Reacting to stimuli: ability to react quickly to stimuli
  Using auditory speed: ability to react quickly to auditory stimulus
  Using visual speed: ability to react quickly to visual stimulus
  Using haptic speed: ability to react quickly to haptic stimulus
  Using olfactory speed: ability to react quickly to visual stimulus
  Using multimodal speed: ability to react quickly to two or more stimuli

SENSATION AND PERCEPTION ABILITIES

Seeing: sensing the presence of light and form, size, shape and color of visual stimuli
  Using near vision: seeing visual stimuli located 20 in. or less from the eye
  Using far vision: seeing visual stimuli located greater than 20 in. from the eye
  Using central vision acuity (form perception): ability to perceive form and contour
  Using visual field: ability to see up/down or right/left
  Using color discrimination: ability to identify and distinguish colors
  Using depth perception: ability to perceive the distance and spatial relationships of objects
  Using visual accommodation: ability to adjust the eye to bring objects into focus
  Using sensitivity: ability to tolerate lighting conditions such as bright or low light.
  Using visual scanning: ability to quickly apprehend, identify, or find a visual pattern or object or accurately compare one or more patterns in a visual field

Hearing: sensing the presence of sounds and discriminating location, pitch, loudness, and quality
  Using noise sensitivity: ability to tolerate auditory stimulus such as loud or high pitch noises
  Localizing sound: ability to determine the location of a source of sound
  Detecting sound: ability to sense the presence of sounds
  Discriminating speech: ability to perceive and accurately distinguish sounds located within the range of normal speech from other sounds
  Auditory scanning: ability to quickly apprehend, identify or find an auditory pattern or object or accurately compare one or more patterns

Sensing odors and flavors: sensing the presence of and discriminating differences in odors/flavors
  Smelling: distinguishing differences in intensity or quality of odors
  Tasting: distinguishing differences in intensity or quality of flavors
  Using odor and flavor sensitivity: ability to tolerate strong odors and flavors

Feeling with skin: ability to cutaneously feel and sense variations in touch and texture
  Discriminating cutaneously: ability to discriminate light touch, pressure, vibration, pain, and temperature and perceiving attributes of objects such as size, shape, temperature, and texture through touch
  Using material sensitivity: ability to tolerate contact with materials or substances encountered
  Using environmental sensitivity: ability to tolerate exposure to environmental variations such as heat, cold, and vibration

(*continued*)

TABLE 2.1
Description of Abilities (*continued*)

COMMUNICATION ABILITIES

Producing communication: expressing meaningful messages using forms of language
  Speaking: ability to understandably express ideas, name and describe objects using spoken language
  Writing: ability to express the literal and implied meaning of messages using written language
  Signing: ability to convey ideas and name/describe objects using formal sign language
  Gesturing: ability to use body gestures to convey messages
  Drawing: ability to use symbols and drawings to convey messages

Receiving communication: decoding messages in different forms of language to obtain their meaning
  Reading: ability to comprehend literal and implied meaning of written language (including Braille)
  Listening: ability to comprehend the literal and implied meaning of spoken language
  Understanding sign: ability to comprehend the literal and implied meaning of formal sign language
  Understanding gestures: ability to comprehend the literal and implied meaning of body gestures
  Understanding drawings: ability to comprehend the literal and implied meaning of symbols and drawings

Conversing: engaging in a purposeful exchange of language with one or more people.
  Conversing: ability to initiate, sustain, and terminate an interchange of thoughts with one or more other people using language
  Discussing: ability to initiate, sustain, and terminate an examination of a matter with arguments for or against with one or more other people using language

Interacting: ability to interact with people in a contextually and socially appropriate manner
  Using social cues: giving and reacting appropriately to signs and hints that occur in social interactions
  Regulating emotion: regulating emotions and impulses, verbal and physical aggression in interactions with others

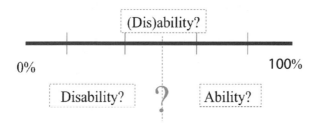

Levels of ability/(Dis)ability.

FIGURE 2.4

intents and purposes, level of ability acts independent of type. As a result, no two people have exactly the same levels of all abilities. For example, one individual can have full 20/20 visual acuity, no ability to ambulate, and mild limitation in reaching ability, whereas another can have 20/200 acuity (legally blind), full ability to ambulate, and mild limitation in reach. Most importantly, few individuals have full levels of ability across all types of abilities, and conversely, few individuals have very low levels of ability across all types. This trend is crucial to understanding the disabling impact of everyday design.

EVERYDAY DESIGN

Design for Population Norms

For any type of ability, the number of individuals at each level of that ability is represented by a normal distribution or bell curve (Figure 2.5). In a normal distribution, the mean, median, and mode correspond to the same centerline. As such, 50% of the individuals have levels of ability above the center point, and 50% lie below. In addition, the majority of the population is clustered around the mean. For example, 68% of the population lies within ±1 standard deviation of the centerline, and 95% of the population lie within ±2 standard deviations.

Few design theories and practices recognize diversity of human form and function (Imrie, 2005). As a result, to the extent that typical everyday designs of buildings, spaces, and objects are based on human ability at all, they are based on technical standards and dimensions of "normal"

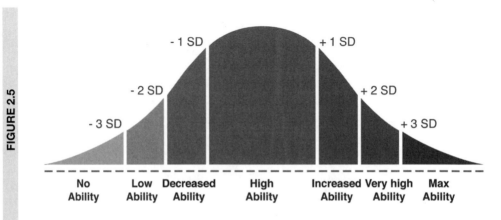

FIGURE 2.5

Distribution of ability levels.

body structure, function, and capacities (Imrie, 2004). These population norms are operationally defined by the 5th and 95th percentiles of the bell curve or 90% of the population that are expected to be able to use a particular design. For example, the 5th percentile (4'11") woman is typically used to determine reach, which conceptually means that 95% of the population over 4'11' should be able to perform reaching tasks required by everyday design. Looking at it from the other point of view, 10% of the population are not expected to use the design and will need to be accommodated.

Although the data used are generally based on anthropometric tables of military personnel, the accuracy of the data is less important here than the practice of everyday design, which not only excludes 10% of the population but also deliberately includes only individuals with moderate to fairly high levels of ability. This approach presumes not only that everyone in the 90% is fit and able-bodied but also that there are no differences across individuals due to gender or other individual attributes that would impact usability of design. In other words, the population norms that are the basis of everyday designs are not norms at all (Finkel & Gold, 1999). Although the inequities in this approach are evident, they are exacerbated by the variability in the levels of each ability within individuals themselves and across their life spans. Clearly, design based on the 95th percentile for one dimension (e.g., height) will not accommodate the 95th percentile on the others (e.g., vision, hearing, perception). Further, the more dimensions that are included at the 90% level, the smaller the actual percent of the population that is accommodated. As Vanderheiden (1990) pointed out, the same people do not fall outside the 5% tail for every type of ability. As a result, no design will actually accommodate 90% of the population across abilities.

Overall, the 95% design approach ensures that the demands exerted by everyday design will invariably result in a misfit between design and some abilities for almost everyone. This suggests that regardless of body function and structure, everyday design is disabling in some ways for many individuals. To compound the problem, when everyday designs are extended beyond the 95th percentile, they typically only do so for one type of ability. Often times, the result is designs that are even more disabling. A classic example of this is the famous butterfly ballot used in Florida in the 2000 U.S. presidential election. The ballot was put on two pages to keep the print size big enough to accommodate older adults with visual limitations. However, the design failed to accommodate their cognitive abilities. The layout of double pages with punch holes in the middle was novel to begin with. Further, reading down the page on the left, the Democratic

FIGURE 2.6

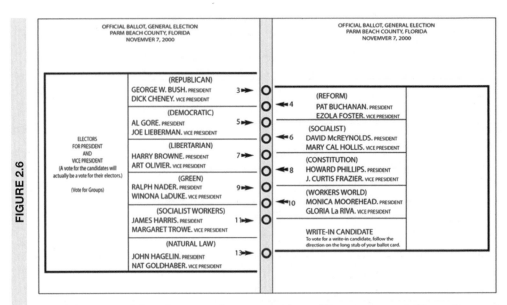

Never Underestimate the Power of Design

Adaptation of Apple Computer advertisement in *USA Today*, Thursday,
November 17, 2000.

candidates were listed second. However, they were the third, rather than second, punch hole in the middle. As a result, the strength of the ballot's unfamiliar and counter intuitive cognitive demands was greater than the reduction on their visual demands, thus causing many voters to misread the ballot and punch the second hole, which cast a vote for Pat Buchanan of the Reform Party. Although the impact of the ballot on the election itself will be debated for years to come, it did lead to the complete overhaul of the U.S. voting system. Seizing the moment, Apple Computer, which prides itself on usability of everyday design, ran a full-page ad in *USA Today* 2 days after the election (Figure 2.6) to sensitize people to the (in this case disabling) power of design. In the end, "If you want designers to design for everyone, then it is incumbent to ensure that data on everyone are available in the same place and in the same way" (Connell & Sanford, 1999).

ENVIRONMENTAL BARRIERS: DESIGN IMPLICATIONS OF ABILITY

As illustrated by the butterfly ballot, everyday design exerts demands that often exceed the level of one or more abilities. The result is design barriers to usability. Usability barriers are common across abilities, affecting motor, sensation/perception, cognition, and communication domains alike. More specifically, barriers act on each of the abilities within the four function domains. Although providing examples of barriers for each of the 91 abilities in the four domains would fill the rest of this text, common examples are provided to illustrate the types of attributes that result in usability barriers for different types of ability.

Within motor abilities, typical barriers to moving one's body include obstacles in the path of travel (Figure 2.7), discontinuity of pathways (Figure 2.8), size of space that restricts maneuvering (Figure 2.9), steep

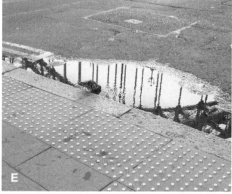

FIGURE 2.7

Over the river and through the woods. A variety of obstacles in the path of travel can create barriers to mobility, such as (A) "security" barricades across the accessible route to a Braves baseball game at Turner Field, Atlanta, GA; (B) a utility pole in the middle of a sidewalk on West Peachtree St., Atlanta, GA; (C) a police car in front of the curb cut in downtown Raleigh, NC; (D) the entrance ramp to the U.S. Embassy in Toronto, Canada (did they really think that yellow "do not cross" tape and orange cone would keep anyone out?); and (E) standing water at a curb cut in Newcastle, England.

FIGURE 2.8

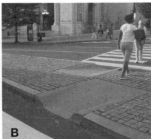

Separation anxiety. (A) Discontinuous paths of travel create barriers to movement, such as an ubiquitous, uncontrolled, middle of the block street crossing with a curb cut only on one side of the street in Mexico City, Mexico; (B) curb cuts with no maneuvering space (and extremely rough pavers in between, see also Figure 2.11) outside Union Station, Washington, DC; (C) a curb cut that dead ends into a utility pole along Ponce de Leon Ave. in DeKalb County, GA, where there is no sidewalk (at least they got the tactile warning in the right place and pedestrian crossing button at the right height); (D) and a very steep ramp on a home in Atlanta, GA, that ends in two steps.

FIGURE 2.9

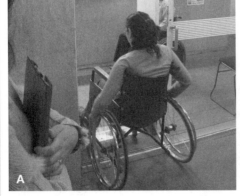
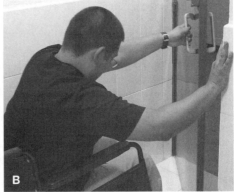

Room to move. Lack of space restricts maneuverability, particularly to individuals who use mobility aids, whether it is (A) the entrance to a library or (B) a rest room.

FIGURE 2.10

Getting over the hump. Steep slopes and cross slopes create difficult and dangerous situations for people who have mobility problems. Sidewalks, which ADAAG permits to follow the slope of the street, can be steep. However, sometimes, there is a hump in the middle of a sidewalk even though there is an otherwise flat street adjacent to it, such as (A) along N. Decatur Rd. in DeKalb Co, GA, and (B) under the Krog St. Bridge along DeKalb Ave. in Atlanta, GA. Other times, ramps follow the slope of stairs, such as (C) in Stockholm, Sweden, which at best is close to a 64% slope (for a 7:11 stair) versus an 8.3% (1:12) maximum slope required for a ramp. Cross slopes at curb cuts, which may be unavoidable due to the slope of the street, are difficult to maneuver, such as (D) in Austin, TX. Finally, a ramp-to-ramp transition (E) in Buenos Aires, Argentina, without a level landing creates a severe cross slope at the transition, that is, presuming that someone could actually get up the extremely steep slope and over the wide and deep grooves in the lower ramp.

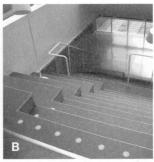

FIGURE 2.11

Stairway to heaven? Steps, for a variety of reasons, create an obvious physical barrier for people who use mobility aids. (A) The magnitude of the barrier is magnified when a sign at the top of the steps at Hofbrau Steakhouse in Dallas, TX, indicates that the restaurant is accessible, but an individual with a disability must call the manager for entry. Stairs can also be difficult and dangerous for all users, particularly people who have gait and balance problems. Stairs that (B) lack handrails, such as the one pictured in the Division of Occupational Therapy at Karolinska Institute, Flemingsberg, Sweden, or (C) lack handrails and have uneven surfaces and riser heights such as the stair in Hibiya Park, Tokyo, Japan, do not provide the support to ensure safe stair use (which is exacerbated by visual distractions). Finally, (D) high steps, such as the unusually high curb pictured from Denver, CO, can be difficult for someone who has difficulty lifting his or her leg, it can also create a hazard for someone without a mobility limitation because it is unexpected.

slopes and cross slopes (Figure 2.10), vertical level changes that have steps (Figure 2.11), long distances (Figure 2.12), and uneven surface materials (Figure 2.13). Barriers to reaching and manipulating objects include height of counters and objects (Figures 2.14 and 2.15), location of objects in space (Figure 2.16), size and shape of interfaces (Figure 2.17), and degree of precision required (Figure 2.18).

Within mental abilities, similar environmental attributes can simultaneously create barriers to multiple abilities (Figures 2.19 thru 2.23). For example, lack of information (e.g., signage, announcements, or instructions), too much information (e.g., visual clutter, auditory distractions), contradictory information (e.g., contradicts either other information or user's expectation), and information that is hard to find (e.g., not where it is expected or not visible) can create barriers to perceiving space, attending

FIGURE 2.12

A long and winding road. (A) Distance by itself, such as the very wide intersection at Clairmont Rd. and N. Druid Hills Rd. in Atlanta, GA, can create a barrier to mobility, particularly when the timing of the traffic light is set at normal walking speed of about 4 ft per second. However, the effects of distance are aggravated when it is combined with (B) crowding, such as an airport concourse at Miami International Airport, Miami, FL, or slope, such as (C) the ramp on the Georgia Tech campus, Atlanta, GA, which takes the user to the end of the building and back again, or (D) the ramp at the architectural award-winning Tokyo International Forum, Tokyo, Japan, which has a sign warning visitors who use wheelchairs or buggies not to use the ramp for safety reasons. (E) Even if a ramp, such as the one in Waterfront Park, Louisville, KY, complies with accessibility standards that require a 1:12 slope and 5-ft landings every 30 ft, an extremely long overall length without places to sit and rest can create a mobility barrier for many individuals.

FIGURE 2.13

FIGURE 2.14

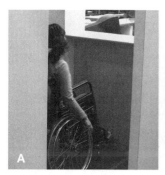

FIGURE 2.15

Seeing eye to eye. Height of counters are almost invariably too high to reach from a seated position, including (A) the checkout desk in the architecture library at the Universidad Nacional Autónoma de México, Mexico City, Mexico, and (B) the concession stand along the Ohio River in Cincinnati, OH, even though there are accessible bathrooms on either side of the facility. (C) Interestingly, no one seemed deterred by the counter height at Giovanni's Shrimp Truck, Kahuku, HI, that was even too high for the 95th percentile male customer.

FIGURE 2.13

One accessible feature does not make an accessible design. Uneven and rough surfaces create barriers to movement even when "accessible features" are included, such as (A) "handicapped" parking at Wills Park, Alpharetta, GA that is unpaved and unlevel; (B) smooth, low-riser stairs with handrails, but a ramp with rough pavers and no rails at Paley Park, NY; (C) no step transitions from smooth sidewalk to rough granite street crossings in the new town of Serenbe, GA; (D) curb cuts across from Union Station leading to rough pavers, Washington, DC; and (E) curb cuts adjacent to cobblestone streets in old Montreal, Canada.

FIGURE 2.14

A higher power. The height of mounted objects can act as barriers to reaching and operating hardware or controls that might otherwise be very usable. This is a common problem in restrooms, where towel and soap dispensers are often too high for someone who is short or seated, such as the ones in the bathrooms at (A) the Universidad Nacional Autónoma de México, Mexico City, Mexico, and (B) Red Rocks Amphitheater, Morrison, CO. (C) Of course, in the rare case when the hand dryer is at the right height for a seated user, the door handle is too high for an individual to reach to pull the door open to exit the restroom (although there is no place for a wheelchair to back up even if the user could reach the handle). Height of pedestrian crosswalk buttons is also a common problem for seated and short users, such as the two examples from DeKalb County, GA, (D) one along North Decatur Rd. and (E) the other at Commerce Drive in Decatur.

FIGURE 2.16

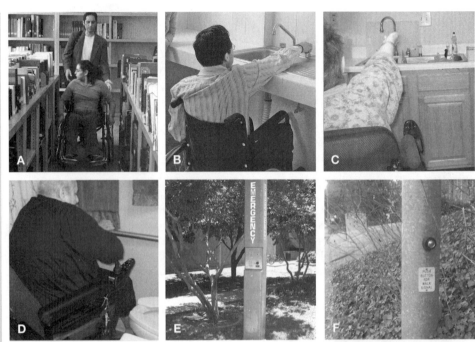

Location, location, location. (A) The location of objects on shelves and counters can also be a barrier due to the lack of maneuvering space as exemplified by narrow widths of library aisles in the architecture library at the Universidad Nacional Autónoma de México, Mexico City, Mexico that create barriers to maneuvering, reaching books close to the floor and to others that want to pass by. (B) The height of sinks and faucet handles can be a barrier to reach even when there is knee space underneath for a forward reach, such as this restroom at the Universidad Nacional Autónoma de México, Mexico City, Mexico. (C) However, when there is no knee space, objects need to be closer to the user to be reached from a side approach, such as this home in Atlanta, GA. (D) Finally, when the grab bar is located on the other side of a toilet that protrudes too far into the room to permit wheelchair access, an alternative approach might be in order (photos C and D courtesy of Sarah O'Brien, Georgia Tech). *And location, location, location.* Location of controls in inaccessible spaces out of the path of travel can create barriers to use, such as (E) the emergency kiosk outside the Architecture Building on the Georgia Tech campus, Atlanta, GA; (F) a pedestrian crosswalk button along North Decatur Rd. at the Emory University campus, DeKalb Co, GA; and (G) an automatic "handicapped" door opener (if a user could reach the button without falling off the landing, how would he or she get around the open door?) at Georgia Perimeter College, Clarkston, GA (Photo C courtesy of Joanna Sanford, Georgia Perimeter student).

FIGURE 2.17

Size matters. The size and shape of interfaces, such as (A) the size of buttons and the space between them, as well as (B, C) those that require dual actions, such as pinching or grasping before turning, can create barriers to individuals with limited strength or fine motor control. However, the old adage, "bigger is better" is usually a pretty good rule of thumb.

FIGURE 2.18

Precision, precision, precision. Objects that require precision to operate are unforgiving and difficult for everyone and particularly for individuals with limited fine motor control. (A) Lining up the combination on a post office box or (B) the two tiny arrows on the display screen support arm for the bulkhead seats on an Airbus A300 require considerable precision. (C) Similarly, precision is required to push the small buttons on the keypad for a locked "handicapped" bathroom in a restaurant in Stockholm, Sweden and (D) a typical pedestrian walk button in Atlanta, GA.

FIGURE 2.19

It's not fair. Fare machines operated by Metropolitan Atlanta Rapid Transit Authority, Atlanta, GA, create multiple demands on our mental abilities by being inconsistent with expectations by (A and B) not being clear what button to touch first (hint: the large easy-to-see letters on each side of the screen are not buttons), (B) not providing a logical sequence of operations (which is why the 5 dollar bill is hanging out of the machine), (A and B) not providing directions for unfamiliar jargon such as what "tap card" means or where to tap, and (C and D) not explaining what the options mean (e.g., a round trip is actually just two trips, regardless of destination, at the same price as two-one way tickets).

to task, reasoning, remembering, learning, executive functioning, and reacting to stimuli.

Within perception and sensation, typical barriers to seeing include size of space, lack of contrast (Figure 2.25), information that is not apparent and hard to find (Figure 2.26), lack of wayfinding information (Figure 2.27), too much information (Figure 2.28), too much or too little light, and reflective surfaces that create glare. Barriers to hearing include size of space, background noise, reflective surfaces that create reverberation, and

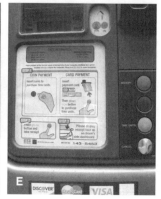

FIGURE 2.20

Who's on first? Parking kiosks in the City of Atlanta, GA, create a variety of demands on mental abilities, including by creating visual clutter, not meeting expectations, and providing contradictory information. (A, B, C) Clutter is created by the random placement of visual information on the meter rather than as an orderly sequence of steps. (C, D) Unmet expectations and contradictory information are apparent in the location of the green start button (labeled print receipt, not start), at the bottom of the interface rather than at the top where one would expect Step 1 to be. (E) Contrast this with the photo of a meter from New York City, which also has three steps to operate but has different color buttons for each different function. By the way, it took 10 minute before the gentleman in the first photo to get frustrated and walk off without ever putting any money in the machine. No wonder there were no cars parked on this side of the street, whereas the parking spaces across the street that had old-fashioned put-the-coin-in-the-meter were filled.

Visual overload. (A) Getting in this door at the VA Medical Center, Decatur, GA, (B) crossing the street, or (C) going down a stair in Tokyo, Japan, may be difficult because too much information becomes confusing visual clutter. But clutter is not just limited to people who can see; (D) the overuse of textured surfaces at Hibiya Park, Tokyo, Japan, can make a confusing maze of tactile wayfinding information for people with visual limitations.

frequency, intensity, and pitch of auditory information. Barriers to sensing by touch are primarily created by new digital interfaces that offer little or no tactile feedback through the skin (Figure 2.29). Finally, because communication and motor, mental and perception, and sensation are interdependent, design attributes that create barriers to these other types of abilities will similarly affect communication. For example, seeing is necessary for all visual communication abilities, whereas hearing is necessary for all auditory communication. Verbal communication abilities are related to moving in space and changing position, whereas communication using hand

FIGURE 2.22

What is behind Door 1? Misinformation, contradictory information, and false positive information make using environments confusing and difficult. (A) If you cannot "enter" the entrance, how do you get into this Target in Atlanta, GA? (B) How do you get into the voodoo shop in New Orleans, LA when the sign on the right door (the one with the handle) states please use other door—the one without the handle? (C) Where is the curb cut/crossing for which the yellow tactile

strip is providing a warning in Santa Fe, NM, and (D) who stole the ramp at this hotel in Kona, HI?

FIGURE 2.23

Where's Waldo? Look closely . . . can you find Door 1? When important information that differentiates the door from the rest of the exterior is lacking, such as this Pinkberry store in New Orleans, LA, it might be difficult to attract customers . . . unless of course you are selling ice cream in New Orleans.

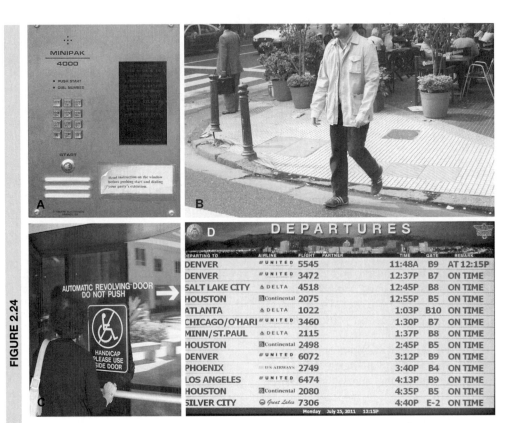

FIGURE 2.24

Dazed and confused. When information is unclear, not presented in sequential order, or counterintuitive, expectations are not met. (A) Directions at the top of the control panel state push to start; yet the start button is located at the bottom. (B) Nonvisual information can also be confusing, such as the tactile warning in Buenos Aires, Argentina, which is relatively small compared with other tactile material at the corner. Planters or other types of physical separation, such as bollards that are on the corner, would be more effective and less confusing. (C) When products work in unexpected ways, signage that tells the user to do something that is counterintuitive is usually ineffective, such as the motion-operated revolving door at Bethesda Memorial Hospital, Boynton Beach, FL. (D) Finally, how do you find your flight when you are in a hurry at the Santa Fe, NM, Airport? The information is seemingly random since the first column of information is the destination city, yet it is not organized alphabetically. To find one's flight, a traveler has to look four columns to the right to see that the information is actually organized by departure time.

Hiding in plain sight. (A) Lack of contrast in white controls on a white appliance makes it difficult to differentiate controls from background. (B) The lack of differentiation in color and texture between the curb cut and the street in Honolulu, HI, not only makes it difficult for wheelchair users with good vision to find the curb cut but also makes it difficult for visually impaired pedestrians to detect where the street begins. (C) Similarly, the lack of contrast between the text and the background on a sign at the Botanical Garden, New Orleans, LA, makes it difficult to read. Raised and incised signage that are the same color as the background are also difficult to read and use, such as (D) the ubiquitous stainless steel elevator panel with raised stainless steel buttons and floor numbers on a stainless steel background plate and (E) a restroom door with incised letters indicating that it is a unisex bathroom.

FIGURE 2.25

Hiding in the front closet. Information is hard to find when it is hidden and you don't know to look for it. (A) while this looks like an ordinary closet at the Hyatt Regency Hotel, Chicago, IL, (B) imagine my surprise when I found the emergency flashlight (A) hidden behind the clothes hangers.

Path to nowhere. (A) The pedestrian walkway in a broad open entry plaza at Olympic Stadium in Montreal, Canada, provides only visual cues (painted lines and an icon of a pedestrian) to indicate where the designated walkway is located (at least until one reaches the middle of the plaza). (B) The sidewalk in Buenos Aires, Argentina, is not at a loss for tactile cues, but none that will provide meaningful wayfinding information for the cane user in the middle of the photo. (C) In contrast, the intersection on Ponce de Leon Ave. in DeKalb Co., GA, also provides tactile cues, but to where?

FIGURE 2.28

TMI. (A) The amount of information and size of text, particularly on directories, such as the Georgia Tech Campus directory and (B) the Concourse Directory and (C) flight departures at Denver International airport, make it difficult for anyone to read, especially when the user has poor vision, is of short stature, or is seated (At least the flight departures are organized alphabetically by city).

FIGURE 2.29

See me, hear me, touch me, feel me. The iPhone has a high-contrast interface with large icons that increase usability for people with low vision and dexterity limitations. It also has a feature for tactile feedback, making some information accessible to individuals who are blind.

(e.g., signing) and facial gestures is dependent on the ability to move body parts.

SUMMARY

Clearly, the fiasco of everyday design can be traced to the logic of designing for the 95th percentile. To the extent that the so-called 5th and 95th percentiles actually encompass 90% of the population, they do so for only one anthropometric dimension at a time. Therefore, from the start, design barriers are expected to create usability problems for at least 10% of the population. However, because no one falls into the 90% across all abilities, design for one type of ability can create barriers for the others. Moreover, design for multiple abilities offers ever diminishing returns on the percentage of the general population that can actually use the design. Nonetheless, for every problem, there is a solution. To overcome the usability barriers created by everyday design, specialized assistive technologies and accessible designs were developed.

THREE

Function Follows Fiasco: Specialized Designs for Enabling Disabling Design

*T*o remove or overcome design barriers for people with disabilities, specialized designs, including adaptive equipment, devices, and products, accessible design (AD) features, and assistive technologies (AT), such as adaptive equipment, devices, and products, have traditionally been added to everyday designs. Acting as enablers or facilitators that address barriers created by everyday designs, specialized designs serve as prosthetic supports to improve function and compensate for a (dis)ability (i.e., limitations in ability). For example, a ramp compensates for an inability to ambulate or lift one's leg, whereas grab bars compensate for loss of ability to raise and lower oneself. With the assistance of specialized designs, disabling everyday design can be enabled, allowing many individuals with disabilities to safely and independently carry out basic activities associated with daily living and receive personal assistance from caregivers that would otherwise not be possible.

Five Facts About Specialized Design as a Rehabilitation Strategy

- It is design and technology for people with limited abilities
- It has prescribed rules of what must be done
- It is design for improving performance in daily activities
- It is added on to everyday design and often institutional in nature
- It often adds cost to everyday design

Although the various different types of specialized designs are sometimes used interchangeably, they clearly represent different approaches to achieve usability. Nonetheless, the distinction, or lack thereof, among types of specialized designs is generally an artifact of disciplinary bias. For example, as clinicians, therapists tend to distinguish among adaptive equipment, AT, and environmental interventions/AD. Building contractors tend to adopt a similar approach differentiating between those things that are attached to the environment (i.e., AD) from objects that are purchased and freestanding (e.g., adaptive products). In contrast, rehabilitation engineers tend to consider all specialized design to be assistive technology (AT), as the definition below might suggest. Finally, designers typically consider all specialized designs to be AD because they are all part of the environment. To avoid confusion and for simplicity, when referred to in this text, specialized designs are either AT or AD.

ASSISTIVE TECHNOLOGY

An AT device, as defined by the Technology-Related Assistance for Individuals with Disabilities Act of 1988, as amended in 1994, is "any item, piece of equipment, or product system, whether acquired commercially, modified, or customized, that is used to increase, maintain, or improve functional capabilities of individuals with disabilities" (U.S. Congress, 1988, 1998). Clearly, the reference to "any item, piece of equipment, or product system" seems to designate every design or technology as AT. In fact, this is the often the accepted interpretation, particularly among rehabilitation engineers. However, the operant terms in this definition are related to *scale* and *individuals with disabilities*.

First, the definition clearly limits the scale of AT to products or interfaces. Moreover, it implies that these designs are independent in function as well as of space. As a result, specialized products, such as an adaptive keyboard, are considered AT, whereas everyday products that include specialized features, such as a computer with large text capability, are not. As interpreted here, neither are spatial changes, site-built designs, and installations of products (specialized or otherwise) in a space. For example, a tub-mounted, clamp-on grab bar would be considered AT, as would a freestanding aluminum ramp and a portable patient lift (Figure 3.1). However, wall-mounted grab bars, a site-built ramp, and a ceiling-mounted lift, because they are part of the space, would not be considered AT.

Second, the definition implies that an AT product is one that is specifically intended to compensate for functional capabilities of individuals with disabilities. A common interpretation of this statement is that everyday designs would be considered AT if it is used to compensate for loss of ability by an individual with a disability. However, because AT is intended to compensate for barriers in everyday design, using an alternative everyday design to compensate for one that is disabling is clearly a contradiction in

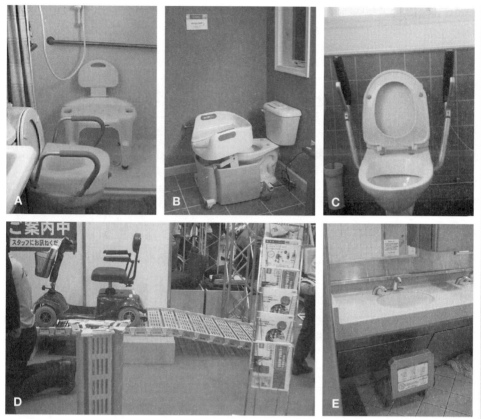

Examples of AT that are added into everyday design include (A) a raised toilet seat and shower chair for people who have difficulty raising and lowering or standing for extended periods, respectively; (B) a toilet stander-upper and (C) grab rails for people who have difficulty raising and lowering to the fixture; (D) a Roll-a-Ramp for wheeled mobility aids; (E) and a Step'nWash for children who cannot reach a faucet.

FIGURE 3.1

terms. Moreover, because universal design (UD) is everyday design that accommodates all abilities, this interpretation would also imply that all UD is AT. If that were the case, "the book would stop here."

Therefore, as used here, AT refers to any off-the-shelf product (e.g., a portable aluminum ramp) that is an independent device *added to* everyday design for (a usually small group of) individuals with specific limitations in ability. In addition, AT may also be any modification to an everyday product that is not a permanent part of the product or attached to a physical structure (e.g., it can be installed or removed without tools such as an adaptive lever door handle that fits over a doorknob or a grab bar that clamps onto a bathtub) to facilitate use by an individual or individuals with explicit limitations in ability. In other words, AT is not everyday design.

ACCESSIBLE DESIGN

Most definitions of AD (e.g., Erlandson, 2008; Salmen, 2001) link it to compliance with legal mandates, guidelines, or code requirements associated with the ADA and other pieces of U.S. accessibility legislation (e.g., Architectural Barriers Act [ABA] and Fair Housing Amendments Act) that set minimum levels of design necessary to accommodate people with disabilities. This may be true in public facilities that come under the *Americans with Disabilities Act Accessibility Guidelines (ADAAG)*; however, residential and work environments, while influenced by the *ADAAG*, are not subject to them. As a result, AD, as used here, will refer to a type of design approach, regardless of the forces driving it.

Specifically, AD includes specialized designs based on accepted dimensional requirements that are intended to remove barriers by minimizing demands on people with disabilities (i.e., people with specific types and levels of ability). Like AT, AD is a disability-specific approach that applies separate designs for different types of (dis)abilities. In other words, each specialized design is only useful to individuals with specific types of functional limitations (Figure 3.2). For example, a ramp and curbless shower are useful to people who have difficulty or cannot walk or lift their legs by minimizing demands on one's lower body motor abilities (i.e., eliminate need to lift one's leg onto or over a step); high-contrast signage or tactile warnings are useful to people with poor vision by minimizing demands on visual abilities; and flashing alarms are useful to individuals with hearing loss by minimizing demands on auditory abilities.

Whereas AD, in general, has many benefits, the codes themselves focus primarily on mobility issues and, in some cases, pose barriers to people with other types of disabilities (Finkel & Gold, 1999). A good example is the use of curb cuts or curb ramps at crosswalks to enable wheelchair users to cross the street. Although curb cuts provide access for a variety of users today, including people who use mobility devices, parents with strollers, bicyclists, and travelers with rolling luggage, an early unintended consequence of changing the curb design was that blind individuals who used canes to detect the curb unknowingly walked into the street. To compen-

FIGURE 3.2

Accessible designs are intended for one individual or a group of individuals with similar types of functional limitations. The raised dome tactile cues that are used in many transit stations around the world are intended to support visually impaired travelers by (A) providing wayfinding information, such as in Tokyo, Japan, warning. travelers of dropoffs at platform edges, such as in (B) Vancouver, Canada and (C) Tokyo, Japan. The focus of AD on one group of individuals is highlighted by the removal of barriers for people with vision loss, whereas (C) the 3-in. height differential between the platform and the train creates a barrier for wheelchair users and a trip hazard for individuals with other mobility limitations.

sate, curb cuts today are designed with tactile and high-contrast warnings for individuals who are blind or who have low vision (Figure 3.3).

Simply, AD includes those specialized designs that are not included in the definition of AT. More specifically, it is composed of specialized designs that are added to everyday products and spaces, such as adding grab bars to the walls around a toilet, mechanical lifts to a stair, or detectable warnings to a street corner (Figure 3.4), to change the attributes of those everyday designs. Thus, like AT, AD is a reactive approach to design that is intended to compensate for barriers in the everyday environment. However, unlike AT, which is more individualized and usually follows the person, AD, because it is part of the built environment, is often aimed at and typically impacts larger populations of individuals with more generalized types of limitations (e.g., unable to walk). Nonetheless, when ADs, such as curb cuts, become ubiquitous, they, themselves, become everyday designs used by everyone, regardless of ability, and are therefore universal.

In the United States, AD in public facilities, multifamily housing, workplaces, transportation, and telecommunications is legislated by a variety of federal laws, including the ABA of 1968, the Rehabilitation Act

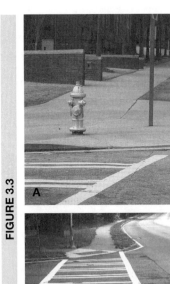

FIGURE 3.3

Viva la différence. Curb cuts may be ubiquitous, but the tactile surfaces on them come in a myriad of shapes and sizes, which makes it hard to figure out what to expect when you encounter them. Some examples include (A) the "naked" curb cut on the Georgia Tech campus, Atlanta, GA; (B) the no-to-low-contrast warning on the 16th street mall in Denver, CO, which has no visual differences, although it has some small textural changes; (C) the low–low-contrast warning in a Publix parking lot in Boynton Beach, FL, which has low visual and textural changes; and (D) the SOP (standard of practice) high-contrast visual and tactile warning in DeKalb County, GA.

of 1973, the Fair Housing Amendments Act of 1988, and the ADA of 1990, which is not only the centerpiece of the U.S. disability civil rights policy but also represents a landmark piece of disability legislation throughout the world. The accessibility guidelines and standards mandated by these laws, such as the ABA–ADA Accessibility Guidelines,[1] which is arguably the most comprehensive set of accessibility specifications worldwide that

---

[1] In 2004, the ADA and ABA Accessibility Guidelines were combined to form a uniform set of guidelines called the *ADA–ABA Accessibility Guidelines* to cover both Acts and to be more compatible with the American National Standards Institute ICC-ANSI A117.1, the model accessibility code that is referenced in most U.S. building codes. As of this writing, three of the four standard-setting federal agencies that enforce the ABA had adopted these guidelines as standards to replace the Uniform Federal Accessibility Standards. However, neither the Department of Justice nor the Department of Transportation, which are vested with enforcement of ADA in public and private sector facilities and transportation systems, had adopted the new guidelines.

are mandated by legislative act, prescribe minimum technical require-ments for design attributes (e.g., clearances, space, height, width, dis-tance, and slope). For example, to minimize demands on individuals who cannot ambulate, a ramp is specified to have a maximum slope of 1 in. of rise for every 12 in. of run and a maximum length of 30 ft between level landings. Whereas these requirements are intended to minimize demands primarily on wheelchair users, the specifications may or may not actually achieve that end, depending on the interaction between the ramp characteristics and the actual motor abilities of the individual who is using the wheelchair.

Although legislated guidelines and standards only apply to public facil-ities, individualized interventions in housing and workplaces are strongly linked to these guidelines. As a result, specifications for AD (e.g., types and sizes of grab bars) are often used as the basis for individualized home modifications and workplace accommodations (Table 3.1). This is easier to understand in the workplace, where the ADA mandates reasonable accom-modations where they are needed to perform essential job tasks, although specific interventions are not identified. There is no such requirement in residential settings, although most local building codes have adopted tech-nical specifications from the *ADAAG* (e.g., maximum ramp slope of 1:12) to regulate safety rather than accessibility.

Unfortunately, because AD is mandated by a set of rules without an understanding of why these rules are applied, it is often misinterpreted, misapplied, or misunderstood. In practice, much of the AD that is imple-mented does not adhere to the *ADAAG*. As a result, it is not uncommon to find toilet grab bars that are too short or located in the wrong place

TABLE 3.1
Differences in Approaches to Accessible Design Across Types of Settings

SETTING	ACCESSIBILITY REQUIREMENTS	APPROACH
Public facilities	Mandated in ADA Title III (ADAAG) ⇕	Technical requirements for accessible design
Workplace	Mandated in ADA Title I ⇕	Individualized accommodations (AT, AD)
Housing	Not mandated (Comply with local building codes)	Individualized modifications (AT, AD)

(Figure 3.5). Alternatively, AD is routinely and repetitively applied regardless of context and whether it is warranted or not, such as Braille labeling on a drive-through teller or curb cuts and tactile warnings in the absence of a sidewalk (Figure 3.6). Worse, it is often applied when "accessible" specialized designs are less "accessible" than the typical everyday designs,

FIGURE 3.4

Stuck on you. Examples of accessible designs that are added on and not integrated into everyday design, such as (A) the inclined stair lift at the Archeology Museum in Mexico City, Mexico; (B) tactile surfaces that appear randomly placed at the corner along Ponce de Leon Ave. in DeKalb Co., GA; (C) a grab bar attached to the back of an out-swinging door at Lund University, Lund, Sweden that enables wheelchair users to pull the door shut after entering the bathroom; (D) light contrasting tape to mark the stair tread in this clothing store in Santa Fe, NM . . . with a handwritten sign (taped to the rail to the left of the stair) to "to watch your step" and (E) a "handicapped" button for a power-assisted door in Newcastle, England, although the older woman in the photo does not seem too thrilled with the help.

such as the use of lever faucets instead of those with electronic sensors (Figure 3.7). As a result, AD is often unused or unusable by the individuals who need it, whereas those who do not are left wondering why it was put there in the first place.

STIGMA OF SPECIALIZED DESIGN

By design, AT and AD are prosthetic specialized designs that compensate for deficiencies in everyday design through a reduction or elimination of

How hard is it to follow the rules? The ADAAG are prescriptive rules that clearly specify attributes of accessible design. Although rules are not hard to follow, they are rarely applied correctly. (A) The tub grab bars at the Hotel Orrington in Evanston, IL, are too high, too short, and too few. (B) The grab bars in a ubiquitous restroom anywhere in the United States almost meet the code, although the side bar is more than 6 in. from the wall behind the toilet, but the location of the toilet paper, which is clearly specified in the ADAAG, is unreachable even for someone without limitations. (C) An accessible guest room in the Swisshotel, Chicago, IL, does not have grab bars in the bathtub that are low or long enough and a sink apron that is not high enough at 24 in. above the floor for a wheelchair user to roll under. (D) The one-tactile-surface-fits-all approach to crosswalk warnings is not going to provide useful information to a blind person that there is a crosswalk straight ahead and one to the right.

FIGURE 3.5

FIGURE 3.6

Too much of a good thing. Accessible design is often applied in places where it is not needed, such as (A, B) Braille on a drive-through teller at a Wells Fargo Bank in Atlanta, GA or (C) the accessible toilet stall in this inaccessible restroom at Wills Park, Alpharetta, GA. Hint—the door is wide enough, but how do you get across the gravel lot and past the planters at either end, even when there are no cars blocking the walkway?

usability barriers for individuals with limitations in specific abilities. They are, by nature, reactive approaches that are added on to everyday products and building features. As band-aids, specialized designs tend to be institutional looking and stand out. Thus, although they enable disabling everyday design, they are typically associated with the stigma of disability and institutional care.

Stigma, according to Goffman (1963), is an "undesired differentness" from what is socially expected and results from a trait (e.g., physical deformity) that often has extensive negative social implications of being classified as inferior and socially unacceptable. For people who are already predisposed to being stigmatized because their abilities are different than the "normal" 90% of the population, specialized designs and devices, much of which were originally designed for institutional settings (e.g., hospitals) and are medical in appearance, reinforce societal stereotypes by emphasizing and directing attention to these differences in public or residential settings (Figures 3.8 to 3.11). As a result, AT and AD are equally objects of stigma as the traits from which the stigma is derived.

Moreover, because specialized designs are symbols of stigma, their presence is sufficient for people associated with their use to be targets of that stigma, regardless of whether they possess stigmatizing traits or not. For example, the presence of a ramp on an individual's home creates the presumption that the individual is "disabled," whether he or she is or not. Not surprisingly, many individuals would rather face a variety of

FIGURE 3.7

Not enough of a better thing! (A) Among the 20 lavatories in the restroom at the Palais des Congrès de Montréal, Montréal, Canada, all have no-touch, electronic sensor faucets that require no physical effort to operate, except the one "accessible" lavatory at the end, which has a typical wing lever handle, requiring longer reach and dexterity. (B) Meanwhile, who would have ever thought to ask for a ramp (sign above the number 1 to the right of door) at the Tesuque Glassworks, Teseque, NM? Maybe the sign should also say "yell loud, the proprietor is hard of hearing."

environmental barriers than be labeled as "disabled." As a result, they will often decline to use the AT and the AD. The abandonment rate for pre-scribed AT is high. Even AT that is used at home is frequently left there when people go out into community settings. Others may not go out at all. Some individuals, particularly older adults, refuse to modify their homes to make them accessible or make such minimal modifications (that are also minimally useful) so as to not attract attention.

On the other side of the coin, the stigma of specialized design has im-pacted its social acceptance. Historically, it has been viewed as expensive, clinical looking, and out of place. As a result, developers, builders, and owners have resisted including AD because they believe that such addi-tions will increase cost, have undesirable aesthetics, and decrease market-ability. Ultimately, even if specialized designs enable disabling design, they cannot minimize barriers for anyone if they are equally disdained by users and society alike.

To overcome the stigma of specialized design, some AT devices (i.e., per-sonal AT such as mobility aids) have been designed to celebrate and flaunt the stigmatizing trait, thus giving them a positive rather than negative charac-teristic (e.g., designer glasses and hearing aids, racing wheelchairs, or euro walkers). This type of design is well documented in Graham Pullin's re-cent book, *Design Meets Disability*, which illustrates how disability-inspired

FIGURE 3.8

When more is not better. Handicapped signs that tell us the obvious only add to the stigmatization of accessible design by drawing attention to differences in ability. For example, (A) a sign to identify where a curb cut is located at the street crossing in Mexico City, Mexico, or (B) the accessible drinking fountain in Cincinnati, OH, which has a handicapped symbol on the top (is it supposed to be only for people with disabilities?). (C) Then there are cases where the obvious is not even obvious with one sign, so multiple signs are used, such as the lift at the Maui Aquarium, Maui, HI (as if someone using the wheelchair would not recognize that a lift was an accessible feature with only one sign). (D) However, the general overkill award goes to the signage at the multipurpose bathroom at the Kokusai-Tenjijo Station in Tokyo, Japan, which is accessible to everyone, and there is enough signage to prove it. (E) Finally, *who says two heads are better than one?* This two-toilet, one-person restroom in a Target store (photo courtesy of Carrie Bruce, Research Scientist, CATEA, GA Tech, Atlanta, GA) shows that it is not just signage that is overdone. Would it not have been simpler and cheaper for everyone to use the "handicapped" toilet?

FIGURE 3.9

And when bigger is not better. Large signage is good, but supersized is unwarranted, as illustrated by the signage used to identify the handicapped parking along this road in Gateshead, England . . . unless these parking spaces are intended either for drivers with very low vision or perhaps helicopter pilots with disabilities.

FIGURE 3.10

It may look hot . . . but accessible design, no matter how good it looks, segregates users and causes stigma by drawing unnecessary attention to people with disabilities, as illustrated by (A) the accessible seating at the National Aquarium, Baltimore, MD, which is fire engine red set against a gray concrete floor and aluminum-colored bleachers; (B) the glass ramp on a church in Rome, IT (photo courtesy of Carrie Bruce, Research Scientist, CATEA, GA Tech, Atlanta, GA); or (C) the "handicapped" entrance to Bethesda Memorial Hospital, Boynton Beach, FL, to the left of the main revolving door (see also Figure 2.21), even though the large revolving door was specifically designed to accommodate mobility aids and luggage.

FIGURE 3.11

When different makes no difference. (A) The accessible sink in the Occupational Therapy building at Towson University, Towson, MD, is higher (not a bad idea to have different height sinks for tall and short individuals), and the pipes are wrapped to prevent scalding, but it is also a slightly different shape and has a different faucet. However, both sinks, at the appropriate heights, could have been the same and met the needs of all users. (B) The accessible entrance (left door) at the National Aquarium, Baltimore, MD is labeled as such, although there is no reason why it had to be different than the "general" entrance. (C) The appropriately signed access ramp to the right in the photo at the National Zoo, Mexico City, Mexico, enables wheelchair users to access the main ramp used by everyone. However, had the entire ramp been extended across the walkway, it would have eliminated the step, which is not only a tripping hazard but also segregates wheelchair users and forces them to travel a greater distance than other visitors.

design can take specialized design from medical necessity to fashion accessory. For other types of AT and AD, stigma can be overcome by integrating enabling aspects of design into everyday design rather than adding them on. In this type of design, functionality follows form, thus making enabling design the norm rather than the exception. As a result, design enablers that are embedded in everyday design are naturally invisible, not stigmatizing band-aids.

FOUR

Form Follows Function and Functionality: Universal Design as Enabling Design

Although accessible design (AD) is intended to provide greater access for individuals with disabilities, it is primarily designed to promote independent functioning among young adult wheelchair users who have a single disability. Moreover, much of the knowledge about AD is based on 30-year-old research and assumptions (mostly unvalidated consensus opinion) about the population of people with disabilities (i.e., American National Standards Institute Accessibility Standards, A117.1-1980). However, since the development of these early standards, the demographics of the population of people with disabilities have changed dramatically.

Five Facts About Universal Design as a Rehabilitation Strategy

- It is design for all users regardless of ability
- It has performance guidelines of why something is done
- It is design that equally enables activity and participation
- It is everyday design with specialized design built in
- It does not have to add cost

People are growing older and a larger number of individuals are living longer with disabilities. Not surprisingly, a considerable amount of research over the past three decades has shown that AD does not adequately compensate for the range of comorbidities and secondary conditions, including limitations in strength, stamina, reach, lifting legs, and sit-to-stand, which are common among older adults. Instead, using AD may do more to promote excess disability among older people than to ameliorate it (Sanford, Echt, & Malassigné, 1999; Sanford & Megrew, 1995). These findings suggest that a more universal approach based on the needs and capabilities of a wider range of individuals is warranted.

Similarly, AD, which is intended to promote independent functioning, may not be adequate for older adults who are often dependent in one or more basic activities of daily living or for their caregivers, for whom AD is not intended. In fact, even the definition of independence is different for elders. For older adults, independence often means staying out of a nursing home at any cost, even if that cost is dependence on caregiver assistance and the stigma of disability.

To overcome the stigma, segregation, and other functional shortcomings of AD, Ron Mace, an architect with a disability and a staunch advocate of AD throughout his life, developed the concept of universal design (UD). Although the concept first began to emerge in the late 1980s, Mace's ideas were fittingly first published in 1991, the same year as the initial *Americans with Disabilities Act Accessibility Guidelines*. The definition of UD included in that first publication is still the most generally accepted definition of UD today. In that seminal work, Mace defined UD as "the design of products and environments to be useable by all people, to the greatest extent possible, without the need for adaptation or specialized design" (Mace, Hardie, & Place, 1991).

Erlandson (2008) suggested an adaptation of the original definition, which used the term *entities* instead of *products and environments* to convey a broader sense of application to include buildings, workplaces, products, services, and educational materials and activities. To that, we could add technologies, hardware and interfaces, and systems. Regardless of the scale of the design, the essence of UD is simply "everyday design that minimizes demands for people with the broadest range and types of abilities."

Conceptually, UD does not view disability as a single point requiring specialized intervention, but a continuum of (dis)ability that would benefit from less-demanding design. It is neither based on accessible dimensional requirements nor a one-size-fits-all "McDonalds" approach to enhancing function. Rather, it is an approach to design that accommodates the widest possible range of body shapes, dimensions, and movements (Imrie, 2004) through contextually appropriate solutions. Because every context represents a unique set of needs and opportunities, a UD approach allows for contextual problem solving. As a result, UD, by its very nature, represents a distinctive situationally derived alternative in which function and functionality are built into everyday form. Moreover, by making everyday products, communications, and built environment more useable for as many people as possible, UD not only has built-in accessibility but also undetectable accessibility.

UNIVERSAL DESIGN VERSUS SPECIALIZED DESIGN

Universal design differs from specialized designs both conceptually and in physical form. Conceptually, specialized design is an add-on component that addresses the symptoms of person–environment misfit. Assistive technology (AT) is based on a medical model of disability, where design is added on to the person as a technological improvement to compensate for a medical limitation in body function or structure that underlies a disability in order to remove barriers to use of everyday designs. AD is added on to the environment to remove the barriers created by the misfit between everyday design and an individual or group of individuals with a specific type and level of functional limitation (e.g., people with low vision or poor dexterity).

In contrast, UD is an integral component of everyday design that addresses person–environment fit from the very beginning of the design process. As such, UD supports the broadest range of types and levels of all abilities for all individuals. According to Steinfeld (1994), there are two ways in which design can broaden the population of users from one or a few to as many as possible. First, designs can "forgive" limitations by accommodating different ways in which they can be used. Examples might include a door handle that can be used with different grips or body parts. Second, designs can "adapt" to users' abilities rather than the other way around, such as increasing timing of traffic lights to enable slower pedestrians to cross a street rather than making them rush to beat the light.

Universal Design Versus Specialized Design as a Rehabilitation Strategy
Specialized Design increases function of design for individuals or groups of individuals with similar ability limitations by adapting the person to everyday design or everyday design itself to make it more usable (*function = usability*). **Universal design** increases functionality of design for everyone by making everyday design more usable and inclusive (*functionality = usability + inclusivity*).

In addition, although many features might be both accessible and universal, such features will comprise the whole of the AD but will generally be only one component of the overall UD. In addition, the attributes of the design features will differ between the two. The attributes of AD features are based on *prescribed rules* that mandate design requirements for accessibility, whereas UD is based on *principles and guidelines* on how the overall design should perform.

For example, accessible requirements for toilet transfers prescribe attributes of a toilet that is 18 in. to the centerline from an adjacent wall with grab bars a minimum of 42 in. in length located on walls adjacent to and behind the toilet and a 5 ft space on one side the toilet. However, these attributes primarily accommodate independent transfers by wheelchair users with good upper body strength who can pull themselves from the wheelchair to the toilet and back again. As a result, AD attributes fail to accommodate individuals, including many older adults, who do not have good upper body strength, can bear weight, have difficulty going between sitting and standing positions, and/or cannot go up and down by themselves. To accommodate the widest range of users, attributes of a UD toilet, by contrast, would enable both standing and seated transfers either independently or with the assistance of one or two caregivers. Because there are many ways to achieve these ends within different contexts (e.g., bathroom size and configuration), UD principles guide how to design a toilet to meet these ends, rather than prescribe what to design. Thus, attributes of a UD toilet would likely include increased space for caregivers on both sides of the toilet while ensuring that support structures (they may or may not be grab bars or rails) are close enough to the toilet for an individual to grasp for either balance (i.e., assisted use) or bearing weight (i.e., independent use). Further, the supports need to be positioned and at a height to allow someone to go from a sitting to a standing position for a standing transfer or to slide from a wheelchair directly to the toilet for a seated transfer (Figure 4.1).

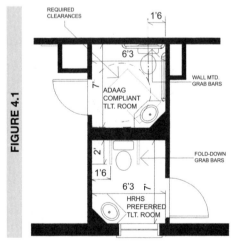

FIGURE 4.1

An alternative to AD? In some long-term care facilities, like this one for Holy Redeemer Health System in Meadowbrook, PA, by Ewing Cole Cherry, Brott, Architects, ADAAG compliance was met (top), and then, additional bathrooms were added (HRHS Preferred) to meet the needs of older residents and caregivers for both independent and assisted transfers.

These differences suggest that design problems to be solved by UD are very different than those addressed by AT and AD. For AT, the problem of someone getting on and off a toilet is defined by, "What product can be added to the context to help an individual with specific limitations get on and off the toilet?" For AD, it is, "What standard kit of attributes can be added to enable either an individual with specific limitations or a group of individuals with similar limitations get on and off the toilet?" For UD, it is, "How can the space be designed so that everyone can get on and off the toilet?" The differences in design solutions produced by these different approaches not only are remarkable but also have implications for who can use the toilet (Figure 4.2).

Universal design has sometimes been equated with human factors design and ergonomics, although it encompasses and transcends them both. Like human factors and ergonomic designs, UD is user centered, that is, designed for the user rather than forcing the user to accommodate the design. The two disciplines, however, differ in their approaches to user-centered design. Human factors, which is modeled after the design process

FIGURE 4.2

From here to eternity. (A) From freestanding AT to (C) unintegrated AD to integrated UD. They all assist with toilet transfers, but are they equal? (A) The toilet safety frame is the least expensive and does not require installation, but it is the least stable, can only be used by someone who can perform a standing transfer and often requires someone to assist. (B) The stainless steel and (C) wood (right) grab bars probably cost about the same because they require installation, but as a result, they are fixed to the wall and stable. Moreover, they can be used by individuals who perform either standing or sliding transfers. However, the stainless steel bars match the toilet paper holder, whereas the wood grab bars match the wood moldings in the bathroom and the rest of the home. So which one would you put in your home?

used by the U.S. military, seeks to achieve comfort, safety, performance, and privacy based on rigorous measures of human physical, sensory, and cognitive abilities. Ergonomics, on the other hand, has well-established applications in the work environment and product design. As such, it is more closely linked to goals of comfort and ease of use based on the physical, psychological, and social needs of individuals. Universal design, by its very nature as design for all, not only incorporates all of the design goals but also is based on the entire set of needs and abilities included in both human factors and ergonomic design.

Also contrasting with specialized design and to some extent ergonomics/human factors design, UD is compatible with the *International Classification of Functioning, Disability, and Health (ICF)* constructs of both activity and participation. Whereas specialized design is predicated on an Americans with Disabilities Act paradigm that engagement in activity begets participation in social roles, it defines function in terms of engagement in activity in hopes that functionality of design will foster participation. The ICF, in contrast, clearly identifies activity and participation as equal and independent, albeit interrelated, constructs. Although it is true that participation cannot occur without activity, activity can occur without participation. As such, design must address the two constructs separately and on their own terms.

Although the accepted definition of UD attributed to Mace does not explicitly state that it encompasses activity and participation, both are basic underlying principles of UD. In fact, Mace, himself, asserted that UD should "integrate people with disabilities into the mainstream" (Story, Mace, & Mueller, 1998, p. 11). On the other hand, other terms used interchangeably with UD are more explicit about inclusion. For example, the definition of *design for all*, the most commonly used term for UD in the European Union, states that it is "design for human diversity, social inclusion and equality" (EIDD Design for All Europe, 2011) and that the aim is so that ". . . everyone, including future generations, regardless of age, gender, capabilities or cultural background, can enjoy participating in the construction of our society" (Design for All Foundation, 2011). To reconcile this omission of inclusion from the original definition of UD, Steinfeld and Seelman (Steinfeld, 2010) have suggested a new consensus definition of UD as "a process that increases usability, safety, health and social participation through design and services that respond to the diversity of people and abilities."

Clearly, UD, by any name, is the only design approach that emphasizes both the usability as well as social inclusivity (which takes into consideration contextual inclusivity) aspects of design. Moreover, these qualities are captured by and articulated in the principles of UD, developed almost a decade and a half ago by a group of researchers, designers, and advocates at the Center for Universal Design, NC State University (1997).

THE PRINCIPLES OF UNIVERSAL DESIGN

With support from the National Institute on Disability and Rehabilitation Research, 10 leading proponents of UD, including architects; industrial, landscape, and graphic designers; and engineers, developed the seven principles of UD (Connell et al., 1997) to define the general performance goals and guidelines for UD. Until that time, there was no guidance other than a conceptual understanding to frame UD. The principles literally turned out to be the UD shot heard around the world. In less than a decade, they had been translated into a number of different languages and reprinted on hundreds of Web sites around the globe. This is not to say that the principles are perfect. On the one hand, they have never been validated. On the other, they may be too broad, too generic, and too difficult to apply. In fact, as discussed below, even the original authors have differing opinions on if or how they should be revised. Nonetheless, the principles have had relative longevity and are clearly recognized as the authoritative source for defining UD.

Developed almost 5 years before the ICF, and by a group of experts representing a completely different profession (i.e., design vs. public health), the seven principles of UD nonetheless capture the constructs of both activity and participation. Participation through inclusivity is the basis of the first principle of equitable use; whereas activity through usability (i.e., designs that forgive and adapt) is reflected in the following six principles: flexibility in use, simple and intuitive use, perceptible information, tolerance for error, low physical effort, and size and space for approach and use (Table 4.1).

Principle 1

Equitable Use. Design should be equally usable by and marketable to everyone. It should avoid segregating and stigmatizing users, and providing the same means of use for everyone (e.g., the same entry) and identical, if possible, should accomplish that goal. Providing the same means of use for everyone eliminates the need not only for specialized designs but also signage that calls attention to the specialized design (Figure 4.3). For example, providing a no-step entrance into a building will enable everyone to enter in the same way and avoid segregating users who cannot climb stairs. In addition, by providing the same design for everyone instead of everyday design for some and special designs for a few, the design should be equally

TABLE 4.1
Principles of Universal Design (Based on Center for Universal Design, 1997)

Principle 1: Equitable use: The design is useful and marketable to people with diverse abilities.

    1a. Provide the same means of use for all users: identical whenever possible; equivalent when not.

    1b. Avoid segregating or stigmatizing any users.

    1c. Provisions for privacy, security, and safety should be equally available to all users.

    1d. Make the design appealing to all users.

Principle 2: Flexibility in use: The design accommodates a wide range of individual preferences and abilities.

    2a. Provide choice in methods of use.

    2b. Accommodate right- or left-handed access and use.

    2c. Facilitate the user's accuracy and precision.

    2d. Provide adaptability to the user's pace.

Principle 3: Simple and intuitive use: Use of the design is easy to understand, regardless of the user's experience, knowledge, language skills, or current concentration level.

    3a. Eliminate unnecessary complexity.

    3b. Be consistent with user expectations and intuition.

    3c. Accommodate a wide range of literacy and language skills.

    3d. Arrange information consistent with its importance.

    3e. Provide effective prompting and feedback during and after task completion.

Principle 4: Perceptible information: The design communicates necessary information effectively to the user, regardless of ambient conditions or the user's sensory abilities.

    4a. Use different modes (pictorial, verbal, tactile) for redundant presentation of essential information.

    4b. Provide adequate contrast between essential information and its surroundings.

    4c. Maximize "legibility" of essential information.

    4d. Differentiate elements in ways that can be described (i.e., make it easy to give instructions or directions).

    4e. Provide compatibility with a variety of techniques or devices used by people with sensory limitations.

Principle 5: Tolerance for error: The design minimizes hazards and the adverse consequences of accidental or unintended actions.

    5a. Arrange elements to minimize hazards and errors: most used elements, most accessible; hazardous elements eliminated, isolated, or shielded.

    5b. Provide warnings of hazards and errors.

    5c. Provide fail-safe features.

    5d. Discourage unconscious action in tasks that require vigilance.

Principle 6: Low physical effort: The design can be used efficiently and comfortably and with a minimum of fatigue.

    6a. Allow user to maintain a neutral body position.

    6b. Use reasonable operating forces.

    6c. Minimize repetitive actions.

    6d. Minimize sustained physical effort.

(continued)

TABLE 4.1
Principles of Universal Design (*continued*)

Principle 7: Size and space for approach and use: Appropriate size and space is provided for approach, reach, manipulation, and use regardless of user's body size, posture, or mobility.

 7a. Provide a clear line of sight to important elements for any seated or standing user.

 7b. Make reach to all components comfortable for any seated or standing user.

 7c. Accommodate variations in hand and grip size.

 7d. Provide adequate space for the use of assistive devices or personal assistance.

FIGURE 4.3

Equitable means providing one means of use by all individuals regardless of body size or means of mobility, such as ramps that provide (A) the main entry to the High Museum, Atlanta, GA; (B) access to the exhibits in the Guggenheim Museum, New York, NY; and (C) general circulation in the Maui Aquarium, HI; and (D) the pedestrian crossing through, rather than over, a median island (thus eliminating the need for curb cuts) on the Georgia Tech campus, Atlanta, GA.

appealing and desirable for everyone. This will enhance not only usability but also marketability.

Principle 2

Flexibility in Use. Design should accommodate a wide range of individual preferences and abilities. Design should be forgiving, allowing use in more than one way, such as being able to use either hand or obtaining information from either visual signage or auditory announcements. It should also be tolerant of different abilities by facilitating and adapting to the user's levels of precision, accuracy, and pace (Figure 4.4).

Principle 3

Simple and Intuitive Use. Regardless of the user's experience, knowledge, language skills, or level of concentration, the way in which the design is

FIGURE 4.4

Flexibility is provided by hardware, such as (A) large light switches in Tokyo, Japan; (B) pedestrian crossing buttons in Toronto, Canada; and (C) lever handles that enable alternative methods of use including open hand, closed fist, or elbow. In addition, (D) the vertical handholds in the Vancouver Metro, Vancouver, Canada, permit grasping by people of almost any height, whereas (E) the ramp at the Archeology Museum in Mexico City, because of its location, has the flexibility to benefit any type of wheeled device.

Simple and intuitive means a few large buttons, an iconic numeric keypad, and bright colors, that are illustrated by (A) a big (red) HELP button that says "push me" in an emergency, (B) arrows pointing to the right for forward and to the left for back, and (C) individual destination buttons with exact fare on the Tokyo subway system.

FIGURE 4.5

used should be easily understood (Figure 4.5). In addition, how the device is used should be natural, intuitive, obvious, and spontaneous, even if the design has never been used before. To accomplish this, unnecessary complexity should be eliminated, and information about use should be presented in a manner that is consistent with its importance. For example, start and stop buttons could be larger, in unique colors, and arranged in a linear order. In addition, the design should provide prompting and feedback, such as a lighted elevator button, so that it is clear that it has been used properly.

Principle 4

Perceptible Information. For a design to effectively communicate with users who have different abilities to see, hear, communicate and understand, it should use as many different modes (e.g., pictorial, verbal, tactile) as possible to provide essential information to users. In addition, regardless of the mode used, it should maximize "legibility" of essential information (Figure 4.6) by providing adequate contrast (e.g., visual, auditory, cognitive) between essential information and its surroundings, such as white text on a black background, differentiating elements in ways that can be described (i.e., make it easy to give instructions or directions, such as "push the red button first"), and enabling users to use any assistive devices, such as low vision or hearing aids, that they might require.

FIGURE 4.6

Perceptible information can be achieved through the use of high-contrast, directional, and tactile information, such as (A) the handrail in European train station; (B) very (very) large, high-contrast signage at Tokyo Big Sight International Exhibition Center; (C) auditory information at the San Diego Zoo, San Diego, CA; (D) highly contrasting handholds on the Arlanda Express, Stockholm, Sweden; and (E) the control panel for a Toto Washlet, which has large buttons, text, pictographs, Braille, and LED lights to indicate water temperature.

Principle 5

Tolerance for Error. Error is both an issue of personal safety (e.g., leaving the oven on or turning the volume up too high on an assistive listening device) as well as prevention of inadvertent mistakes that can lead to loss of objects, data, time, or money. As a result, the design should minimize hazards and unintended actions that could have adverse outcomes. To do so, unconscious actions in tasks that require undivided attention should be discouraged; fail-safe features such as arranging elements so that those that are used most frequently are most accessible and those that are least used and/or hazardous are omitted or protected; and warnings of potential hazards and errors are clearly provided (Figure 4.7).

Principle 6

Low Physical Effort. Physical ease of use is perhaps the one quality that is most commonly associated with UD. However, low physical effort goes beyond ease of use to include efficiency, comfort, and minimizing fatigue. To accomplish these outcomes, the design should minimize strength required by enabling use of low operating forces (Figure 4.8); minimize the need to apply sustained force (e.g., holding a faucet to keep the water on); and minimize repetitive and simultaneous actions (e.g., pushing while turning). In addition, comfort and fatigue are linked not only to strength but also to the position from which the design is used, suggesting that design should be able to be used from a natural body position.

Tolerance for Error can take on many forms, including (A) the use of tactile and visually contrasting floor materials to indicate the location of intersections and stairways such as the black rubber Pirelli flooring top of a stair in the College of Architecture, GA Tech, Atlanta, GA that contrasts with the brick stair and gray carpeting that also has a red edging; (B) repeating highway signage to ensure that the information is conveyed, particularly when the information is confusing, such as the sign near Athens, GA; (C) stairs with integrated reflective nosings to differentiate each tread at the Georgia World Congress Center, Atlanta, GA; and (D) the information painted on the moving walkway at the Minneapolis-St. Paul Airport to remind travelers to walk on the left and stand on right.

FIGURE 4.7

Principle 7

Size and Space for Approach and Use. Size and space is the most architectural of the seven principles, focusing primarily on the amount and configuration of space (e.g., a bathroom that is large enough to turn a wheelchair around) as well as the hardware (e.g., door handles, appliance knobs, and faucet handles) and other product components that are used within a space. In addition, hardware and products should accommodate variations in hand and grip (e.g., door handles that are large enough to grasp). Finally, size of space should accommodate independent and assisted use, including any assistive technologies, such as a wheelchair or a walker that

Low Physical Effort is afforded by (A) an electronic faucet that requires no physical force to operate; (B) controls or objects that are located within comfortable reach, such as the interactive display at the Shedd Aquarium, Chicago, IL; (C) a refrigerator with a bottom freezer; and (D) an inclined moving walkway at the Copenhagen Airport, Copenhagen, Denmark.

FIGURE 4.8

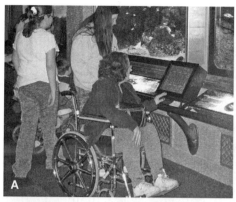

FIGURE 4.9

Size and Space includes maneuvering space for right- or left-handed approach and use as well as a clear line of sight to important elements, such as (A) the interactive display at the Shedd Aquarium, Chicago, IL; (B) the left fare gate at Shibuya Station, Tokyo, Japan that is wide enough for a wheelchair; (C) the bus shelter in Newcastle, England that will accommodate a large number of people with and without assistive devices; (D) an outdoor table in Strasbourg, France that has space for maneuvering and leg clearance for a wheelchair user; and (E) a door handle that is large enough to support a variety of grips (photo courtesy of Jean Yves Prodel, JYP Design, Choisy au Bac, France).

might be needed. In addition, the size and arrangement of space should enable important design features, such as an information kiosk or desk, to be clearly visible, accessible, and obtainable regardless of stature or mode of travel (Figure 4.9).

ACTIVITY, PARTICIPATION, AND THE PRINCIPLES

Activity is clearly the objective of Principles 2–6, as are the human factors and ergonomic goals of performance, ease of use, comfort, security, and privacy. However, the link to participation, which distinguishes UD from other user-centered approaches and its unique link to the ICF, is not as clear. There are several reasons for this lack of clarity. First, Version 1.1 of the principles published in December 1995 predated the ICF by more than 5 years (Story, 2001), so it is understandable that the participation construct is not as clearly identifiable. Second, equitable use, which first appeared in the third draft of the principles in August 1995 as "design does not disadvantage or stigmatize any group of users," was actually intended to address the concept of social equality, not participation (Story, 2001), although egalitarianism is clearly an integral component of participation. In fact, the authors debated whether social equity was a fundamental overarching goal of UD or the only principle that did not focus on usability.

Ultimately, although components of participation were incorporated as social equity/integration in the principle of equitable use, they were articulated as an outcome of use, which is a measure of activity, rather than as inclusivity, which is a measure of participation. The idea that inclusion is an outcome of use fails to recognize that activity and participation, despite being linked, are separate constructs (WHO, 2001) that are likely to be enabled by different design attributes. Without a clear distinction between

FIGURE 4.10

A   B

Is it universal? Universal design is usable by all people . . . without the need for adaptation or specialized design. (A, B) Great Grips are a great idea for retrofitting doorknobs to meet the seven activity principles of universal design. However, they are, themselves, adaptations that are added on. Therefore, although they literally comply with the seven principles, they do not meet the definition of UD itself. They are a good example of why there is a need to clearly define inclusivity as distinct from activity. (photos courtesy of Pat Going, Great Grips, Inc.).

use and inclusion, which is a function of both social and contextual integration, some adaptive designs, such as Great Grips (Figure 4.10), can actually meet all seven principles, yet not fit the definition of UD ("without the need for adaptation or specialized design").

In its attempt to address the various aspects of participation, equitable use not only combines three independent ideas (i.e., sameness of use, social integration, and contextual integration) into one principle but also does not clearly differentiate between the three. First, it implies sameness of activity, such as entering the same door or going to the same floor level, but not necessarily by the same means (Figure 4.11). Therefore, although design that enables all individuals to engage in the same activity offers opportunities for participation, it does not necessarily ensure participation. The same is true for equal provisions for privacy, security, and safety. Being equally available only suggests that, like specialized design, there is a provision for activity to occur. That activity could be separate but equal.

Second, the principle addresses both stigma and segregation. Stigma itself is complex because it is the result of both contextual design and segregation. At the simplest level, stigma can be created by design that is not integrated into the context and hence appears different than everyday

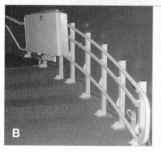

(A) Providing different means to accomplish the same activity, such as the elevator to access the street above on the Riverwalk in San Antonio, TX; (B) the lift at the Maui Aquarium, Maui, HI, which requires people with mobility impairments to ride up alongside the stairs; and (C) street crossings in Sweden, such as this one in Lund, segregate individuals who need curb cuts, to one side of the crosswalk. (D) However, oftentimes the alternate means is not obvious and hard to find, such as the elevator at the National Aquarium in Baltimore that is located at the end of a dark winding hallway.

FIGURE 4.11

design, such as a home with a ramp on the front. Nonetheless, although providing the same means of use for all users (Figure 4.12), such as a sloping walkway rather than different means of use for different users, such as a ramp and stairs, is nonstigmatizing, not all nonstigmatizing design engenders participation.

On the other hand, segregation is clearly a social construct that will preclude participation. Segregation is generally a function of providing different means of use, such as a ramp, elevator, or lift, and often in a different location parking or seating. Thus, segregation not only precludes participation but also causes stigma when it is further exacerbated by signage used to draw attention to the segregated features (Figures 4.13 and 4.14). As such, avoiding segregation addresses social integration, a direct measure of participation outcomes.

To further complicate matters, appealing for all implies sameness of use as well as aesthetics. Although deliberately vague, appealing suggests that a design would be socially acceptable and therefore desirable by anyone because it is everyday design. In other words, it looks the same and is usable by everyone. As a result, it avoids stigma and segregation.

FIGURE 4.12

Stigma can be avoided by providing the same means of use integrated into the design, such as (A, B) the same lavatories in public restrooms and the same circulation systems in (C) the San Diego Zoo, San Diego, CA, and (D) at the Guggenheim Museum, New York, NY, where a ramp is celebrated as the main rather than ancillary circulation.

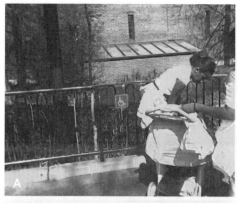

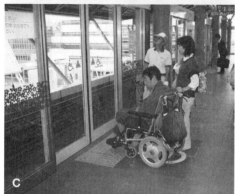

FIGURE 4.13

One is the loneliest number. Signage segregates even when there is contextual integration, such as (A) the designated "handicapped" spaces at the National Zoo, Washington, DC, and (B) the Beluga exhibit at the Georgia Aquarium, Atlanta, GA (photo courtesy of Carrie Bruce, Research Scientist, CATEA, Georgia Tech, Atlanta, GA) that were no different than any other viewing space. (C) The designated wheelchair space at the entry to the train at the Kokusai-Tenjijo Station, Tokyo, segregates passengers even though the particular door is no different than any other door (except for the gentleman in the cap, a station attendant whose job is to lay down a portable ramp to make up for the height difference between the platform and the train). (D) The sign outside of Seamen's Bank in Provincetown, MA, segregates users by stating that it is a *handicapped handrail*. The question is which users are segregated? Does it segregate people with disabilities by reserving the rail? Or does it segregate bicycle riders, who are not allowed to use the rail and have to go around the back of the building (photo courtesy of Carrie Bruce, Research Scientist, CATEA, Georgia Tech, Atlanta, GA)?

FIGURE 4.14

Ramps are not just for wheelchairs anymore. (A) Signage, such as the one pointing to the wheelchair and bicycle ramp for the tram in Pittsburgh, PA; (B) the path for wheelchairs and strollers in Honolulu, HI; and (C) the elevator at the Vancouver Aquarium, which is also for wheelchairs and strollers, can unintentionally segregate a variety of different user groups, even if the ramp, path, or elevator could be used by everyone. On the other hand, if all routes were universal, there would not be a need for a sign in the first place.

Nonetheless, although this creates opportunities for participation to be achieved, it does not necessarily achieve it.

To address these deficiencies, it has been suggested elsewhere (Sanford, 2010) that the principle of equitable use be revised to reflect activity alone and that two new principles, social integration and contextual integration, be added to specifically address participation outcomes (Table 4.2). These changes clearly distinguish between seven "activity" principles and two "participation" principles.

TABLE 4.2
Revisions to Principles of Universal Design

Principle 1. Equitable use and appeal: The design is useful and marketable to people with diverse abilities.

    1a. Provide the same means (i.e., concurrent) of use for all users.
    1b. Provide the same opportunities for privacy and safety/security for all users.
    1c. Is equally suitable for use and in demand by.

Principle 8. Social integration: The design provides opportunities for individuals to participate in activities with others.

    8a. Enables engagement in activities **when** wanted or needed.
    8b. Enables engagement in activities **where** wanted or needed.
    8c. Enables engagement in activities **with whom** is desired or needed.

Principle 9. Contextual integration: The design is appealing for all.

    9a. Is aesthetically compatible with other features of the design for.
    9b. Looks, feels, smells, and sounds like it is an integral part of the overall design.
    9c. Is socially and culturally compatible.

Principle 8

Social Integration. The social integration principle is the essence of inclusion and participation. It promotes inclusion by providing opportunities for individuals to participate in activities with others. It does so by facilitating engagement in activities when, where, and with whom one wants or needs to engage in activities (Figure 4.15).

Principle 9

Contextual Integration. In addition to integrating people, design should also be compatible and integrated with the physical, social, and cultural context. This goes beyond aesthetics to include social and cultural acceptability. By looking, feeling, smelling, and sounding like it is an integral part of the overall design, the design will be aesthetically, culturally, and socially appealing for all (Keates & Clarkson, 2004). Although this does not necessarily mean that a design will be totally integrated (Figure 4.16), the design will not be stigmatizing, and users will want to use it (Figure 4.17).

OTHER APPROACHES TO UD PRINCIPLES

The UD principles have not been without other critics. In fact, several other proponents of UD have lodged similar complaints and proposed alternatives. The most notable suggestions for alternative versions of the UD principles are summarized below.

Steinfeld. Another approach to rectify the activity/participation debate as well as to address concerns that the principles are difficult to interpret

FIGURE 4.15

Social integration enables people to engage with whom they want, when they want, and where they want, such as (A) the kitchen in the Buck Residence, Chicago, IL (photo courtesy of Allan Browne, EHLS, Glenview, IL); (B) the beach in Honolulu, HI; and (C) a water fountain in Cincinnati, OH.

FIGURE 4.16

Contextual but not quite total social integration. This entry to a public restroom in Franklin Square Park, Philadelphia, PA is integrated contextually, but there is a ramp on one side and a stair on the other. The entry is low enough to the ground that a sloping walk on both sides could have been usable by everyone.

and apply to design problems has been proposed by Ed Steinfeld, Director of the IDEA Center and the Rehabilitation Engineering Research Center on Universal Design in the Built Environment at University of Buffalo. Steinfeld (Steinfeld & Danford, 2007; Global Universal Design Commission [GUDC], 2011) has suggested a set of key goals derived from the principles that are stated in concise terms and with clear and measurable outcomes that apply across all scales of design. Four goals (shaded in dark gray in Table 4.3)—body fit, comfort, awareness, and understanding—are activity performance goals derived from human factors and ergonomics (including anthropometry, biomechanics, perception, and cognition). Wellness (unshaded portion in Table 4.3) is focused on health and environmental quality issues, and the remaining three goals (shaded in light gray in Table 4.3)—social integration, personal adaptation, and contextual appropriateness (which is a reflection of social values toward resources and physical context)—are related to support for social participation.

Steinfeld's UD Goals

Body fit—accommodate a wide a range of body sizes and abilities.
Comfort—keep demands within desirable limits of body function and user expectations.
Awareness—ensure that critical information for use is easily perceived.
Understanding—make methods of operation and use intuitive, clear, and unambiguous.

Wellness—contribute to health promotion, avoidance of disease, and protection from environmental hazards.

Social integration—treat all groups with dignity and respect.

Personal adaptation—incorporate opportunities for choice and the expression of individual preferences.

Contextual appropriateness—respect and reinforce cultural values and the social and environmental context of any design project.

Erlandson. Erlandson (2008) offers another view in his book, *Universal and Accessible Design for Products, Services, and Processes,* suggesting that there are

FIGURE 4.17

Contextual integration is the incorporation of prosthetic features into everyday design through the use of compatible materials with appropriate aesthetics and imagery, whether it be (A) molded plastic handholds in a restroom on a Boeing 737-800; (B) an indigenous wooden ramp with wagon wheels at a private home in St. Louis, MO; (C) tactile warnings on stair landings on the Georgia Tech campus that not only provide information by contrasting from the surrounding smooth, light concrete but also match the brick accents in the walkway beyond; or (D) a ramp that blends with the natural rock at the southern entrance to Red Rocks Amphitheater, Morrison, CO.

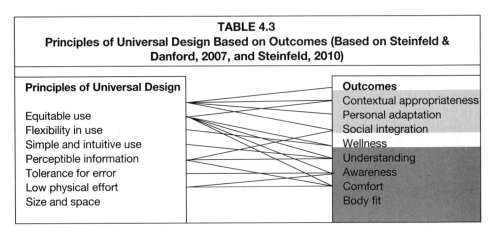

TABLE 4.3
**Principles of Universal Design Based on Outcomes (Based on Steinfeld &
Danford, 2007, and Steinfeld, 2010)**

Principles of Universal Design	Outcomes
	Contextual appropriateness
Equitable use	Personal adaptation
Flexibility in use	Social integration
Simple and intuitive use	Wellness
Perceptible information	Understanding
Tolerance for error	Awareness
Low physical effort	Comfort
Size and space	Body fit

eight principles and categorizing them as human factor principles targeted at the person, including ergonomics, perception, and cognition (shaded in light gray in Table 4.4); process principles dealing with flexibility, error management, efficiency, and stability/predictability (unshaded in Table 4.4); and transcending principles covering equitability (shaded in dark gray in Table 4.4). Like Steinfeld's approach, Erlandson correctly points out that equitability transcends the other principles; imposing constraints force the integration of all the other principles. Further, same as the previously mentioned Principle 9, he suggests that designs should be contextually appropriate. Nonetheless, he does not link equitability and participation despite his use of the ICF as a conceptual framework for disability.

Finkel and Gold. Yet, another variation of the principles was proposed by Finkel and Gold (1999), Canadian researchers based on focus group feedback to validate the seven principles. Focus group participants indicated that all seven principles were essential for good design. However, they voiced a number of concerns. Like Steinfeld's assertions, they suggested that the principles needed wording changes to be more easily understood by the general public. As a result, the researchers suggested wording changes to the principles that included the following: *marketable* rather

TABLE 4.4
Universal Design Principles (Based on Erlandson, 2008)

1. Ergonomically sound	5. Error-managed (proofed)
2. Perceptible	6. Efficient
3. Cognitively sound	7. Stable and predictable
4. Flexible	8. Equitable

than *equitable* for Principle 1, *uncomplicated* rather than *simple and intuitive* for Principle 3, and *understandable* rather than *perceptible* information for Principle 4.

In addition, the focus groups suggested that the principles needed to consider environmental sensitivity issues, including both sensitivity to environmental issues, such as reducing energy expenditures, and sensitivity of individuals to the environment, such as environmental allergies and toxicity of materials. Based on this feedback, the principles were revised and expanded as follows:

1. **Marketable**—The design is saleable and available to a wide range of users.
2. **Flexible**—The design accommodates a wide range of capacities and preferences.
3. **Uncomplicated and understandable**—The design is easy to understand, regardless of the user's experience, knowledge, language skills, or current concentration level.
4. **Safe**—The design provides security.
5. **Easy to use and access**—The design provides for easily getting to, getting at, reaching, using, and handling objects and spaces.
6. **Reasonable effort**—The design is used efficiently and comfortably.
7. **Environmentally sensitive**—The design provides appropriate use of resources and consideration of environmental issues.

UD PRINCIPLES AND THE ICF: A COMPARISON OF ALTERNATIVES

On the surface, Steinfeld's framework appears to be the most divergent from the original seven principles. However, they are, in fact, the most compatible, having been derived from the Principles themselves. As Steinfeld maintains, they are goals, not principles. More precisely, they are human-centered goals that have measureable activity and participation outcomes. The principles, on the other hand, are performance-based criteria that will enable design to support those human-centered goals and achieve the desired activity and participation outcomes. As such, Steinfeld's goals are antecedent to the principles. They provide the ICF health, activity, and participation bases for why design should be the way it is. In other words, the goals provide the rationale for the principles and (as discussed in the next section) a way of determining whether a design is truly universal.

Wording nuances of the principles notwithstanding, the four alternatives discussed above are generally in agreement on the basic principles.

There is also clear consensus that the original seven principles are incomplete. Moreover, all of the authors suggest alternatives for equitability. Three of these, Sanford, Steinfeld, and Erlandson, recognize that equitability is fundamentally different than the other six. Sanford and Steinfeld rectify the discrepancy by deconstructing equitability and creating new principles/ goals that focus on participation-focused concepts of social inclusion and contextual integration to balance the activity-focus manifest by the other principles/goals. Erlandson similarly argues that equitability is a social construct but that it transcends the other principles rather than being a separate but equal construct. In contrast, Finkel and Gold's suggestion, which equates equitability to marketability alone, is furthest from the other three and the ICF. Whereas this approach clarifies the meaning of equitability in a similar manner to Sanford, the latter created two new participation principles not only to compensate but also to elevate participation to an equal level as activity. Finkel and Gold's interpretation totally loses all linkages to the participation aspects of the ICF that make UD unique.

Despite general agreement in principle, there are some notable changes that are suggested. First, although most of us would agree that Finkel and Gold's principle of environmental sensitivity is a desirable design approach and applicable to all good design (and, in their defense, they do use good design interchangeably with UD), we can question whether it is actually UD because it has nothing to do with either the usability or the inclusivity of the design.

A similar question can be asked about Steinfeld's goal of wellness. Clearly, wellness is a universal goal, but does that translate to UD? Wellness differs from the other seven goals in Steinfeld's framework. The other goals embody universal outcomes that are applicable to all design. However, not all designs have wellness-related outcomes. Thus, whereas UD can promote wellness and positive health outcomes (see Part 2), promoting positive health outcomes is not a universal outcome of design. So, although we might agree that all design should minimally do no harm (which is inherent in tolerance for error), the question is whether it must contribute to health promotion, avoidance of disease, and positive health outcomes to be UD. Further, in an attempt to better align UD with the ICF, the focus on wellness as a health outcome loses much of the intent of the principle of tolerance for error, which more broadly encompasses free from mistakes, including those that do not have health consequences (e.g., the undo command on a computer). Ironically, by explicitly identifying health as an outcome of UD, Steinfeld's framework lacks a more universal outcome of all design, which is articulated in the principle of tolerance for error.

In their defense, the original principles were developed prior to the ICF, so it is not surprising that they do not exactly fit the ICF model. Nonetheless, because they are widely accepted and are conceptually compatible with the ICF's activity and participation approach, there is no reason why the principles could not be more closely aligned with the ICF. Whether that is a product of revising the principles to more clearly articulate participation, creating a crosswalk between newly defined sets of UD activity and participation goals and the ICF, as suggested by Steinfeld, is open to discussion. Regardless of how the relationship between the principles and the ICF is ultimately conceptualized, there is no dispute that the goal of UD is to support human-centered function through functionality of form. In UD, activity/usability and participation/inclusivity principles are the embodiment of functionality.

IS IT UNIVERSAL?

Many efforts have assessed function and accessibility of design for people with disabilities based on accepted standards or guidelines. Many others have addressed the functionality of design for the general population. However, no existing instruments address function and functionality of form for the range of users embodied by the concept of UD. In fact, as suggested above, even an assessment instrument based on the seven widely acknowledged principles of UD would only address the activity aspects of UD and without identification of specific user populations.

Frequently and mistakenly, UD is assessed by standards of accessibility. Although the prescriptive accessibility requirements are measureable, they only pertain to people at the lower end of the bell curve. Further, they are one-dimensional, focusing only on activity-related aspects of design. As a result, the focus on activity performance by individuals with disabilities fails to assess whether a design is "usable to the greatest extent possible" as asserted by the most widely accepted definition of UD. For example, a toilet with 42-in. grab bars alongside and behind the toilet and a 5-ft-wide space for transfer meets requirements for AD based on the sliding transfers by nonambulatory wheelchair users. However, this configuration neither effectively accommodates standing transfers by individuals who are semi-ambulatory and only need to use wheelchairs some of the time nor facilitates assisted transfers by one or more caregivers (Sanford et al., 1999).

Basically, the extent to which any design is universal is a function of the degree to which the attributes of design features minimize demands on the widest range of users (Figure 4.18). As a result, the best assessment of whether a design is actually universal would be the measurement of its functionality in terms of positive activity (i.e., usability) and participation (i.e., inclusivity) outcomes for all users under conditions of actual use. Unfortunately, although such an undertaking is the only way to establish whether a particular design is truly universal, the inclusion of all users representing the widest range of abilities is clearly not practical.

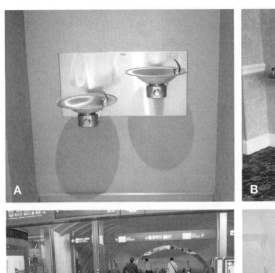

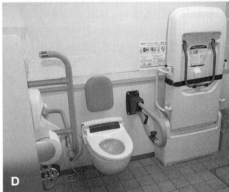

FIGURE 4.18

Is it Universal or is it Accessible? (A, B) Is the design feature one fountain, or is it more than one fountain? Sometimes it is hard to tell. (A) Does the plate on the front make it one fountain and (B) the connection behind the wall make it four fountains? Does it matter as long as everyone can drink water? In many cases, if there is a choice in use, then the feature is universal, even if all of the attributes are not. So, is it universal if an activity can be performed in the same place and the same manner, but the activity is done with different features? (C) Is it universal when anyone without a mobility limitation can use any of the fare gates at Shibuya Station, Tokyo, Japan, but visually impaired travelers who need tactile surfaces for guidance (light flooring leading to and away from the gate) can only use the gate on the left, while travelers who need wheelchairs can only use the wide fare gate in the center of the photo? (D) Finally, is it universal when each fixture in the multipurpose bathroom at Kokusai-Tenjoji Station, Tokyo, Japan, can be used by someone, even if they all cannot be used by everyone?

An alternative, therefore, to determine whether a design is universal is to evaluate the design on the performance guidelines set forth by the UD principles. This can be done prospectively during the design process to measure potential demands on expected users or retrospectively after the design is completed to measure demands on actual users. In prospective assessments, the expected (or potential) impact of design on activity performance and participation can be evaluated based on predefined assumptions of activity and participation among individuals across the (dis)ability continuum. Retrospective assessments, on the other hand, can be used to measure real demands under conditions of actual use based on interactions between design and individuals with measureable abilities.

Assessment of design based on the principles of UD is multidimensional, including function and functional aspects of design. The UD principles also provide a more robust understanding of function as a defined set of usability outcomes (i.e., flexibility, simple and intuitive, perceptibility, ease, limiting error, and sufficient space) rather than the focus on either dependence or difficulty that is associated with accessibility requirements.

Many UD assessments have been reported in the literature. However, few actual assessments have been published, and those instruments that have been published have largely been based on the principles of UD or a variation of them (e.g., City of Winnepeg, 2001; Finkel and Gold, 1999). In other words, the objective of most assessments has been to evaluate how effectively a design exemplifies each principle of UD. On the positive side, the principles have received widespread acceptance and consensus acknowledgement throughout the world. On the negative side, they are based on consensus opinion, not empirical data; they lack measurable outcomes and are therefore open to interpretation; and they have not been validated to any large extent. Moreover, despite their basis in the UD principles, many of the assessments have operationalized the performance-based principles as prescriptive accessibility requirements. For example, just like the accessibility codes, a 1:12 slope is generally considered the maximum slope of a universal designed ramp. Although it might be mandated by accessibility codes as accessible, UD cannot be prescribed. Rather, it must be commensurate with the range of abilities of all users. As a result, a ramp at a senior center might need to be 1:18 to accommodate the many older adults who lack the upper body strength of younger wheelchair users. Unfortunately, most existing assessments focus on specific limitations (e.g., will it be simple and intuitive for people with cognitive limitations) rather than the range of abilities of all users (e.g., will it be simple and intuitive regardless of cognitive ability, and if not, what level of ability will be needed?).

UD Checklist. In contrast to other assessments that focused on limitations, Finkel and Gold (1999) developed a process of evaluating how well a proposed design would respond to both the principles of UD and the range of human abilities, including vision, hearing, stature, balance, upper body strength and mobility, lower body strength and mobility, cognition, dexterity, communication and speech, and life span. The checklist was further developed for the City of Winnepeg (2001) Universal Design Policy. In this later version, design was assessed in two ways. First, it was measured against the range of functioning (i.e., ability) by shading boxes (Figure 4.19) to indicate the degree to which (e.g., 20% per box) the solution met each type of ability. Second, it was measured against the Statements of Good Design (i.e., the principles) by again shading boxes to indicate the extent to which the design met the criteria for each statement.

Although the UD Checklist was the first to assess design according to abilities rather than limitations, it did not directly evaluate the principles by ability. Rather, after the checklist was completed, the results of the two sections were compared (in some way) to be able to make decisions about appropriateness. In addition, the scale of design was not defined, other than the suggestion that in large designs the process may need to focus on a number of individual issues, such as the entry, reception, offices, washrooms, lunchroom, and so forth. This approach only considers architectural space and does not consider specific features in each area. Third, the checklist was intended for proposed designs, not actual designs in use. As a result, it does not consider how space is used, only how it is intended to be used.

Universal Design Assessment Protocol. A second approach to assessment is the Universal Design Assessment Protocol (UDAP) Sanford, 2004, 2010), developed at the Center for Universal Design at NC State at about the same time as the Canadian UD Checklist. In contrast to the checklist, UDAP (Figure 4.20) not only directly assesses the principles by ability but also does so across the entire range of abilities (e.g., moving body parts, maintaining posture, changing position) rather than just at the macro level (e.g., upper and lower body motor function). Similarly, it evaluates design more at the level of each performance guideline, not just each principle, thus affording greater precision of analysis. Finally, UDAP provides an understanding of the universal nature across all scales of design either prospectively or retrospectively.

The development of such an assessment instrument was challenging. The instrument, itself, had to be universal in its approach, application, and

Design under consideration:					
Facilitator:					
Range of Functioning					
	Rating				Comments
Vision					
Hearing					
Stature					
Balance					
Cognition					
Lower body strength and mobility					
Upper body strength and mobility					
Communication					
Dexterity					
Life Span					
Statements of Good Design:					
	Rating				Comments
Marketable					
Flexible					
Uncomplicated & Understandable					
Safe					
Easy to Use and Access					
Reasonable Effort					
Environmentally Sensitive					
Appropriateness and Actions to be Taken					

FIGURE 4.19

Universal Design Checklist (Adapted from Finkel and Gold, 1999)

audience. At a minimum, the assessment had to be useful to and consequently used by people who were likely to make or influence decisions about design. Therefore, the assessment had to be able to be implemented by and useful to a diverse group of rehabilitation and design professionals, including experts in the functional and social needs of individuals (e.g., rehabilitation engineers, occupational therapists, gerontologists, clinicians) as well as experts in design and construction (e.g., architects, interior designers, product designers, contractors, and remodelers).

The UDAP is based on the environmental press model (Lawton & Nahemow, 1973). As detailed in Chapter 1, the model predicts that demands imposed by the environment related to a particular ability (e.g., reaching) will differentially affect people based on the level of their abilities (e.g., no limitations to severe limitations in reach). It is also based on the ICF (WHO, 2001), which promotes both activity and participation as important health outcomes. The more supportive a design is, the more demands match abilities, the lower the press and the easier it is to engage in activities and participate in society. Thus, the greater the level of UD, the lower the press.

However, how press should be measured has been debated for 40 years. In the UDAP, press is measured by the level of impact that environmental demands will have on users' motor, mental, sensation, perception, and communicative abilities. As a result, assessments of UD can be performed either prospectively in the design phase or retrospectively in use.

Performance guidelines in the seven activity principles and two participation principles described above are the basis for the assessment. In total, the nine principles included 34 performance guidelines, each representing a different type of environmental demand. Each of the 34 guidelines was assessed across the full range of motor, mental, perception, and sensation and communication abilities described earlier to assess design from the perspective of the full range of users.

Demand strength was rated for each guideline by the level of ability (on a scale from *severe* [4] to *no limitation* [1]) that was supported by a specific design feature. The higher the overall score is (i.e., the greater the severity of functional limitations supported by a particular feature), the more universal a particular environmental feature is. Thus, (1) for any environmental feature limitation (e.g., ramp), (2) a performance guideline provides an evaluation criterion (e.g., is it used in same/equivalent manner) that is assessed, (3) for each type of ability (e.g., motor functions of maintaining posture, changing position, moving around, manipulating objects, and coordinating movements), (4) based on the specific level of ability (i.e., 0–4) that the design feature is able to support. A score can be assessed for each criterion/each principle for all abilities (add row scores) or for each type of ability for all principles (add column scores). A total UD score for any environmental feature assessed is merely the sum of all columns or rows.

Although the assessment was designed to embrace activity and participation of people with all types of abilities, the 612-cell matrix (34 guidelines × 18 abilities) proved, in the end, to be overly complex, unwieldy, and impractical for the intended audiences to actually quantify UD. This is not to suggest that the instrument is not useful. It can be applied as a conceptual framework either prospectively or retrospectively to identify and understand both barriers and facilitators and to whom at any scale of design.

FIGURE 4.20

PRESS

COMPETENCE

	MOTOR FUNCTIONING						ABILITIES

Moving Body
Moving muscles and joints to complete tasks
- ☐ Head & Neck Movement
- ☐ Upper Extremity Movement
- ☐ Hand Movement
- ☐ Lower Extremity Movement
- ☐ Trunk Movement

Maintaining Posture
Initiating & sustaining body positions to perform tasks
- ☐ Balancing
- ☐ Standing
- ☐ Sitting

Changing Position
Transitioning from lying, standing or sitting positions to other positions
- ☐ Whole Body Positioning
- ☐ Lying
- ☐ Sit to Stand
- ☐ Whole Body Transfer

Moving Around
Moving oneself across space
- ☐ Ambulation
- ☐ Device-aided Mobility
- ☐ Climbing
- ☐ Crawling

Manipulating Objects
Reaching, lifting, handling and transporting objects
- ☐ Reaching
- ☐ Grasping
- ☐ Lifting/Lowering
- ☐ Pushing/Pulling
- ☐ Carrying
- ☐ Releasing
- ☐ Turning

Coordinating Movements
Performing movements in a purposeful, orderly combination
- ☐ Hand Coordination
- ☐ Eye-Hand-Foot Coordination
- ☐ Lower Body Coordination
- ☐ Upper Body Coordination
- ☐ Foot-Hand Coordination

Environmental Demands related to:

1) Design Feature		2) Performance Guideline		3) Ability Level		4) Environmental Demand									TOT DEF
AB	N/A	AB	N/A	AB	N/A	AB	N/A	AB	N/A	AB	N/A	AB	N/A	AB	N/A	TOT APP DEMANDS

Person-Environment Fit

Personal Abilities

0 = No one w/ or w/o limitations in…

VEL

LE

1 = People w/o limitations in …
2 = People w/ moderate limitations in
3 = People w/ severe limitations in …

COMPETENCE

Universal Design Assessment Protocol

FIGURE 4.20 (*continued*)

PRESS

Environmental Demands related to: / Person-Environment Fit	MENTAL FUNCTIONING								
	Perceiving Space Identifying oneself in relation to location and time	**Attending to Task** Initiating and sustaining focus on tasks	**Understanding and Interpreting Numbers** Understanding & applying numerical concepts	**Remembering** Using memory to complete tasks	**Learning** Understanding instructions, reasoning and making judgments	**Reasoning** Developing concepts & processing abstract information	**Executive Functioning** Engaging in complex goal directed behaviors to complete tasks.	**Reacting to Stimuli** Ability to react quickly to stimuli	ABILITIES
	❑ Orientation ❑ Wayfinding ❑ Spatial Relations	❑ Selective Attention ❑ Sustained Concentration ❑ Divided Attention	❑ Numeracy ❑ Telling Time ❑ Calculation ❑ Mathematical Reasoning	❑ Short-term Memory ❑ Long-term Memory ❑ Prospective Memory ❑ Procedural Memory	❑ Learning	❑ Abstract ❑ Logical ❑ Sequencing	❑ Organization and Planning ❑ Time Management ❑ Cognitive Flexibility ❑ Insight ❑ Judgment ❑ Problem Solving	❑ Auditory Speed ❑ Visual Speed ❑ Haptic Speed ❑ Olfactory Speed ❑ Multi-modal Speed	
Personal Abilities LE / VEL *0 = No one w/ or w/o limitat...* ... *1 = People w/o limitations in…* *2 = People w/ moderate limitations in* *3 = People w/ severe limitations in…*	1) Design Feature 2) Performance Guideline 3) Ability Level 4) Environmental Demand								
	AB N/A	AB N/A	AB N/A	AB N/A	AB N/A	AB N/A	AB N/A	AB N/A	TOT DEF TOT APP DEMANDS

COMPETENCE

COMPETENCE

PRESS

COMPETENCE

SENSATION AND PERCEPTION

ABILITIES

Seeing
Sensing the presence of light and form, size, shape and color of visual stimuli

☐ Near Vision
☐ Far Vision
☐ Central Visual Acuity
☐ Visual Field
☐ Color Discrimination
☐ Visual Accommodation
☐ Light Sensitivity
☐ Visual Scanning

Hearing
Sensing the presence of and discriminating the location, pitch, loudness and quality of sounds

☐ Noise Sensitivity
☐ Localization of Sound
☐ Sound Detection
☐ Speech Discrimination
☐ Auditory Discrimination

Sensing Odors and Flavors
Sensing the presence of and discriminating differences in odors/flavors

☐ Smell
☐ Taste
☐ Odor Sensitivity
☐ Flavor Sensitivity

Sensing and Feeling by Touch
Feeling and sensing variations in touch and texture

☐ Cutaneous Discrimination
☐ Material Sensitivity
☐ Environmental Sensitivity

1) Design Feature   2) Performance Guideline   3) Ability Level   4) Environmental Demand

| AB | N/A | AB | N/A | AB | N/A | AB | N/A | AB | N/A | AB | N/A | AB | N/A |

TOT DEF
TOT APP DEMANDS

Environmental Demands related to:

Person-Environment Fit

Personal Abilities

0 = No one w/ or w/o limitations
1 = People w/o limitations in....
2 = People w/ moderate limitations in....
3 = People w/ severe limitations in....

LEVEL

COMPETENCE

FIGURE 4.20 *(continued)*

FIGURE 4.20 (continued)

COMPETENCE

PRESS

COMPETENCE

COMMUNICATION

ABILITIES

| | | | | | | | | TOT DEF |
| | | | | | | | | TOT APP DEMANDS |

Producing Communication
Expressing meaningful messages using forms of language
□ Speaking
□ Writing
□ Formal Sign
□ Gesturing
□ Drawing

Receiving Communication
Decoding messages in different forms of language to obtain their meaning
□ Reading
□ Listening
□ Understanding Sign
□ Understanding Gestures
□ Understanding Drawing

Conversing
Engaging in a purposeful exchange of language with one or more people.
□ Conversation
□ Discussion

Interpersonal Skills
Interacting with people in a contextually and socially appropriate manner
□ Social Cues
□ Regulating Emotion

1) Design Feature   2) Performance Guideline   3) Ability Level   4) Environmental Demand

| AB N/A | AB N/A | AB N/A | AB N/A | AB N/A | AB N/A | AB N/A | AB N/A |

Environmental Demands related to:

Person-Environment Fit

Personal Abilities

0 = No one w/ or w/o limitations in

1 = People w/o limitations in...
2 = People w/ moderate limitations in
3 = People w/ severe limitations in ...

LEVEL

100

P1. EQUITABLE USE

	C1	C2	C3	C4	C5	C6	C7
1a. Provide the same means (i.e., concurrent) of use by:	□	□	□	□	□	□	□
1b. Is equally private/secure/safe for:	□	□	□	□	□	□	□
1c. Is equally suitable for use and in demand by:	□	□	□	□	□	□	□
TOTAL DEF/ TOTAL # APPLICABLE DEMANDS P1							

P2. FLEXIBILITY IN USE

	C1	C2	C3	C4	C5	C6	C7
2a. Provides choice in methods of use by:	□	□	□	□	□	□	□
2b. Permits right- or left-handed use by:	□	□	□	□	□	□	□
2c. Requires minimal accuracy & precision by:	□	□	□	□	□	□	□
2d. Is adaptable to pace of:	□	□	□	□	□	□	□
TOTAL DEF/ TOTAL # APPLICABLE DEMANDS P2							

P3. SIMPLE & INTUITIVE USE

	C1	C2	C3	C4	C5	C6	C7
3a. Is not too complex for:	□	□	□	□	□	□	□
3b. Is consistent with expectations of:	□	□	□	□	□	□	□
3c. Provides a range of literacy & language for:	□	□	□	□	□	□	□
3d. Arranges information consistent w/ importance for:	□	□	□	□	□	□	□
3e. Provides effective prompting & feedback for:	□	□	□	□	□	□	□
TOTAL DEF/ TOTAL # APPLICABLE DEMANDS P3							

P4. PERCEPTIBLE INFORMATION

	C1	C2	C3	C4	C5	C6	C7
4a. Has different modes for redundant presentation for:	□	□	□	□	□	□	□
4b. Provides legible essential information for:	□	□	□	□	□	□	□
4c. Differentiates elements for:	□	□	□	□	□	□	□
4d. Is compatible w/ devices and strategies used by:	□	□	□	□	□	□	□
TOTAL DEF/ TOTAL # APPLICABLE DEMANDS P4							

FIGURE 4.20 *(continued)*

FIGURE 4.20 (continued)

P5. TOLERANCE FOR ERROR								
5a. Arranges elements to minimize hazards and errors by:	☐ ☐	☐ ☐	☐ ☐	☐ ☐	☐ ☐	☐ ☐	☐ ☐	☐ ☐
5b. Provides warnings of hazards & errors for:	☐ ☐	☐ ☐	☐ ☐	☐ ☐	☐ ☐	☐ ☐	☐ ☐	☐ ☐
5c. Provides fail safe features for:	☐	☐	☐	☐	☐	☐	☐	☐
5d. Excludes unconscious actions in tasks of vigilance by:	☐	☐	☐	☐	☐	☐	☐	☐
TOTAL DEF/ TOTAL # APPLICABLE DEMANDS P5								
P6: LOW PHYSICAL EFFORT								
6a. Is usable w/ a neutral body position by:	☐	☐	☐	☐	☐	☐	☐	☐
6B. Has reasonable operating forces for:	☐	☐	☐	☐	☐	☐	☐	☐
6c. Requires minimal repetitive action by:	☐	☐	☐	☐	☐	☐	☐	☐
6d. Requires minimal sustained physical effort by:	☐	☐	☐	☐	☐	☐	☐	☐
TOTAL DEF/ TOTAL # APPLICABLE DEMANDS P6								
P7. SIZE & SPACE FOR APPROACH AND USE								
7a. Provides a clear line of sight to important elements for:	☐	☐	☐	☐	☐	☐	☐	☐
7b. Has reachable components for:	☐	☐	☐	☐	☐	☐	☐	☐
7c. Provides variations in hand and grip size for:	☐	☐	☐	☐	☐	☐	☐	☐
7d. Has adequate space for AT or personal assistance for:	☐	☐	☐	☐	☐	☐	☐	☐
TOTAL DEF/ TOTAL # APPLICABLE DEMANDS P7								
P8. SOCIAL INTEGRATION (individual or group)								
8a. Enables engagement in activities with **when** wanted or needed by:	☐	☐	☐	☐	☐	☐	☐	☐
8b. Enables engagement in activities with **where** wanted or needed by:	☐	☐	☐	☐	☐	☐	☐	☐
8c. Enables engagement in activities with **whom** is desired or needed								
TOTAL DEF/ TOTAL # APPLICABLE DEMANDS P8								

P9. Contextual Integration								
9a. Is aesthetically compatible with other features of the design for:	☐ ☐	☐ ☐	☐ ☐	☐ ☐	☐ ☐	☐ ☐	☐ ☐	☐ ☐
9b. Looks, feels, smells, and sounds like it is an integral part of the design for:	☐ ☐	☐ ☐	☐ ☐	☐ ☐	☐ ☐	☐ ☐	☐ ☐	☐ ☐
9c. Is appealing for:	☐ ☐	☐ ☐	☐ ☐	☐ ☐	☐ ☐	☐ ☐	☐ ☐	☐ ☐
TOTAL DEF/ TOTAL # APPLICABLE DEMANDS P9								
TOTAL PRESS								

PRESS

FIGURE 4.20 (continued)

As a result, it represents a conceptual model for how to identify UD, rather than a practical measure of it.

GUDC Rating System. Another approach to assessment that has been proposed by the GUDC is a rating system for a set of consensus standards that can be adopted to incorporate UD principles into new and existing commercial designs. The standards, currently in development, will cover (1) design process, (2) site elements, (3) building elements, (4) customer service, and (5) facilities management and will be assessed by a numerical rating system, developed through an open consensus process involving a wide range of stakeholders. Unlike the other assessments, the GUDC rating system is building type specific. It will assess the relevant set of components and systems for a particular type of occupancy based on a set of performance guidelines and potential strategies to meet users' needs and the goals of UD, respectively. Performance guidelines are evaluated based on a subset each of the eight UD goals. For example, the goal of body fit has the following subset of goals:

1. Does the guideline address differences in height and/or weight?
2. Does the guideline address differences in the size and function of body parts?
3. Does the guideline address differences in the space clearances needed to complete tasks, including space for assistive devices?
4. Does the guideline address differences in fields of view?

Each goal has a total possible score based on the number within the subset. In the example above, body fit would have a total maximum score of 4. Other goals may have five to seven subgoals. The total *goal score* for each performance guideline is then the sum of the actual number of subgoals achieved for each of the eight goals for that guideline (Figure 4.21).

Unlike the other assessments described, the GUDC rating system does not explicitly address differences in ability. These differences are addressed through weighting the goals themselves. In other words, each goal addresses different abilities or needs. For example, the needs of people with visual impairments are addressed through the awareness goal. Thus, the

FIGURE 4.21

		Total Points	Body Fit	Comfort	Awareness	Under-standing	Wellness	Social Integration	Personali-zation	Contextual Appropriateness
Design Feature	Performance Goal 1	9	3	1	1	1	2		1	0
	Performance Goal 2	8	1	2	1	1		2		1

Conceptual framework for assessing design features.

point total for each performance guideline gives that guideline more or less weight relative to a specific population's needs and abilities.

Further, the rating system also includes possible strategies that can be used to achieve each performance guideline. For example, "signs identify all site access points" is a strategy to achieve the guideline that site entrances/exits are conveniently located and distinguishable from their surroundings. One to three points are then assigned to each strategy based on how innovative it is. The sum of points for strategies used is the total *strategy score* for a performance guideline. Finally, multiplying the total number of points by the weight derives the point total for each performance guideline.

So, Is It Universal?

Only time will tell if any of these assessments will actually be adopted. The UD checklist is the simplest to apply, but also the broadest. As such, its use is questionable because it lacks the specificity to actually assess all levels of design and for all abilities. The UDAP is the most detailed and complete, assessing both the breadth of ability and design, but its depth makes it cumbersome and impractical. The GUDC rating system, because it rates a myriad of performance guidelines, suffers from cumbersomeness similar to the UDAP. However, it will have the strength of a consensus standard behind it, if and when that standard is completed and adopted. Moreover, although the other assessments are essentially unbiased, the GUDC includes a number of strategies that can be used to achieve UD and awards points accordingly. This not only helps interpret the principles but also provides guidance on how they can be achieved.

However, let us go back to the original question—Do any of these rating systems actually measure UD? Although they measure the UD principles or some variation of the principles, the principles and their derivatives are all the result of expert and consensus opinions of what UD should be, not what UD is. Neither the principles or the guidelines or the design strategies have been empirically validated. Until they are, they represent ideals that we believe, in both our heads and hearts, define what UD is and how it should be achieved. So, in the absence of data, the basic principles, regardless of terminology, are all we have to really hang our hats on. Let us make sure that the hat rack provides the same means of use for all, provides choices in methods of use, is consistent with expectations, differentiates elements, provides fail-safe features, is usable with a neutral body position, has reachable components, enables engagement in activities when desired, and is aesthetically compatible with the space that it is in.

Author. (1985). *American heritage dictionary*. Boston, MA: Houghton Mifflin Company.

Brandt, E., & Pope, A. M. (Eds.). (1997). *Enabling America: Assessing the role of rehabilitation science and engineering*. Washington, DC: National Academy Press.

Bruce, C., & Sanford, J. A. (2009). Assessment for workplace accommodation. In T. Oakland & E. Mpofu (Eds.), *Assessment in rehabilitation and health* (pp. 205–221). Upper Saddle, NJ: Prentice Hall.

Canadian Association of Occupational Therapists. (1997). *Enabling occupation: An occupational therapy perspective*. Ottawa, ON: CAOT Publications.

Center for Universal Design. (1997). What is universal design? Retrieved from www.design,ncsu.edu/cud/univ_design/princ_overiview.htm

Christiansen, C., & Baum, C. (1997). *Occupational therapy: Enabling function and well-being* (2nd ed.). Thorofare, NJ: Slack.

City of Winnipeg, Mayors Access Advisory Committee. (2001). *Universal design policy*. Winnipeg, Canada: Author.

Connell, B. R., Jones, M. L., Mace, R., Mueller, J., Mullick, A., Ostroff, E., Sanford, J. A., Steinfield, E., Story, M., & Vanderheiden, G. (1997). *The principles of universal design: Version 2.0*. Raleigh, NC: The Center for Universal Design.

Connell, B. R., & Sanford, J. A. (1999). Research implications of universal design. In E. Steinfeld & S. Danford (Eds.), *Measuring enabling environments* (pp. 35–57). New York, NY: Springer Publishing.

Department of Labor, Employment and Training Administration. (1991). *The revised handbook for analyzing jobs*. Washington, DC: U.S. Government Printing Office.

Design for All Foundation. (2011). Retrieved April 7 from http://www.designforall.org/en/dfa/dfa.php

Dijkers, M. (1998). Community integration: Conceptual issues and measurement approaches in rehabilitation research. *Topics in Spinal Cord Injury Rehabilitation*, 4(1), 1–15.

Dunn, W., Brown, C., & McGuigan, A. (1994). The ecology of human performance: A framework for considering the effect of context. *American Journal of Occupational Therapy, 48*(7), 595–607.

EIDD Design for All Europe. (2011). Retrieved June 12 from http://www.designforalleurope.org/Design-for-All

Erlandson, R. F. (2008). *Universal and accessible design of products, services and processes*. Boca Raton, FL: CRC Press.

Finkel, G., & Gold, Y. (1999). Actualizing universal design. *Journal of Leisurability*, *26*(1), 25–30.

Gaudino, E., Matheson, L., & Mael, F. (2001). Development of the functional assessment taxonomy. *Journal of Occupational Rehabilitation*, *11*(3), 155–175.

Goffman, E. (1963). *Stigma: Notes on the management of spoiled identity*. New York, NY: Simon & Schuster.

GUDC. (2011). Retrieved May 2 from http://globaluniversaldesign.com/index.php?option=com_content&view=article&id=12&Itemid=13

Hagedorn, R. (1995). *Occupational therapy: Perspectives and processes*. Edinburgh, Scotland: Churchill Livingstone.

Imrie, R. (2004). From universal to inclusive design in the built environment. In J. Swain, S. French, C. Barnes, & C. Thomas (Eds.), *Disabling barriers—Enabling environments*. London, UK: Sage Publications.

Iwarsson, S. (2004). Assessing the fit between older people and their home environments: An occupational therapy research perspective. In H.-W. Wahl, R. Scheidt, & P. Windley (Eds.), *Annual review of the Gerontological Society of America 2003, Vol. 23: Focus on aging in context: Socio-physical environments* (pp. 85–109). New York, NY: Springer Publishing.

Iwarsson, S. (2005). A long-term perspective on person-environment fit and ADL dependence among older Swedish adults. *Gerontologist*, *45*, 327–336.

Keates, S., & Clarkson, J. (2004). *Countering design exclusion: An introduction to inclusive design*. London, UK: Springer-Verlag.

Kielhofner, G. (1995). *A model of human occupation: Therapy and application* (2nd ed.). Baltimore, MD: Williams & Wilkins.

Law, M., Cooper, B. A., Strong, S., Stewart, D., Rigby, P., & Letts, L. (1996). The person-environment-occupation model: A transactive approach to occupational performance. *Canadian Journal of Occupational Therapy*, *63*, 186–192.

Lawton, M. P., & Nahemow, L. (1973). Ecology and the aging process. In C. Eisdorfer & M. P. Lawton (Eds.), *The psychology of adult development and aging* (pp. 619–674). Washington, DC: American Psychological Association.

Lewin, K. (1951). *Field theory in social science*. New York, NY: Harper.

Mace, R., Hardie, G., & Place, J. (1991). *Accessible environments: Toward universal design*. In E. T. White (Ed.), *Innovation by design* (pp. 155–175). New York, NY: Van Nostrand Reinhold Publishers.

Nagi, S. (1976). An epidemiology of disability among adults in the United States. *Milbank Memorial Fund Quarterly, Health and Society*, *54*, 439–467.

Nagi, S. Z. (1965). Some conceptual issues in disability and rehabilitation. In M. B. Sussman (Ed.), *Sociology and rehabilitation* (pp. 100–113). Washington, DC: American Sociological Association.

Oliver, M. (1990a, July 23). *The individual and social models of disability.* Paper presented at the Joint Workshop of the Living Options Group and the Research

Unit of the Royal College of Physicians. Retrieved April, 21, 2009, from http://www.leeds.ac.uk/disability-studies/archiveuk/Oliver/in%20soc%20dis.pdf

Oliver, M. (1996). *Understanding disability, from theory to practice.* London, UK: Macmillan.

Rigby, P., & Letts, L. (2003). Environment and occupational performance: Theoretical Considerations. In L. Letts, P. Rigby, & D. Stewart (Eds.), *Using environments to enable occupational performance* (pp. 17–32). Thorofare, NJ: Slack.

Rochette, A., Korner-Bitensky, N., & Levasseur, M. (2006). Optimal participation: A reflective look. *Disability and Rehabilitation, 29*(19), 1231–1235.

Rubenstein, L. Z. (1999). The importance of including the home environment in assessment of frail older people. *Journal of the American Geriatrics Society, 47,* 111.

Salmen, J. P. S. (2001). U.S. accessibility codes and standards: Challenges for universal design. In W. F. E. Preiser & E. Ostroff (Eds.). *Manual of universal design* (pp. 12.1–12.8). NY, New York: McGraw Hill.

Samaha, A. D. (2007). *What good is the social model of disability?* The University of Chicago Law Review. Retrieved January 20, 2009, from http://lawreview.uchicago.edu/issues/archive/v74/74_4/Samaha.pdf

Sanford, J. A. (2004, June 2). *Development and Testing of a Universal Design Assessment Protocol.* Paper presented at the 35th Annual Meeting of the Environmental Design Research Association, Albuquerque, NM.

Sanford, J. A. (2010). Assessing universal design in the physical environment. In T. Oakland & E. Mpofu (Eds.), *Rehabilitation and health assessment* (pp. 255–278). New York, NY: Springer Publishing.

Sanford, J., & Bruce, C. (2010). Measuring the impact of the physical environment. In T. Oakland & E. Mpofu (Eds.), *Rehabilitation and health assessment* (pp. 207–228). New York, NY: Springer Publishing.

Sanford, J. A., Echt, K., & Malassigné, P. (1999). An E for ADAAG: The case for accessibility guidelines for the elderly based on three studies of toilet transfer. *Journal of Physical and Occupational Therapy in Geriatrics, 16*(3/4), 39–58.

Sanford, J. A., & Jones, M. L. (2001). Home modifications and environmental controls. In D. A. Olson & F. DeRuyter (Eds.), *Clinician's guide to assistive technology* (pp. 405–423). Chicago, IL: Mosby.

Sanford, J. A., & Megrew, M. B. (1999). Using environmental simulation to measure accessibility for older people. In E. Steinfeld & S. Danford (Eds.), *Measuring enabling environments* (pp. 183–206). New York, NY: Plenum Press.

Scheidt, R., & Windley, P. (2006). Environmental gerontology: Progress in the post-Lawton era. In J. E. Birren & K. W. Schaie (Eds.), *Handbook of the psychology of aging* (6th ed., pp. 105–125). Amsterdam, Netherlands: Elsevier.

Schkade, J., & McClung, M. (2001). Occupational adaptation in practice: Concepts and cases. Thorofare, NJ: Slack.

Shakespeare, T., & Watson, N. (2001). The social model of disability: An outdated ideology? In S. N. Barnartt & B. M. Altman (Eds.), *Research in social science and disability, Volume 2, exploring theories and expanding methodologies* (pp. 9–21). New York, NY: Elsevier Science.

Steinfeld, E. (1994). The concept of universal design. Paper presented at the Sixth IberoAmerican Conference on Accessibility, Centre for Independent Living, Rio De Janeiro, Brazil, June 19.

Steinfeld, E., & Danford, G. S. (2007, June 6). *Universal design and the ICF*. Paper presented at 12th Annual North American Collaborating Center Conference on ICF, Vancouver, Canada.

Steinfeld, E., Schroeder, S., Duncan, J., Faste, R., Chollet, D., Bishop, M., Wirth, P., & Cardell, P. (1979). *Access to the built environment: A review of the literature.* Prepared for the U.S. Department of Housing and Urban Development, Office of Policy Development and Research. Washington, DC: Government Printing Office.

Stineman, M. G., Ross, R. N., Maislin, G., & Gray, D. (2007). Population-based study of home accessibility features and the activities of daily living: Clinical and policy implications. *Disability and Rehabilitation, 8*(2), 34–45.

Stark, S. L., & Sanford, J. A. (2005). Environmental enablers and their impact on occupational performance. In C. Christiansen & C. M. Baum (Eds.), *Occupational therapy: Performance, participation, and well-being* (pp. 298–337). Thorofare, NJ: Slack.

Story, M. F. (2001). Principles of universal design. In W. F. E. Preiser & E. Ostroff (Eds.), *Universal design handbook* (pp. 10.3–10.19). New York, NY: McGraw-Hill.

Story, M., Mace, R., &Mueller, J. (1998). *The universal design file: Designing for people of all ages and abilities.* Raleigh, NC: Center for Universal Design, NC State University.

U.S. Access Board. (2002). *ADA accessibility guidelines for buildings and facilities (ADAAG).* Retrieved February 3, 2010, from http://www.access-board.gov/adaag/html/adaag.htm

Vanderheiden, G. C. (1990). Thirty-something million: Should they be exceptions? *Human Factors, 32*(4), 383–396.

Wahl, H.-W. (2001). Environmental influences on aging and behavior. In J. E. Birren & K. W. Schaie (Eds.), *Handbook of the psychology of aging* (5th ed., pp. 215–237). San Diego, CA: Academic Press.

Winkler, D. C., Unsworth, C., & Sloan, S. (2006). Factors that lead to successful community integration following severe traumatic brain injury. *Journal of Head Trauma Rehabilitation, 21*(1), 8–21.

World Health Organization. (1980). *The international classification of impairment, disability and health* (p. 143). Geneva, Switzerland: Author.

World Health Organization. (2001). *International classification of functioning, disability and health.* Geneva, Switzerland: Author.

PART II

DESIGN FOR THE AGES: UNIVERSAL DESIGN AS A REHABILITATION STRATEGY FOR AGING IN PLACE AND AGING IN THE WORKPLACE

*A*ging is a constant. We age from the day that we are born until the day we die. With aging comes naturally occurring changes in our abilities, from progressively increasing in our infancy and youth to progressively declining in our senior years. At the same time, our needs and preferences also change along with changes in our lifestyles and life situations, from student, to employee, to parent, to retiree. Yet, despite the dynamic nature of our needs and abilities throughout our lifetimes, the environments within which we live, work, and play are static. To the extent that they support any of our needs and abilities, they are designed to support only some of those needs and abilities at specific points in time. Even then, our environments do not exhibit much understanding of how we function on a daily basis. As a result, our environments support only part of our needs and abilities only part of the time.

To further complicate the person–environment misfit, people are living longer, working longer, and remaining in the community longer than in any time in history. Moreover, all indications are that they will continue to do so. At the same time, our needs and abilities are continuing to evolve and place new demands on old environments. The home itself is no longer just a castle and symbol of the American dream; it is becoming the preferred health care environment of the 21st century, supporting a home health industry that is expected to grow by leaps and bounds over the next decade. The work environment is no longer just a place of goods and services required to ensure our self-worth and economic well-being; it is becoming a measure of our psychological health as more and more individuals retire from one career and begin another. The community is no longer an environment that represents mobility as a means to get to a destination at the end; it is becoming an end itself where activity and participation are tantamount to physical health and participation.

Not surprisingly, our environments, which continue to be designed according to the Peter Pan Paradox, where people never grow up and never grow old (Hare, 1992), are struggling to keep up with our ever-changing lives. Being static, they have difficulty adapting to our changing lives. As a result, we most often adapt to our environments, rather than the other way around. Unfortunately, when our abilities are exceeded by the strength of environmental demands to the point where we can no longer adapt, the environment must change or be left behind.

Design for the ages means exactly that—design that will meet the needs and abilities of individuals throughout their lifetimes. As such, the focus on specific environments for aging does not imply that Part 2 is limited to rehabilitation interventions for seniors. Rather, it means that regardless of how old we are, design should support our needs and abilities at that point in time and continue to do so at every point in time as we age. Leaving an environment should be by choice. No one should be forced to move from his or her home or retire from his or her workplace because environment does not support his or her needs and abilities. As detailed in the following chapters, universal design is a rehabilitation strategy that can support individuals at any point in time as they age in place and in the workplace.

FIVE

Housing Environments: Universal Design as a Rehabilitation Strategy for Aging in Place

There is a direct relationship between rehabilitation and housing. When an individual has a chronic condition, impairment, or age-related functional declines, health concerns are virtually indistinguishable from housing concerns, particularly in an aging housing stock (Lawler, 2001). Housing can be, at the same time, prosthetic and therapeutic, compensating for limitations in functional abilities and enabling health maintenance and management. As a prosthetic, the home can facilitate basic activities associated with safe and independent living, participation in social roles, and provision of personal assistance from caregivers as needed. Therapeutically, it can facilitate health-promoting behaviors and provision of health care services.

Unfortunately, many homes are not designed to provide either prosthetic or therapeutic support. Physical barriers in the home are common and pervasive (Gill, Robison, Williams, & Tinetti, 1999). They are the primary source of misfit between rehabilitation and health needs of community-dwelling individuals and the places within which they live. Barriers, such as stairs, narrow doorways, low lighting, poor visual contrast, shower curbs or tub sidewalls, low toilets, narrow halls and doors, small spaces, and cluttered layout can create physical hazards and social isolation that can put community-dwelling individuals with functional limitations at significant risk for adverse health events, such as falls and injuries, difficulty in performing activities of daily living (ADLs), loss of independence, depression, inactivity, and obesity (CDC, 2010; Holt-Lundstad, Smith, & Bradley, 2010).

Our homes can also make it difficult to accommodate health care equipment, care providers, and communications infrastructure necessary to share information with remote service providers. Such barriers can minimize the effectiveness of caregivers, assistive technologies, and health care devices and can even lead to early institutionalization (Carter, Campbell, Sanson-Fisher, Redman, & Gillespie, 1997; Clemson, Roland, & Cumming, 1997; Cumming et al., 1999, 2001; Fange & Iwarsson, 2003; Iwarsson, 2005; Lau, Scandrett, Jarzebowski, Holman, & Emanuel, 2007). In fact, a lack of space and inability to accommodate prosthetic and therapeutic supports can cause the support themselves to become clutter and safety hazards, thus becoming barriers to aging in place. As a result, it is not surprising that family caregivers have a 10% increase in risk of being injured or having physical ailments and higher mortality rates than those who are not caregiving (Pinquart & Sorenson, 2003). These statistics become even more alarming when we consider that over the life span of a home that is occupied by four to five different families, approximately 25% to 60% of all new homes will be occupied by a resident with severe long-term mobility impairment (Smith, Rayer, & Smith, 2008).

Exacerbating the lack of fit between individuals and their homes, rehabilitation and health promotion are typically treated autonomously and with different contextual implications, although homes that promote independence could reduce health care needs and those that promote health could facilitate independence. Although the World Health Organization has suggested that environments be created to support healthy living and well-being (World Health Organization, 1991), the home environment is perceived differently by the individuals who function within it and the systems that regulate it. Not surprisingly, the rehabilitation and home health goals that should be mutually supportive (i.e., activity independence and participation should promote health, and health should promote activity and participation) often occur without consideration for each other.

Nonetheless, the home has become, not by choice and often in spite of its design, a de facto therapeutic environment. On the one hand, a home should provide a prosthetic rehabilitation environment within which individuals can live and function safely as long as they choose to remain there. On the other hand, the cost of health care and development of new communication and medical technologies have made the home a convenient place for self-management and remote health care delivery.

Homes vary widely in their location, size, condition, and physical design characteristics, and each of these factors affects provision of prosthetic and therapeutic interventions. The success of housing as a rehabilitation setting is, therefore, more complicated than simply adding a ramp to the front of house or grab bars around the toilet. It involves a diverse set of contextual factors (i.e., physical, social, cultural, and policy environments and personal factors) and an array of rehabilitation interventions that go beyond merely accommodating activity needs of an individual with functional limitations. For such interventions to occur, there must be fundamental paradigm shift with regard to the importance of the home environment in promoting activity, participation, and health in general. Further, changes must occur in a number of different and mutually exclusive systems that are not particularly aware of the role of the environment in supporting activity, participation, and health needs or of each other.

Universal design (UD) applied across the various scales of design, including products, technologies, and interfaces that are used in the home, as well as the design of the home itself, is a strategy that can engender a more holistic approach to activity, participation, and health needs and provide home environments that are more supportive of those needs. Whereas supportive housing is dependent on a complex set of systems that include the physical attributes of the home, social and cultural influences, personal preferences (e.g., willingness to use health technologies or make changes to the home to improve health, activity, and participation outcomes), public health, and social service policies and governmental regulations, this chapter focuses on the attributes of physical environments as they apply to rehabilitation in the home. Specifically, this chapter examines the therapeutic role of home health technologies in promoting positive health outcomes and the prosthetic role of specialized design in enhancing activity outcomes and proposes that UD can provide a more holistic rehabilitation strategy that promotes the health, activity, and participation outcomes that are necessary for successfully aging in place.

HOUSING HEALTH:
HEALTH TECHNOLOGY AS A THERAPEUTIC INTERVENTION

By 2015, an estimated 150 million Americans will have at least one chronic condition due to a variety of causes such as congestive heart failure, cardiopulmonary diseases, deterioration in musculoskeletal system and connective tissue, and injury (Wu & Green, 2000). With the increase in chronic health conditions, there has been a dramatic increase in the level of care requirements, including the need to engage teams of multiple physicians, specialists, and formal and informal caregivers. As a result, chronic diseases account for 75% of all U.S. health care costs (Scheschareg, 2005).

As the intensity and cost of chronic care have increased, the home environment has played an ever-expanding role in health management and prevention. With the dramatic increase in home care services provided by Medicare in the past two decades, the boundary between hospital and home has become blurred (Binstock & Cluff, 2000). Not surprisingly, home health care is the fastest growing sector in the health care industry with a 66% rate of growth projected over a 10-year period from 2008 to 2018 (Bureau of Labor Statistics, 2008). This growth has been fueled not only by a desire for reduced lengths of hospital stays and controlling cost but also by a variety of new home-based therapeutic products and technologies that support aging in place through more active care management and passive monitoring of safety and activity. In addition, the home has become the primary setting for the 42.1 million unpaid informal family caregivers (in 2009) who provide 80% of all home care to older adults limited in daily activities (Binstock & Cluff, 2000; Feinberg, Reinhard, Houser, & Choula, 2011).

Types of Technologies

By placing a greater emphasis on prevention and wellness than on acute care, home-based technologies are changing the way health care is provided and the way in which the home environment is used and conceptualized. Such technologies enable family members and health care providers to manage and promote health by (a) actively monitoring health status (e.g., vital signs, weight, and oxygen saturation); (b) passively monitoring activity (e.g., bathing, toileting, eating, medication adherence, and physical movement) and potential safety hazards (e.g., turn off stove burners, maintain water temperature to prevent scalding, adjust lighting levels to prevent falls risks, detect smoke, and lock doors to prevent wandering of individuals with dementia); and (c) promoting communication with social networks and clinicians via cell phones, videophones, Internet, television, camcorders, and communications software.

Active Technologies for Care Management. Active systems require engagement of individuals to manage their own care in their own homes but are not necessarily tied to the home, itself. The devices are used for treatment, prevention, and communication of information to health care providers. Treatment technologies tend to be large, independent devices that provide a variety of therapies and assist bodily functions, including assistance in breathing, medicine delivery, body function, and suction. Smaller, preventative technologies often monitor a singular condition, such as an implanted cardiac device, that can be linked to a modem to transmit information over telephone lines to care providers so individuals can adjust medication dosage at home.

Passive Technologies for Monitoring Activity and Safety. In contrast to active technologies, passive systems do not depend on active engagement of individuals in the home. These technologies use networks of sensors (e.g., radio frequency identification chips), transmitters, and receivers embedded in the home environment (e.g., woven into carpet) to monitor activity and location (e.g., bathing, toileting, eating, medication adherence, and physical movement) and to identify and reduce potential safety hazards. Recently, passive technologies have been developed that communicate physiological status (e.g., vital signs, weight, and oxygen saturation) to health care providers via the Internet or telephone lines.

Despite the unobtrusive nature of embedded passive monitoring systems, the installation and potentially the appearance of these technologies can be somewhat intrusive in the home environment. However, simply getting this technology into homes is only part of the problem. Like other technologies, there will be issues with the design of sensor networks that fit unobtrusively in the home environment (e.g., visibility of packaging and antennas), are easy to install and maintain, and are integrated with each other and with other home technology systems.

Communication Technologies to Improve Social Connectedness. Communication technology to foster social connectedness and prevent deterioration in psychological health is an important, although sometimes overlooked component of the home-based care system. These include a number of technologies to reduce isolation, including computer-based products, cell phones, video telephones, and a variety of Internet-based communication applications.

Implications of Health Technologies for Aging in Place

Like specialized designs, medical devices and technologies can have a large impact on the home environment and on the individuals living there. Many health care devices and technologies were developed for institutional settings, which are very different in size and appearance than residential settings. Moreover, these devices and technologies were designed to be used by trained health care professionals, not consumers. As a result, equipment often exceeds the skills and abilities of care recipients and their informal care providers.

Whereas large pieces of equipment have obvious space requirements, smaller items, such as pulse oximeters or blood pressure cuffs, need to be stored somewhere, as do medical supplies. Disposal of medical supplies, particularly used needles, is also a major consideration. In general, smaller monitoring and communications technologies have little impact on the structure of the home. However, they require space for both the communications hardware and any biometric tools (e.g., glucose meters, blood pressure cuff, and digital scale) that are needed. Clearly, the larger the number of different systems and biometric tools that are introduced into the home, the more space is required. To compound the space needs of equipment, insufficient space to operate equipment can make it difficult, if not a safety risk, for caregivers to provide assistance. Of equal importance in residential environments is aesthetics. Devices that look institutional are neither compatible with residential settings, nor do they consider the personal needs and tastes of the residents. This not only creates stigma but also leads to disuse and abandonment.

Many independently functioning health care technologies are being shoe-horned into home environments that were not designed for them. As such, homes already bulging at the seams with security systems, music systems, fire alarm systems, cable systems, and communication systems are being bombarded with an array of independent health care systems, each with its own set of sensors, hardware, and communications. Homes are being wired up, and sensors are being put everywhere—under chairs and stairs, in beds and over heads, and in the drawers, doors, and floors—each to its own, special piece of "connected" hardware that communicates via broadband, cell tower, or POTS (plain old telephone system) line to a Web site, a family member, or a health care provider. For individuals with chronic conditions, all this stuff is likely to be piled on top of a variety of personal assistive technologies, such as wheelchair or walker, and general medical equipment, such as a hospital bed and lift, which similarly impact space and space use. The plethora of devices paints a picture of a home environment cluttered with stuff that take up large amounts of space and potentially get in the way of each other. Oh, and don't forget the back-up generator.

ADVANCING ACTIVITY: SPECIALIZED DESIGN AS A PROSTHETIC INTERVENTION

Unlike public environments that come under the *Americans with Disabilities Act Accessibility Guidelines (ADAAG)*, the approach to supportive housing in the United States is terribly underdeveloped. Accessibility codes do not apply to single-family housing and only have minimal impact on individual units in multifamily dwellings. Moreover, there is not a single federal law or program that regulates home design such that individuals are able to successfully age in place. As a result, providing a facilitating home environment is very different than providing an accessible environment in work or community settings. Rather than relying on accessibility codes to provide at least basic levels of access for people with acknowledged disabilities, rehabilitation interventions in home environments or "home modifications" are *individualized, customized,* and *personalized* to best fit an individual's rehabilitation needs and/or his or her caregivers for providing assistance.

Evidence Base for Home Modifications

Prior to past decades, home modification research was primarily descriptive in nature. Most studies treated the environment as an independent variable that served as either a facilitator or barrier (Gitlin, 2003). As a result, studies described home environmental contributions to a variety of positive (facilitators) and negative (barriers) outcomes, such as functional consequences of home conditions (e.g., Connell & Sanford, 1997, 2001), number and type of home hazards (e.g., Carter et al., 1997; Clemson et al., 1997), falls risk (Gitlin, Mann, Tomita, & Marcus, 2001), and needs for and use of assistive technology (AT) and home modifications (Gitlin, 2001; Mann, Hurren, Tomita, Bengali, & Steinfeld, 1994; Manton, Corder, & Stallard, 1993).

More recently, there has been a growing interest in evaluating the effectiveness of home modification interventions, consisting to a large extent of specialized assistive technologies and accessible designs, to overcome the negative impact of physical barriers. By reducing task demand (Verbrugge & Sevak, 2002), home modifications have been shown to contribute to increased independence in activity, autonomy, and safety and greater confidence in performing routine household activities; to prevent functional decline and disability; to promote independent activity and enhance health outcomes; to increase the effectiveness of caregivers; and to decrease the likelihood of institutionalization (Allen, Resnick, & Roy, 2006; Gitlin, Corcoran, Winter, Boyce, & Hauck, 2001; Gitlin, 2003, 2007; Mann, Ottenbacher, Fraas, Tomita, & Granger, 1999; Oswald et al., 2007; Sanford, et al., 2006; Sanford & Hammel, 2006; Schaie et al., 2003; Tinetti, et al., 2002). In addition, when used in a multifactorial intervention in conjunction with exercise and medical risk assessment, home modifications can reduce the risk of falls among older adults (Pynoos, Steinman & Nguyen, 2010).

Overall, most of the studies have shown home modifications to be effective in reducing disability-related outcomes, having had some level of success in 90% of 64 studies reviewed by Wahl et al. (2009) and effecting significant improvements in experimental group participants in 10 of 11 randomized clinical trials reported by Gitlin, Liebman, and Winter (2003). In fact, one study (Freedman, Martin, & Schoeni, 2002) suggested that gains in functioning of older adults over the past few decades may be the result, in part, of the introduction of facilitators that reduce environmental barriers.

However, linking specific environmental facilitators in the home directly to performance of activities is a formidable task (Connell & Sanford, 1997; Connell, Sanford, Long, Archea, & Turner, 1993). For any given environmental barrier to activity performance (e.g., getting on and off a toilet), there are a number of different modifications that can be used to eliminate the barrier (e.g., toilet safety frame, raised toilet seat, grab bars, increased space around the toilet). Some of these modifications can be used alone (e.g., toilet safety frame), whereas others are often (although not always) used together (e.g., raised toilet seat and grab bars) to achieve the same type of barrier removal. In research, as in practice, the decision for determining which interventions to use is a function of a variety of situational factors (e.g., functional ability, home design, user preferences, and cost). This approach typically results in a "prosthetic cocktail" of changes (e.g., Gitlin et al., 2001, 2003; Sanford & Hammel, 2006), rather than one single modification to the home environment.

Unfortunately, this situational approach creates its own research challenges. First, it makes it difficult to define what the modification is. Is it a single product, device, technology, or alteration of spatial, or is it a cocktail of changes to facilitate a specific activity? Second, it makes it difficult to determine a one-to-one relationship between specific modifications and activity performance. Are some interventions more effective than others in facilitating activity and under what circumstances? What are the cost–benefits of different alternatives? Thus, although there is fairly good evidence for the effectiveness of home modifications in general, there is very little evidence to suggest that specific modifications, in and of themselves, are more effective than others.

Modification Strategies

Home modifications are "any alteration, adjustment, or addition to the home environment through the use of specialized, customized, off-the-shelf, or universally designed technologies, equipment, products, hardware, controls and cues, finishes, furnishings, and other features that affect the layout and structure, to remove physical environmental barriers, to minimize environmental demands on, and improve functional capability of individuals and their caregivers in order to meet the situational needs for promoting performance of daily activities as independently and safely as possible" (Sanford, 2004).

By definition, home modifications are broad and are intended to encompass any changes in the physical environment of the home that remove environmental barriers. They can range in scale from small assistive technologies to whole house renovations. They can be simple changes that have no or little cost, such as rearranging furniture to make space for a wheeled mobility device or adding lighting to make it easier to read labels on medicine bottles. They can also be more complex such as adding a curbless shower or a ramp.

In general, modification strategies are varied, including specialized and UD to change the layout or configuration of space, equipment, appliances, fixtures, and/or other products that are used, and assistive or adaptive devices that change the way the environment is used. Although the definition encompasses both specialized and UD strategies, several factors dictate that most modifications are based on a specialized design strategy. First, most modifications are made after-the-fact to remove or overcome barriers from existing homes. As a result, adding patches are more economical and more easily applied than UD, which, as an integral part of the home design, often requires more substantial changes to accomplish similar functional (if not aesthetic) outcomes for the individual who needs it. Second, both third-party reimbursement policy (and hence, rehabilitation practice) favors a person-centered, activity-based approach that favors individualization of interventions that best fit a client's functional needs (at a reasonable cost) over those that best fit the situational needs of the household. This approach also promotes specialized design strategies and AT in particular because AT, which can typically be purchased off the shelf, is a known quantity with known costs.

Modifications to Remove Barriers to Independent Function

Although problems can and do occur throughout the home, research and experience suggest that modifications to improve independence and safety of individuals in the home, particularly those with motor, vision, and cognitive loss, are linked to three primary activities: getting in and out of the house, moving around the house, and performing self-care (toileting, bathing, and grooming). For example, an AARP study (2000) found that among people older than 45 years, a substantial percentage of respondents had made modifications for moving around the house, including changes to lighting (24%) and handrails (17%) on stairs, changes to live the first floor so they did not have to climb stairs (14%), and widening doorways (9%). In addition, 4% added a ramp or lift to facilitate getting in and out of the house. Another study (Freedman, 2011) found that adults older than 75 years were more likely to make bathroom modifications.

Clearly, mobility and transfer tasks are integral to each of these activities. Not surprisingly therefore, most home modifications have traditionally focused on modifying entrances to remove barriers to *getting in and out of the home*, circulation paths and stairs to remove barriers to *moving around the home*, and the bathroom to remove barriers to *performing self-care activities*. In contrast, modifications to other areas of the home, such as the kitchen, are much less common, particularly for older adults, unless they are intended to improve safety and mobility. In addition, for people with hearing and cognitive loss, for whom receiving auditory information is a major problem, modifications primarily focus on communication systems (e.g., doorbell, alarms).

Getting In and Out of the Home. Many homes are built above ground level with steps leading up to a porch, deck, or landing at the door. Stairs not only are a barrier to wheelchair users but also can become an obstacle to individuals with gait and balance problems, as well as those who use walking aids. In addition, walkways and stairs are frequently in poor condition, lack handrails for support, and lack adequate lighting at night.

To increase general safety getting to the door, common exterior home modifications include replacing walkways so they have smooth surfaces, repairing broken steps, adding handrails on both sides and using contrasting nosings (the rounded edges of stair treads), adding a ramp or mechanical lift to eliminate use of stairs, and adding adequate lighting operated by motion detectors or timers. At the door, thresholds and steps are usually eliminated to minimize tripping, doorways are widened, furniture is moved to provide sufficient space to maneuver, and doorknobs are changed or modified to eliminate twisting and turning.

- ■ *Lower extremity limitations.* For individuals with lower extremity impairments, mobility-related problems getting in and out of the house are caused by decreased range of motion, strength, speed, and accuracy, and are manifest in difficulties walking on uneven surfaces, using stairs, and getting through doorways. To address removing barriers to these individuals, common home modification strategies include the following:

1. *Removing obstacles on walkways* (e.g., uneven surfaces, clutter) by moving obstructions; widening paths; installing smooth, slip resistant path surfaces; and repairing or rebuilding steps with a typical 7:11

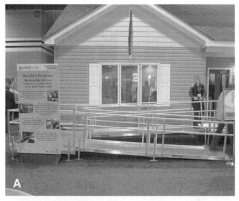

FIGURE 5.1

Eliminating or reducing the demands of stairs to get to the door using ramps, lifts and better stairs. Ramps, such as (A) the prefabricated Aluminum ramp on the NextGen Home at Medtrade 2010 in Atlanta and (B) the wooden ramp (photo courtesy of Jane Gustafson, Beyond Barriers, Wyoming, MN) are typically used when the height of the entry is 30 in. or less. (C) A lift (photo courtesy of Carrie Bruce, Research Scientist, CATEA, Georgia Tech, Atlanta, GA), shown on a home in Washington DC, typically has lower initial installation costs when entry height exceeds 30 in, though it has higher long-term maintenance costs than a ramp. (D) A low-riser, wide-tread stair integrates specialized design into everyday design by enabling people who have gait problems, such as difficulty lifting their legs, and/or who use ambulatory aids, such as walkers, to use stairs safely and easily (photo courtesy of Louis Tenenbaum, CAPS, CAASH, Independent Living Strategist, Potomac, MD).

FIGURE 5.2

Providing or changing the location of support at level changes such as (A) adding handrails on both sides of the stairs and then extending into the walk, which has another level change, help individuals with gait and balance problems (photo courtesy of Melinda Ickes, New Bern, NC) and (B) adding visual contrast to the edge of a step (photo courtesy of Carrie Bruce, Research Scientist, CATEA, Georgia Tech, Atlanta, GA).

tread/riser ratio or a lower riser and wider tread (e.g., 4:24 ratio) for walker users).

2. *Eliminating or reducing demands of stairs or level changes* (Figure 5.1) by constructing ramps, sloping walkways, mechanical lifts (e.g., stair or vertical power lift), wide-tread/low-riser stairs or moving the entry.

3. *Providing or changing the location of supports at level changes* (Figure 5.2) by installing handrails at a convenient height on both sides of a stair or ramp.

FIGURE 5.3

Removing obstructions at the door by installing (A,B,C) threshold ramps provide a smooth transition through doorways (A and B photos courtesy of Sarah O'Brien, Georgia Tech).

4. *Removing obstructions at the door* (Figure 5.3) by moving furniture, reducing the threshold height, widening the doorway, changing the door swing, removing a screen/storm door, or creating space to maneuver.

■ *Upper extremity limitations.* For individuals with upper extremity impairments, mobility problems are related to getting in and out of the home are caused by decreased range of motion, strength, speed, and coordination, and are manifest in difficulties using handrails to climb stairs or ramps, operating door handles, and using keys. To address these barriers, common home modification strategies include the following:

1. *Changing the attributes of gripping surfaces* (e.g., handrails, door handles, and keys) by altering size, shape, and texture to facilitate gripping, pushing, and pulling and eliminate pinching and turning.
2. *Changing the location of gripping surfaces* (particularly handrails) by installing handrails at a convenient height on both sides of a stair to minimize reaching.
3. *Using alternative or automatic opening systems* by installing electronic or remote-controlled locks, door handles, or keypads that eliminate reaching and handling.

■ *Vision and cognitive limitations.* For individuals with vision and cognitive loss, mobility problems related to getting in and out of the home are related to decreased acuity, contrast and color sensitivity, and visual discrimination and are manifest in difficulties seeing objects and hazards, reading text, and finding one's way. To help maintain independence and ensure safety of individuals with vision and cognitve loss when getting into and out of the home, modifications to remove barriers for these individuals include the following:

1. *Increasing light levels* by adding enough light where it is most needed including lights (preferably equipped with a motion sensor or dusk-to-dawn photo cell) at every door to the house, along commonly used paths, and wherever there are steps or a change in grade.
2. *Increasing visual contrast* by painting or using natural materials to make doors, gates, and stair nosings a contrasting color so they are visually distinctive from the background.
3. *Decreasing unnecessary pattern* by paving walks in solid colors or muted patterns to eliminate visual ambiguity.
4. *Eliminating hazards in the path of travel* by providing lighting and visual contrast.

5. *Enhancing way finding and orientation* by providing high-contrast, tactile cueing on or along walkway surfaces.

Moving Around the Home. Inside the home, people who use mobility aids such as wheelchairs frequently lose access to rooms or different parts of their homes because hallways or doors are too narrow, furniture obstructs the path of travel, or stairs prevent travel to other floors in the home. Stairs are also a potential safety hazard, accounting for a greater number of falls than any other single location in the home. According to an AARP report (Kochera, 2002), 14% of all falls took place on stairs, compared with 4%, which involved the bathtub, shower, or toilet.

In a survey of 1,231 individuals, 65 years and older, 68% had stairs inside their homes (Wylde, 1997). Among these respondents, slightly more than one fourth said they experienced difficulty going up and down the stairs, and almost 16% said there were times when they were nervous about using the stairs. Approximately 41% of the respondents who had stairs in their homes indicated that they had to climb the stairs to reach their bedroom, bathroom, or kitchen. Overall, 26% lived in homes in which stairs posed a barrier to essential activities such as toileting, bathing, sleeping, or eating. Stairs are also common places for people to have accidents in the home.

■ *Lower extremity limitations.* For individuals with lower extremity limitations, typical modification strategies to ensure activity and increase safety are similar to those for outdoor settings, although stair lifts are commonly used instead of ramps between levels of a home because the height differential between floors would require a prohibitiviely long ramp. Common home modification strategies to remove barriers to moving around the house are parallel those for getting in and out of the house including the following:

1. *Removing barriers on routes* (e.g., clutter, furniture) by moving obstructions; widening paths, hallways, and doorways; eliminating stairs or level changes; or installing smooth, nonskid surfaces.
2. *Providing or changing the location of supports* by installing handrails at a convenient height on both sides of a stair and locating handrails or supports (e.g., furniture) at strategic places (e.g., doorways, corridors, level changes) in the home.
3. *Removing obstructions at doorways* (Figure 5.4) by moving furniture, reducing the height of the threshold, widening the doorway, changing the door swing, and creating space to maneuver.

FIGURE 5.4

Removing obstructions at doorways can be accomplished by using (A) swing clear hinges (photo courtesy of Sarah O'Brien, Georgia Tech), which push the door out and away from the door frame to provide a fully clear opening and (B) pocket doors that open fully and do not require stop molding around the frame, thus typically increasing the opening by 1 inch.

4. *Eliminating stairs or level changes* by constructing ramps (not between full levels of a house) or installing mechanical lifts (e.g., stair or inclined stair lift) or elevators.
5. *Eliminating the need to use stairs* (Figure 5.5) by moving functions to one level, such as moving an upstairs bedroom to the main floor.

FIGURE 5.5

Eliminating stairs can be accomplished by (A) a residential elevator (photo courtesy of Sandra McGowan, FASID, Atlanta, GA); (B) a vertical power lift, which is like an open elevator (photo courtesy of Allan Browne, EHLS, Chicago, IL); or (C) a stair lift, which requires a wheelchair user to be able to transfer and have a wheelchair at each level (photo courtesy of Jane Gustafson, Beyond Barriers, Wyoming, MN).

FIGURE 5.6

Using alternative or automatic opening systems such as an automatic door opener eliminates the need to grasp a door handle and reduces strength required to push/pull a door (photo courtesy of Jane Gustafson, Beyond Barriers, Wyoming, MN).

■ *Upper extremity impairments.* People with upper extremity impairments encounter similar barriers to in-home mobility as those that are experienced during outdoor travel. Common modifications to remove barriers to getting around the home include the following:

1. *Changing the attributes of gripping surfaces* (e.g., handrails, door handles, and keys) by altering size, shape, and texture to facilitate gripping, pushing, and pulling and eliminate pinching and turning.
2. *Changing the location of support surfaces* (particularly handrails) by installing handrails at a convenient height on both sides of a stair to minimize reaching.
3. *Using alternative or automatic opening systems* (Figure 5.6) by installing electronic or remote-controlled door openers that eliminate reaching and handling.

FIGURE 5.7

(A, B) *Increasing contrast* by using different colors, textures and materials to differentiate between spaces/activities can help locate spaces and potentially reduce the incidence of falls as most falls occur in transitions spaces, such as doorways (photos courtesy of Sandra McGowan, ASID, Atlanta, GA).

■ *Vision limitations.* Individuals with vision loss often experience difficulty with visual tasks such as seeing at night, seeing edges, going up and down stairs, and transitioning between dark and bright spaces. These problems are often due to a variety of barriers such as insufficient lighting or contrast, too much glare, and abrupt transitions between dark and light. Modifications to overcome these barriers to enable individuals with vision loss get around the home include the following:

1. *Increasing light levels,* especially at night, by installing night lights along paths used at night, adding task lighting in the kitchen and bathroom, putting additional lamps throughout the house, and increasing wattage of bulbs at the top and bottom of stairs.
2. *Increasing contrast* (Figure 5.7) by using natural colors of materials or painting doors and adjacent walls contrasting colors, painting the doorway threshold in a color that contrasts with the surrounding floor, changing a doorknob to contrast with the door, using decals on glass doors, marking the edges of steps with contrasting colored tape or other materials, painting the handrail to contrast with the wall, or using carpet or other contrasting material at top and bottom stair landings.
3. *Decreasing unnecessary pattern* by replacing patterned carpet or floor coverings with solid colors or muted patterns to eliminate visual ambiguity.
4. *Controlling glare* by using sheer curtains or translucent shades (as opposed to metal mini blinds that reflect light) to buffer bright sunlight.

FIGURE 5.8

Increasing the height of a toilet seat and providing supports by adding (A) a vertical pole (photo courtesy of Melinda Ickes, New Bern, NC), (B) raised toilet seat with arm supports (photo courtesy of Sarah O'Brien, Georgia Tech), and (C) toilet grab bars (photo courtesy of Sarah O'Brien, Georgia Tech), can facilitate transfer even when there is little maneuvering space.

5. *Reducing dark/light transitions* from inside to outside or between hall-ways and rooms by adding light to dark areas or shading to bright outside areas (e.g., porch or canopy) to create more similar lighting levels between areas.

■ *Cognitive limitations.* Individuals with cognitive limitations often have difficulty remembering where things are located in the home. To overcome barriers to remembering, many of the same modifications that are used to reduce barriers for people with vision loss can serve as reminders for people with cognitive limitations by drawing attention to important design features such as hallways, stairs, and bathroom. In addition, physical prompts and reminders can be intentionally added to the home environment. Common home modification strategies to overcome barriers to moving around the house for people with cognitive limitations include the following:

1. *Increasing light levels,* especially at night, by installing night lights along paths used at night, adding task lighting in the kitchen and bathroom, putting, additional lamps throughout the house, and increasing wattage of bulbs at the top and bottom of stairs.
2. *Increasing contrast* by using natural colors of materials or painting doors and adjacent walls contrasting colors, painting the doorway threshold in a color that contrasts with the surrounding floor, changing a doorknob to contrast with the door, using decals on glass doors, marking the edges of steps with contrasting colored tape or other materials, painting the handrail to contrast with the wall, or using carpet or other contrasting material at top and bottom stair landings.
3. *Using prompts and reminders,* such as labeling rooms, leaving doors open, and using cues to mark paths to important destinations (like the bathroom), provide orientation and wayfinding information.

Performing Self-Care. For many individuals who have difficulty rising up and lowering down, including those who use wheeled or ambulatory mobility aids, transferring to the toilet, bathtub, or shower can be extremely problematic and a falls risk. Although individuals who use wheelchairs often lack space to maneuver or get close enough to a fixture, ambulatory individuals with gait and balance problems often lack support (i.e., something to hold onto) to safely lower themselves down onto a toilet or the bottom of a tub or conversely to pull themselves back up from these positions.

The bathroom is one of the most common places in the home where injuries occur. Maneuvering, transferring, changing position, and stepping over obstacles on hard, often wet slippery surfaces in small, cramped spaces can easily lead to falls, particularly among individuals with motor, vision, and cognitive limitations. As a result, toileting, bathing, and grooming are three of the most hazardous activities in the home. To overcome barriers to general safety, mobility, and usability of toilets, bathtubs/showers, and sinks, an array of seats, benches, and support rails are typically provided to reduce the barriers to raising and lowering down to a toilet or into a tub; the need for stepping and lifting legs over the side of the tub or shower curb; and the need to stand in a shower or sink. In addition, people with upper extremity and vision limitations encounter barriers with reaching, grasping, and locating objects. Unlike most other environmental barriers in the home, those that occur in the bathroom are generally sequential. In other words, barriers to approaching each fixture need to be overcome before transfers can occur, and barriers to transfers need to be removed prior to removing barriers to reaching objects (e.g., toilet paper or soap) required for personal care.

A. *Toileting* is perhaps the most critical ADL for aging in place because loss of independence in toileting is the highest predictor of relocation from home to a nursing home. Unfortunately, difficulty toileting is common because it is impacted by an array of normal and widespread limitations in motor abilities, including gait, balance, strength, stamina, and range of motion that affect an individual's ability to sit-to-stand, maintain or change positions, travel, and reach. Moreover, many individuals also have vision and cognitive losses that limit their ability to see or differentiate the toilet from the background (e.g., white toilet on a white tile floor with white walls) and remember where the toilet is located, respectively.

■ *Lower extremity limitations.* For people with lower extremity limitations, getting on and off the toilet is the most common problem. Typical modification strategies that can remove barriers to getting to get on and off a toilet include the following:

1. *Creating space for transfer* by removing walls, moving the toilet or other fixtures, or enlarging the bathroom.
2. *Increasing the height of the toilet seat to facilitate getting up and down* (Figure 5.8) by raising the toilet off the floor, adding a raised seat, or replacing the toilet with a comfort-height toilet.
3. *Providing or changing the location of supports at the toilet* (Figure 5.8) by installing grab bars, safety frame, or floor-to-ceiling pole.
4. *Using alternative or automatic transfer systems* like a lift system, rollover commode chair, or lifting toilet seat.

Increasing contrast of toilet and grab bars by using (A) a toilet or toilet seat and (B) grab bars (photo courtesy of Anne Long Morris, FAOTA, OTR/L) that have colors that stand out from the walls and floor.

■ *Upper extremity limitations.* Individuals with upper extremity limitations typically encounter problems reaching, grasping, handling, and bending for supports (e.g., grab bars), toilet paper, and flush handles. To remove barriers to these tasks, common modification strategies include the following:

1. *Providing or changing the location of hardware* by relocating the toilet paper holder so it is closer to toilet; positioning or reconfiguring grab bars (e.g., angled, vertical) so they are closer to the user at all times during transfer (i.e., approaching the toilet, getting on the toilet, getting off the toilet); and using a push-button or pull-up flush handle mounted on the top of the toilet tank.
2. *Changing the attributes of supports* by using bars with a smaller diameter or different surface material (e.g., knurled or coated) that are easier to grasp.
3. *Installing an alternative or automatic standing, cleansing, or flushing system* to eliminate reaching and handling can be accomplished through installation of lift systems, hands-free cleansing systems, and automatic flushing systems.

■ *Vision limitations.* Individuals with vision limitations who have losses in acuity, contrast sensitivity, or visual field often have difficulty seeing or differentiating the toilet in the bathroom. Typical modification strategies that can remove barriers to locating the toilet include *increasing contrast of toilet and grab bars* by changing the color of adjacent walls (e.g., painting or retiling) so that it contrasts from the toilet and grab bars (e.g., dark walls for a white toilet or vice versa) or using a toilet, toilet seat, and grab bars that contrast with the walls and floor.

■ *Cognitive limitations.* Cognitive limitations can affect an individual's ability to remember where the toilet is located or to remember to use the toilet. For people with cognitive limitations, typical modification strategies that can remove barriers to remembering and finding the toilet include the following:

1. *Using lighting to direct behavior* by installing night lights along routes to the bathroom or using a motion sensor to turn on the bathroom lights before an individual gets to the room to draw attention it.
2. *Providing prompts and reminders* by labeling the bathroom door or keeping it open to provide cueing.
3. *Increasing contrast of toilet and grab bars* (Figure 5.9) to draw attention to them by using fixtures that stand out from the surrounding context.

B. *Bathing/showering,* like toileting, bathing is crucial to successful aging in place. Although inability to bathe independently is not as high of a predictor of movement to a higher level of care as the inability to toilet, the presence of wet slippery surfaces add a high risk factor for falls because of the variety of positional changes that are necessary for getting in and out of the fixture and for washing. This risk is compounded by a variety of common motor and visual losses that limit an individual's ability to step over obstacles, maintain balance, change and position, and reach and see objects.

■ *Lower extremity limitations.* For people with lower extremity limitations, who have difficulty balancing or lifting their legs over the side of the tub or curb of the shower, getting in and out of the fixture and maintaining balance while bathing/showering are common problems. Typical modification strategies that can remove barriers to getting in and out/ maintaining balance in the tub include the following:

1. *Creating space at the bathtub/shower* for mobility aids and caregiver assistance during transfers by removing walls and/or by rearranging fixtures and furnishings around the bathtub or shower.
2. *Decreasing the height of the tub wall or shower curb* (Figure 5.10) by installing a tub with a lower wall height, a walk-in tub with a side-opening door, or a curbless or roll-in shower.
3. *Providing or changing the location of supports* (Figure 5.10) at the tub or shower by installing grab bars in appropriate places on the outside and inside the tub or by using a shower or tub chair/seat.

FIGURE 5.10

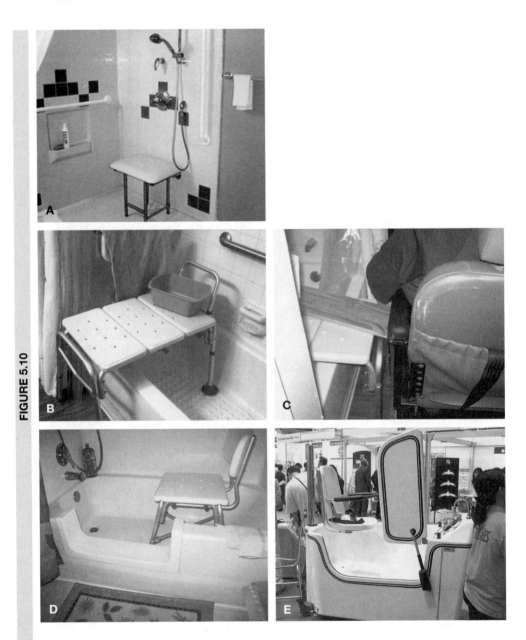

Providing supports, decreasing the height of the tub wall, and using alternative transfer systems, by adding (A) grab bars and a tub seat (photo courtesy of Andrea Hubbard, ASID, Bremen, GA); (B,C) a tub transfer bench (photos courtesy of Sarah O'Brien, Georgia Tech); (D) a tub cut out and seat (photo courtesy of Melinda Ickes, New Bern, NC); and (E) a transfer tub with a pivoting side wall and optional lift seat facilitate or eliminate or minimize stepping over the side of the tub, standing, and having to lower down to and rise up from the tub bottom.

FIGURE 5.11

Changing the location of the faucet to (A) the outside edge of the tub or (B) shower (photo courtesy of Carrie Bruce, Research Scientist, CATEA, GA Tech, Atlanta, GA) eliminates reaching to turn the water on or off.

4. *Using alternative or automatic transfer systems* (Figure 5.10) by adding a tub transfer bench or installing an overhead or portable lift system (although the portable system will also require raising the tub off the floor).

■ *Upper extremity limitations.* Individuals with upper extremity limitations typically encounter problems reaching, grasping, and handling supports (e.g., grab bars), faucet handles, towels, soap, and other items used for washing. To remove barriers to reaching and grasping objects for bathing/showering, common modification strategies for people with upper extremity limitations include the following:

1. *Providing or changing the location of hardware (e.g., supports and faucet handles) and accessories (e.g., soap, shampoo, towels)* by adding a hand-held shower with a shut-off or moving faucet handle to the outside of the fixture from the centerline of the wet wall (Figure 5.11); positioning and configuring grab bars so that they are located in as many heights and places around the fixture to be as close to the user as possible at all times; adding shelves for soap, shampoo, and other items so that they are within reach during and after bathing/showering; and moving/lowering towel racks so that they are within reach before and after bathing/showering.
2. *Using alternative or automatic soap-dispensing systems* by installing a hands-free soap dispenser.

3. *Changing the attributes of supports* by using bars with a smaller diameter or different surface material (e.g., knurled or coated) that are easier to grasp.

■ *Vision limitations.* Individuals with vision limitations who have losses in acuity, contrast sensitivity, or visual field often have difficulty seeing the side wall of a bathtub or curb of a shower. In addition, they have difficulty locating supports and accessories. For people with vision loss, modifications to remove barriers to seeing fixtures and supports include the following:

1. *Increasing contrast* by adding colored nonskid tape to the edge of the tub or shower curb; placing a nonskid textured mat in the shower or tub; or installing grab bars that are visually distinct from the surrounding walls.
2. *Relocating accessories* by installing shelves so that accessories are in the same place all of the time or using bottles with different sizes and shapes or an automatic dispensing system to differentiate between body wash, shampoo, and cream rinse.

■ *Cognitive limitations.* Cognitive limitations can affect an individual's ability to remember where the bathtub/shower and supports are located or an event to bathe/shower. For people with cognitive limitations, typical modification strategies that can remove barriers to remembering and finding the bathing fixtures and supports include the following:

1. *Providing prompts and reminders* by labeling the bathroom door or keeping it open to provide cueing.
2. *Increasing contrast of fixture and grab bars* to call attention to them by changing colors or a contrasting colored tape on the edge of tub or shower curb.

C. *Grooming* to maintain personal appearance, including brushing teeth, washing face and hands, shaving, combing hair, and putting on makeup, is an important predictor of engaging in social interaction. Like other self-care activities, barriers to the completion of these tasks are common among individuals with motor, vision, and cognitive limitations.

■ *Lower and upper extremity limitations.* For people with motor limitations, the limitations are caused by decreased range of motion, endurance,

Creating space beneath the sink for a seated user can be accomplished by (A) using a wall hung sink (photo courtesy of Jane Gustafson, Beyond Barriers, Wyoming, MN) or (B,C) removing/eliminating a cabinet (Photo B courtesy of Melinda Ickes, New Bern, NC, and Photo C courtesy of Charles Schwab, AIA, Moline, IL).

strength, and accuracy. Specific issues include standing for extended periods, difficulty in reaching faucet or accessories, turning the water on/off, and requiring ample space for a mobility device or caregiver. To remove barriers to grooming for people with motor limitations, modification strategies include the following:

1. *Creating maneuvering space at the sink* by rearranging fixtures and furnishings and removing walls to provide sufficient space for individuals with poor gait or those who use mobility aids.
2. *Creating space beneath the sink* (Figure 5.12) for a seated user by raising the height of the sink for a wheelchair or lowering the height for a standard chair/bench; using a pedestal or wall hung sink; or removing the cabinet from beneath the sink.
3. *Reducing reach* by moving the faucet handles from the back to the outer edge of the sink; relocating shelving, medicine cabinets, and other storage to a lower height; or moving toiletries to the vanity or sink top.
4. *Reducing gripping* by replacing knob faucet handles with lever handles or a motion-activated faucet.
5. *Providing or changing location of supports* at the sink by installing grab bars or a sink with integral handholds to enable an individual to maintain balance or stand for extended periods at a time.

FIGURE 5.12

6. *Providing storage/accessories within reach* by raising or lowering shelves as needed, using pullout drawers, and relocating items to the counter.

■ *Vision limitations.* For people with vision limitations, loss of independence and safety risks in grooming are caused by poor lighting and contrast and difficulty differentiating between objects. To overcome barriers to grooming for these individuals, common modification strategies include the following:

1. *Increasing light levels* by using higher wattage bulbs, installing additional lights over the sink, or adding task lighting, such as a makeup mirror.
2. *Increasing contrast* by using highly contrasting colors for sinks, faucets, and countertops or painting adjacent walls contrasting colors.
3. *Controlling glare* by using sheer curtains or translucent shades (as opposed to metal mini blinds that reflect light) to buffer bright sunlight.
4. *Changing the mirror* to bring it closer to the user by lowering and/or adding a swivel or angled mirror or adding a magnifying makeup mirror.
5. *Relocating and differentiating accessories to be more visible* by installing shelves or pullout drawers so that accessories are closer to the user and in the same place all the time; putting colored tape on different bottles to easily distinguish among them; and relocating the most used accessories to the sink or countertop.
6. *Avoiding accidents and injuries* by installing pressure-balanced, anti-scald valves.

■ *Cognitive limitations.* For people with cognitive limitations, loss of independence and safety risks in grooming are caused by poor judgment, forgetfulness, and decreased ability to initiate and sequence an activity. To overcome barriers to grooming, typical modifications aimed at calling attention to different features in the environment include the following:

1. *Increasing light levels* by using higher wattage bulbs, installing additional lights over the sink, and adding task lighting to highlight specific objects.
2. *Increasing contrast* by using sink, faucet, and countertop colors that are highly differentiated from the walls and floor as well as each other, or painting adjacent walls colors that contrast from the fixtures and counters.
3. *Relocating and differentiating the most important accessories* by installing shelves so that accessories are in plain sight; putting colored tape on

different bottles to easily distinguish among them; and relocating the most used accessories to the sink or countertop.

4. *Providing prompts and reminders* by putting notes on the mirror or on grooming accessories.

5. *Avoiding accidents and injuries* by installing pressure-balanced, anti-scald valves; insulating exposed plumbing; installing a grab bar at the sink for balance; covering outlets; or putting away products that could be dangerous (e.g., hair spray).

Receiving Environmental Information. Most home technologies rely on either auditory (e.g., doorbell, telephone, e-mail, timer, smoke detector, alarm system) or visual signals (e.g., thermostat microwave time, oven temperature, video monitoring) to convey important information about the condition, status, and safety of the home environment (e.g., current temperature, or there is a fire) as well as who is trying to communicate (e.g., knocking at the door, calling on the telephone, or skyping). Unfortunately, individuals with hearing and cognitive limitations are likely to have difficulty receiving information when conveyed through an auditory modality, whereas those with vision losses are likely to have difficulty receiving information when conveyed only through a visual one.

■ *Hearing and Cognitive Limitations*. People with hearing loss and individuals with cognitive loss are more likely to have difficulty recognizing and responding to auditory information, such as hearing the telephone, doorbell, timer, smoke detector, or other auditory signals. To remove barriers to receiving and responding to environmental information, modification strategies for people with hearing and cognitive limitations include the following:

1. *Reducing/isolating/relocating background noise* by replacing sources of noise, such as appliances, with quieter ones; replacing window air-conditioners with a central unit; moving sources of noise to other locations such as basement or closet; and covering or removing large expanses of hard reflective surfaces such as tile, glass, or mirrors.

2. *Conveying information by alternative means* by using flashing lights, vibration (e.g., vibrating oven timer), or a code (e.g., number of flashes or vibrations) to identify a specific signal.

3. *Amplifying desired sound* by adding a transmitter and the receiver to an existing source of sound or by purchasing a unit that has amplification.

■ *Vision limitations.* People with vision loss often have difficulty receiving visual information, such as reading a digital display or using a video monitor to see who is at the door. For these individuals, typical modification strategies to overcome environmental barriers include the following:

1. *Increasing light levels* by adding enough light where it is most needed.
2. *Increasing contrast* by using equipment with high-contrast LED or backlit control panels.
3. *Increasing size of text* by using large text digital readouts.
4. *Eliminating the need to read text* by using audio signals or synthesized speech to provide voice output or tactile outputs such as vibration to convey information.

Modifications to Improve Dependent Function and Caregiver Assistance

Unfortunately, not all modifications permit independent activity. When modified home environments continue to place demands that exceed the abilities of individuals to engage in independent and safe mobility and transfer, caregiver assistance and/or supervision is often required.

Given the strenuous nature of these tasks and the many barriers in the home, including clutter, lack of space, and other safety risks (Gershon, Pogorzelska, Qureshi, et al., 2008), it is not surprising that caregivers experience considerable difficulty and have an increased incidence of injury compared with other health care and human services workers (Galinsky, Waters, & Malit, 2001; Myers, Jensen, & Nestor, 1993). To reduce injury and facilitate caregiver assistance, a number of technologies have been developed to enable moving around the home and transferring to be easier, safer, more efficient, and more dignified, both for the care recipient and the caregiver. These include lift systems for moving individuals through the home and products that assist with, or eliminate the need for, transfers in bathing and toileting.

Moving Around the Home. Portable, freestanding, Hoyer-type lift systems roll along the floor and can be moved from room to room by a caregiver. However, portable lifts are difficult to push on carpeting or over thresholds, turn in tight spots, get through narrow doorways, maneuver in bathrooms, and facilitate transfers into a bathtub. As a result, doorways may need to be widened, thresholds and carpeting removed, bathrooms and other tight spaces enlarged, and tubs raised off the floor to allow lift legs to slide underneath. In contrast, overhead (or ceiling or track) lifts solve the

FIGURE 5.13

(A,B,C) Ceiling lifts for facilitating caregiver-assisted mobility through the home typically requires cutting of door headers for the track (Photos A and B courtesy of Jane Gustafson, Beyond Barriers, Wyoming, MN; Photo C courtesy of Louis Tenenbaum, CAPS, CAASH, Independent Living Strategist, Potomac, MD).

maneuverability problems of floor-based lifts by having a track mounted to the ceiling. However, they create a whole new set of problems, including institutional-looking metal tracks on the ceiling and more expensive modifications to the home, such as reinforcement in the ceiling to support more than 25 lb/ft^2 and cutout door frames to allow the track to pass over the door (Figure 5.13). Instead, some lift combine the qualities of both overhead and portable lifts with a light portable lift that can be attached to a floor-supported overhead track. Although this eliminates the need for permanently installed ceiling tracks and cutting door headers, it does necessitate having a full-scale erector set of tracks throughout the home.

Bathing Transfers. Ceiling and floor lifts are also used for bathing transfers (Figure 5.14). Alternatively, battery-powered tub lifts that allow an individual to sit on the seat platform, rotate their legs into tub, and lower down into the tub offer alternatives to traditional tub benches. Although the back separates from the base for storing, storage of the device, when the fixture needs to be used by someone else, is not convenient because bathrooms rarely have a place to put it. As a result, these, and other devices, typically clutter the bathroom where they become safety hazards and barriers themselves.

Toilet Transfers. Raising and lowering an individual within the "corner" or closet in the bathroom to which the toilet is generally relegated

FIGURE 5.14

(A,B) Ceiling lifts (Photos A and B courtesy of Jane Gustafson, Beyond Barriers, Wyoming, MN) and (C) floor lifts are also used to facilitate assisted bathing.

FIGURE 5.15

(A,B,C) Fold-down grab bars provide flexibility for assisted transfers by enabling the assisted individual to hold onto a grab bar for balance during disrobing and providing space for a caregiver(s) to stand on either (or both) sides of the toilet during sitting and standing (Photo A courtesy of Melinda Ickes, New Bern, NC; Photos B and C courtesy of Jane Gustafson, Beyond Barriers, Wyoming, MN).

creates one of the most difficult and demanding tasks for caregivers. To facilitate these transfers, a variety of products are available to provide support during transfer and to reduce the distance that an individual has to lower down or raise up from the toilet. Unlike standard fixed grab bars that are often institutional looking and ineffective in home environments, fold-up grab bars that mount on both sides of the toilet and swing up out of the way (Figure 5.15) enable one or more caregivers to stand beside and brace the individual. However, to be mounted securely, these grab bars need reinforcement in the walls. In a remodeling this often requires a considerable amount of construction to open the wall and to replace the surface finish, which is often tile.

In addition to supports, reducing the distance that an individual must go between a standing and sitting position facilitates transfers. A number of products are available to increase the toilet seat height 2–5 in. from the standard 15 in. from the floor. Some of these merely raise the height, whereas others include integral grab bars and lock down for safety. However, like other bathroom devices that are intended for specific individuals, these devices must be stored when others in the household need to use the toilet. Like other products, they often end up cluttering the bathroom.

Modifications to Improve Safety and Caregiver Supervision of Individuals With Cognitive Loss

For people with cognitive loss, home modifications are made to either maintain independence or to enhance the ability of a caregiver to provide supervision. Generally, there is an inverse relationship between these two goals and the level of cognitive loss. Autonomy is generally the goal with mild cognitive loss when the individual is capable of maintaining autonomy and performing routine activities independently or with little assistance. As a result, home modifications for these individuals are intended to ensure safety by maintaining independence for basic and instrumental ADLs as described in the previous sections. However, people with more severe cognitive loss, such as individuals at later stages of dementia, typically exhibit a variety of negative behaviors, including wandering and exiting, agitation, rummaging, and shadowing that pose risks to aging in place. As these behaviors grow worse, autonomy tends to give way to ever-increasing levels of caregiver supervision. As a result, modifications for behavior problems are primarily intended for the caregiver, rather than the individual, and to ensure safety through facilitating supervision.

Wandering and Exiting. Wandering is associated with poor judgment, forgetfulness, and perseveration behaviors. When an individual who is prone to wandering or lacks an understanding of perimeter boundaries, access to spaces with a means of egress can potentially result to exiting. To remove barriers to safety and to support of caregiver supervision, access to spaces can be selectively provided by the following:

1. *Camouflaging* design elements, such as covering doorknobs or locks, painting doors to match the walls, or hanging a curtain in front of the door.
2. *Permitting selective access* to space by using "do not enter signs" on doorways, removing doorknobs, using gates or furniture to block access, or installing complicated locks or a second doorknob.
3. *Increasing caregiver awareness* of the care recipient's location by using notes, bells on the door, motion sensors that turn on lights or alerts, or alarm systems.
4. *Differentiating boundary lines* by clearly marking pathways and using fencing and putting locks on gates or doors.

Agitation. Agitation often results from overstimulation. Stimulation can be regulated by the following:

1. *Minimizing glare and reflections* that can cause hallucinations, by covering mirrors and using low glare wax on floors; and
2. *Reducing auditory and visual noise,* by using calming colors; reducing volume on telephones, television, radio, and alarms; and minimizing changes in the home that can cause confusion.

Rummaging. Rummaging is unwanted searching, handling, or arranging the contents of drawers, closets, boxes, and other places of storage. Rummaging can be controlled by the following:

1. *Denying access* to valued items such as jewelry or even the mail by placing them out of sight, providing low-cost substitutes, or simply locking them up.
2. *Decreasing the number of places where rummaging can occur* by removing clutter, cleaning out drawers and closets, or locking them.
3. *Allowing access to some items by creating appropriate places to rummage,* such as junk-filled drawers, that can divert attention away from other places where rummaging is unwanted.

FIGURE 5.16

Too many devices in relatively small spaces can themselves create barriers and often must be moved or stored. Here, the tub transfer bench is hung up in the tub so that it does not block access the toilet (photo courtesy of Sarah O'Brien, Georgia Tech).

Shadowing. Shadowing is following someone (i.e., the caregiver) surreptitiously. Because shadowing is a response to agitating situations, *minimizing agitating situations* will help minimize shadowing. In addition, *providing areas for activities*, such as painting, gardening, or preparing a meal that have visible lines of sight to the caregiver will help reduce incidences of shadowing.

Implications of Specialized Design for Aging in Place

The plethora of prosthetic technologies and accessible design features that need to be brought into the home to improve function and promote independent, assisted, and supervised activity creates an environment that is filled with a variety of independent technologies that are only useful to the individual with functional loss and his or her caregivers. Many of these devices, such as tub benches or toilet safety frames, often interfere with activities of others in the household who do not need them. In cases where they must be moved and/or stored when others need to use the space, not only is storage an issue but also the device must be repeatedly removed and set up (Figure 5.16).

Unfortunately in one's home, devices and modifications that will provide the best fit for supporting aging in place cannot be based simply on function alone. The home is a complex environment that is composed of a large number of confounding contextual factors, such as personal tastes and preferences of a particular individual and others living in the home, social constraints of the living situation, structural limitations of the home, building and zoning codes and cost, that have nothing to do with activity and health outcomes but mediate and influence decisions on which interventions should be implemented. Although the number of potential mediators is large, those related to cost, and to a lesser degree aesthetics, are by far the most common and most influential. In the end, the best therapeutic and prosthetic interventions for the situation may or may not be an "ideal" fit with the functional abilities and needs of the client, but how much it costs and whether it will fit in the home.

PROMOTING PARTICIPATION: VISITABLE DESIGN AS EVERYDAY INTERVENTIONS FOR AGING IN PLACE

The lack of federal legislation for accessible housing in the United States spawned the concept of visitability. *Visitability*, as first defined by Eleanor Smith of Concrete Change in Atlanta, GA, and promulgated in the United States through various state and local regulations, is an affordable, sustainable, and inclusive design approach for integrating basic accessibility features as a routine construction practice (Maisel, 2010).

Visitable design is neither AD nor UD, but lies somewhere in between. As its name implies, visitability is intended to enable people with disabilities to visit homes that they would not otherwise be able to access. In other words, the driving force behind visitability is more about participation than activity. In that respect, it is closer to UD than accessible design and home modifications, as both share a common goal of creating homes that are inclusive—enabling, to the greatest extent possible, all people of all abilities to participate equally in society.

However, unlike UD, which considers all features of the home to enable all aspects of our daily lives, visitable design focuses on basic

FIGURE 5.17

A visitable no-step entrance can be any exterior door, including the garage.

access by prioritizing a limited number of essential features that are absolutely necessary to enable participation of the broadest spectrum of the population.

To accomplish this, visitability most frequently embraces three design features, not all of which are required by accessible design, that are essential for access by individuals with lower extremity motor limitations. By targeting this population of individuals who are most excluded from participating in social roles by physical barriers in the home, visitability ensures that housing is as inclusive as possible. The three critical visitability features include a no-step entrance, wide hallways and doors on the entry level, and at least a half bath on the main entry level that a wheelchair can get into even if the bath itself is not accessible (e.g., no grab bars or space to maneuver).

No-step Entry. The no-step entry (Figure 5.17) can be any entrance to the house including one through a garage. The no-step can be accomplished in a variety of ways such as ramp or walkway, although using mechanical means such as a lift is typically more intrusive and more expensive. Using a porch or portico to cover the entry will help protect it from weather.

Wider Doors and Halls. Like accessible design, visitable design prescribes a minimum of a 32-in. clear width door opening. Therefore, a 2 ft 8 in. sliding pocket door will work because it has no stop molding, but a typical standard swinging door will require at least a 2 ft 10 in. opening. Nonetheless, 3-ft doors throughout the house are desirable. Moreover, while an individual using a wheelchair or walker can get through a typical 36 in. wide hallway, maneuvering into adjacent rooms is difficult. Hallways that are at least 42 in. allow for better maneuvering and for the installation of handrails if they are necessary.

A visitable bathroom on the main floor should have a door that is wide enough for a wheelchair to get through and enough space for a wheelchair user to get to the toilet, although it can be a half bath and grab bars and other accessible features are not required (photo courtesy of Andrea Hubbard, ASID, Bremen, GA).

FIGURE 5.18

Main Floor Bathroom. Locating a bathroom on the entry floor ensures that there is at least a restroom that is available to an individual who uses a mobility aid (Figure 5.18). Although the bathroom could be a half bath (presuming that there would be a full bath if a bedroom was located on the main floor), prescribed accessible design features are not required. The doorway should already be at least 32 in. clear based on the requirement for wider doors on the main floor; however, if door swing into the room is an issue, swinging the door out will provide the extra maneuvering space in the room. Although grab bars are not required, providing blocking in the wall for future installation saves having to rip the walls out later.

Unlike UD, visitability does have prescriptive requirements and is much more limited than the nine principles. Like accessible design, it is intended for only a small segment of the population, in this case people who use wheelchairs, although the prescriptive requirements for visitable design are much less extensive than those required for accessible design.

Although visitable design is much less comprehensive than either AD or UD, it does set a basic level of access that will enable everyone to get into a house, regardless of ability to ambulate. Moreover, while it is intended primarily for visitors, an added benefit is that a resident will not have to adapt the entire home if ambulatory status of a resident changes. Whereas this does not ensure usability of the home, particularly with no bedroom on the main level, it does simplify making future modifications should they be needed (Truesdale & Steinfeld, 2002). As a result, individuals are better able to age in place as their rehabilitation needs change over time.

Visitability programs for both new and existing housing have also begun to spread across the United States through various mechanisms at the local level. These include tax incentives, voluntary programs, and regulatory requirements in the building or zoning codes. By 2008, mandatory or voluntary visitability programs existed in at least 57 U.S. cities (Maisel, Smith, & Steinfeld, 2008). Nonetheless, visitable design, in itself, only covers the home, and then, only three design features in the home. It is, to a large extent, prescriptive and does not cover all scales of design as does UD. As a result, many visitability ordinances use visitable design as a starting point with incentives to go beyond the three basic features to include a wider range of UD features throughout the home.

ADVANCING ACTIVITY AND PROMOTING PARTICIPATION: UD AS EVERYDAY INTERVENTIONS FOR AGING IN PLACE

Whereas therapeutic interventions promote health and prosthetic interventions promote activity, neither promotes participation. What is lacking is a rehabilitation strategy that promotes participation plus activity and health. Clearly, the provision of such a rehabilitative and chronic care strategy to support aging in place will have a profound impact on the home environment that goes well beyond just adding ramps and grab bars.

In addition to the lack of participation-focused interventions, traditional rehabilitation, and chronic care strategies (characterized by a large number of assistive technologies, home modifications, medical devices, and health care technologies combined with a variety of typical personal technologies, including multiple wheelchairs, walkers, and scooters) create a home environment that is cluttered with devices that take up large amounts of space, can potentially get in the way of each other and others in the home, and can themselves become hazards. When these conditions are introduced into homes of older adults or individuals with other chronic conditions, they can negatively impact aging in place by exacerbating conditions in which many health and safety hazards already exist, including lack of space, clutter, poor lighting, and loose rugs (Gershon et al., 2008).

Space in the home is always limited, and there are ever-increasing technologies and devices vying for it. Nonetheless, new housing is not being designed, and existing housing often is not being remodeled, with these needs in mind. The challenge therefore is to incorporate all the stuff needed for aging in place into the home environment without violating the housing market's prime directive, which states that "outside forces are not to interfere in the cost and aesthetics of any home, especially the natural development of everyday design, either by direct intervention, or technological revelation."[1] Thus, although space might be the great equalizer for incorporating all the stuff needed for successful aging in place, the size of a home increases cost, which violates the prime directive. Similarly, health technologies and specialized designs are not perceived as being residential in scale and appearance. Therefore, despite improving health and activity, the perception is that the appearance of these interventions is the cause of stigma for residents and unsold homes for builders.

The success of rehabilitation strategies to promote aging in place depends on fundamental changes in the way rehabilitation interventions are conceived and carried out. This will require new approaches to product and housing

---

[1] With acknowledgment of and apologies to Starfleet Command.

design that not only integrate technological systems with each other and within the everyday home environment but also integrate the relevant and necessary technologies within the home in a rational organized manner, such that costs remain stable and the home remains a home and not a hospital.

To achieve these aims, housing and technology must support all three constructs in the *International Classification of Functioning, Disability, and Health*—health, activity, and participation. In contrast to everyday and specialized design, both visitable design and UD are intended to promote participation. Although visitable design achieves activity and participation, it is still focused primarily on removing barriers to specific types of disability, that is, people with lower extremity motor limitations. Moreover, it does not address health aspects of design. On the other hand, UD as rehabilitation strategy for aging in place is relevant to and would achieve health, activity, and participation goals at all scales of design. Universal design not only supports function of people with a wide range of abilities and health conditions, their caregivers, families, and health care providers but also is functional for them as well. It is a rehabilitation strategy where housing and technology can work together as a seamless, integrated system of everyday design to support aging in place.

Evidence Base for UD

Universal design is everyday design at all scales of design that is usable by everyone living in or visiting a home. As such, it eliminates the need for specific modifications or extensive remodeling of homes to make them suitable for individuals to age in place. In addition, because it is everyday design, it is residential in both scale and character, thus avoiding the stigma of specialized design. Logically, UD as a rehabilitation intervention for aging in place provides cost–benefits by being functional for all users across their life span and across the life span of the home.

Unfortunately, logic and faith are better rationalizations for UD as a rehabilitation strategy for aging in place than evidence of its outcomes. Unlike home modifications, which have a considerable, if not, wide-ranging focus of outcome research, there are no studies that have specifically examined the health, activity, or participation benefits of UD interventions in housing. Instead, UD has typically been included as an intervention in home modification studies. Although there are some clear benefits of home modifications, the extent to which UD is represented in these interventions is not clear and open to debate.

The lack of an evidence base of positive health, activity, and participation outcomes of UD or its cost effectiveness is not surprising. First, the lack of a common understanding, if not measurable criteria, of what UD is makes it effectiveness open to interpretation and debate. In fact, most home modification studies have misidentified specialized design as UD. Second, studying UD as an intervention is difficult. As discussed earlier, in practice, decisions about rehabilitation interventions in the home are often based on a variety of factors, including reimbursement by third-party payers, that have more to do with minimizing cost than with maximizing function. As a result, assistive technologies and inexpensive accessible designs are more likely to be implemented in a retrofit situation than UD. Implementing UD interventions in an existing home as part of a controlled research study is similarly impractical because of cost and time constraints. Finally, the naturally occurring opportunities to conduct outcomes research in the handful of UD demonstration homes that have been constructed have never been realized due to either developers being reluctant to work with researchers or the sale of the homes to private individuals.

Nonetheless, whereas the evidence base of UD outcomes is lacking, there is substantial data on the effects of home modifications to infer that UD alternatives will at least equally improve activity and health-related outcomes. Therefore, on the basis of existing evidence on the effectiveness of home modifications, implementing UD because it is a broader, more cost-effective home modification strategy seems like a logical approach.

Universal Design Features to Enable Activity and Participation

Unlike home modifications that are designed to remove barriers to activity performance for residents with specific functional limitations and unlike visitable design that is intended to promote activity and participation for (primarily) visitors with lower extremity motor limitations, UD in housing treats everyone who lives in or might visit the home, regardless of ability, as the target population. As a result, it is intended to enable everyone in the home to perform activities and participate in social roles.

The amount and configuration of space, the location of products and fixtures in that space, or the design of the products and fixtures for the home are all strategies that can achieve UD. Oftentimes, UD features are merely standard building products, hardware, fixtures, or appliances that have been placed differently, such as standard electrical outlets that are located higher above the floor than usual to minimize bending and reaching or switches and environmental controls that have been lowered to

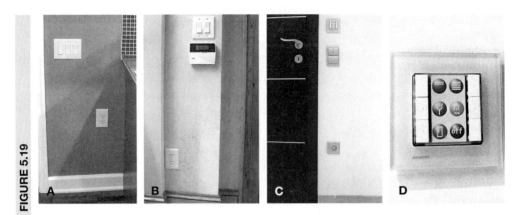

FIGURE 5.19

(A,B,C) Raising outlets and lowering switches and controls (Photos A, B, C courtesy of Jean Yves Prodel, JYP Design, Choisy au Bac, France) can enable everyday designs to meet Principles P1, Equitable Use and P6, Low Physical Effort. (D) Switches and controls that have larger interfaces and contrasting colors (photo courtesy of Jean Yves Prodel, JYP Design, Choisy au Bac, France) can meet the other five usability principles: P2, Flexibility in Use; P3, Simple and Intuitive Use; P4, Perceptible Information; P5, Tolerance for Error; P7, Size and Space for Approach and Use; as well as P9, Contextual Integration.

minimize reaching controls and facilitate viewing of displays (Figure 5.19). Alternatively, UD is built into design features with specific attributes that have both function and functionality, such as pocket doors that increase clear opening or toilets that are higher to reduce the distance of raising or lowering. In still other cases, design features that create barriers, such as stairs, might be omitted altogether (Center for Universal Design, 2006).

Lists of UD housing features to promote activity and participation abound, such as the one published by the Center for Universal Design at NC State University. Although much of the list is composed of features (e.g., open plan design), some are closer to prescriptive guidelines that specify accessible attributes, such as a minimum 5 × 5-ft curbless shower or a 60-in. diameter turning space for maneuvering a wheelchair. This list has been adapted and included here (Table 5.1) to illustrate the range of features that could be included. However, from a rehabilitation perspective, it is more important to understand how to use UD to promote activity, participation, and health than where the designs are typically found in the house. Therefore, to compare UD solutions with accessible home modifications described earlier in the chapter, UD exemplars are similarly organized by typical activity-related problems associated with aging in

TABLE 5.1
UD Features (adapted from Center for Universal Design, 2006)

ENTRANCES
- At least one stepless entrance is essential; if only one, it should not be accessed through a garage or from a patio or raised deck.
- More than one stepless entrance is preferred, particularly for emergency egress.
- Avoid ramps, but if used, they should be integrated into the design.

Site Design Methods for Integrated Stepless Entrances
- Level bridges to uphill point.
- Driveway and garage elevated to floor level so vehicles do the climbing.
- Earth berm and bridge with sloping walk.
- Site grading and earth work (with foundation waterproofing) and sloping walks at 1:20 maximum slope.

Other Entrance Features
- 1/2 inch (1/4 preferred) maximum rise at entrance thresholds.
- Minimum 5' × 5' level clear space inside and outside entry door. (Can be smaller if automatic power door provided.)
- Power door operators whenever possible.
- Weather protection such as a porch, stoop with roof, awning, long roof overhang, and/or carport.
- Built-in shelf, bench or table with knee space below located outside the door.
- Full length sidelights, windows in doors, and/or windows nearby.
- Wide-angle viewers and TV monitors.
- Lighted doorbell at a reachable height, intercom with portable telephone link, and/or hardwired intercom.
- Light outside entry door and motion detector controlled lights.

INTERIOR CIRCULATION
- Clear door opening width (32" minimum, 34" – 36" wide doors), for all doorways.
- Flush thresholds at all doorways.
- Clear floor space (18" minimum) beside door on pull side at latch.
- Circulation route (i.e., hallways) 42" minimum width.
- Turning space (minimum of one 5' minimum diameter clear floor space) in all rooms.
- All stairs should allow use of handrails on both sides and have space at the bottom for later installation of a platform lift, if needed.
- Handrails to extend horizontally beyond top and bottom risers.
- A residential elevator with minimum 3' × 4' clear floor area or at least one set of stacked closets, pantries, or storage spaces with knockout floor.

BATHROOMS
- Minimum 5' × 3' (5' × 5' preferred), curbless shower or tub with integral seat.
- When possible, arrange at least one shower control for right-hand use and one for left-hand use.
- Adequate maneuvering space: minimum 5' diameter turning space in the room and 30" × 48" clear floor spaces at each fixture. Spaces may overlap.
- Clear space (3') in front of and to one side of toilet.
- Cantilevered fold up grab bars preferred with toilet centered 24" from side walls or adjacent fixtures. If a traditional side wall bar is used center toilet 18" from side wall.
- Broad blocking in walls around toilet, tub, and shower for future placement and relocation of grab bars.

(continued)

TABLE 5.1
UD Features (*continued*)

- Lavatory counter height 32" minimum.
- Knee space under lavatory (maximum 29" high). (May be open knee space or achieved by means of removable vanity or foldback or self-storing doors. Pipe protection panels should be provided to prevent contact with hot or sharp surfaces.)
- Countertop lavatories preferred with bowl mounted as close to front edge as possible. Wall hung lavatories acceptable with appropriate pipe protection.
- Long mirrors should be placed with bottom no more than 36" above the finished floor and top at least 72" high.

Fixture Controls

- Offset controls toward the outside edge of the tub/shower with adjacent clear floor space.
- Single-lever water controls at all plumbing fixtures and faucets.
- Adjustable height, movable hand-held shower head or 60"–72" flexible hose (on /off valve on shower head preferred).

KITCHENS

- Clear knee space (minimum 29" high) should be provided under sink (with pipe protection), counters, and cook tops. May be open knee space or achieved by means of removable base cabinets or fold-back or self-storing doors.
- Variable height (from 28"–42") work surfaces such as countertops, sinks, and or cooktops.
- Stretches of continuous countertops particularly between refrigerator, sink, and stove top.
- Adjustable height shelves in wall cabinets.
- Full-extension, pull-out drawers, shelves and racks in base cabinets.
- Full height pantry storage with easy access pull-out and/or adjustable height shelves.
- Loop handles or push latches on cabinet doors.
- Front-mounted controls on all appliances.
- Cooktop or range with staggered burners and front or side-mounted controls. Cooktop with low profile preferred to provide smooth transition to countertop.
- Glare-free task lighting to illuminate work areas without too much reflectivity.
- Side-by-side or French door refrigerator with pull out shelving.
- Under-counter or refrigerator drawers.
- Built-in oven with knee space beside, set for one pull-out oven rack at the same height as the adjacent countertop and with pull-out shelf below or drop-in range with knee space beside, top set at a maximum of 34" above finished floor.
- Dishwasher raised on a platform or drawer unit, so top rack is level with adjacent countertop.
- Single-lever water controls at all plumbing fixtures and faucets.

LAUNDRY AREAS

- Front-loading washers and dryers, with front controls, raised on platforms or drawers. Doors should open in opposite directions for easy transfer from washer to dryer.

(*continued*)

TABLE 5.1
UD Features (*continued*)

- Laundry sink and countertop surface no more than 34" above finished floor with knee space below.
- Clear floor space at least 36" wide across full width in front of washer and dryer and extending at least 18" beyond right and left sides. (Extended space can be part of knee space under counter tops, sink, etc.)
- Some hanging and shelf storage should be less than 54" high with adjustable height closet rods and shelves.

STORAGE/CLOSETS

- Some hanging and shelf storage should be less than 54" high with adjustable height closet rods and shelves.

GARAGES/CARPORTS

- Power operated overhead doors.
- 8' minimum door height or alternate on-site parking for tall vehicles.
- 5' minimum access aisle on both sides of cars, 3' aisle in front of vehicles.
- Sloping garage floor (with through-the wall vents at bottom of slope to release fumes) in lieu of stepped entrance with ramp from garage to house interior.

WINDOWS

- 36" maximum sill height.
- Casement, or other type of crank operated windows.

HARDWARE

- Lever door handles
- Push plates
- Loop handle pulls on drawers and cabinet doors
- Touch latches on cabinet doors
- Magnetic latches on doors in lieu of mechanical locks

SWITCHES AND CONTROLS

- Light switches (motion detector or remote controlled preferred) 44"–48" high, and thermostats 48" maximum height.
- Electrical outlets at beds and desks, four-plex boxes each side for computer and electronic equipment as well as personal use equipment.
- Electrical outlets, 18" minimum height.
- Remote controls for heating and cooling.
- Doorbell intercoms that connect to portable telephones.
- Audible and visual alarms for doorbell, smoke detectors, etc.
- Electrical panel with top no more than 54" above floor located with a minimum 30" × 48" clear floor space in front.

place. In addition, it is important to note that, unlike some home modifications that are either intended for independent functioning or caregiver assistance with ADLs, UD accommodates both independent and assisted use.

Like home modifications, UD is focused on design of entrances for getting in and out of the home, circulation paths and stairs for moving around the home, and bathroom space and fixtures for performing self-care activities. However, unlike specialized designs, which are rarely used to modify kitchens, UD features are used often in kitchens to facilitate preparing meals. Perhaps, this is an artifact of limited coverage by third-party payers for kitchen modifications, but it is just as plausible that UD products are more functional than everyday design and at the same time more integrated into the design of the kitchen and house than specialized design. This functionality by integration, rather than by addition, is a key difference between UD and specialized design as a rehabilitation strategy to accomplish essential everyday activities of getting in and out of the home, moving around the home, performing self-care activities, and preparing meals.

> Functionality by integration rather than by addition is a key difference between UD and specialized design as a rehabilitation strategy to accomplish essential everyday activities.

Getting In and Out of the Home. In general, sloping walkways (i.e., less than 1:20 slope) are the most desirable UD solution because they enable all individuals to get to the door in the same manner and with low effort, while being integrated with the overall context of the home and community (Figure 5.20). In the absence of one point of access/egress for all users, flexibility is increased by providing multiple means of getting to the door, such as wide-tread–low-riser steps in addition to a ramp or lift, that are integrated into the overall design. Paths to the home are smooth, with hard surfaces to minimize obstructions or falls risk and are wide enough to accommodate two people side by side, whether they are walking or using mobility devices, such as strollers, bicycles, wheelchairs, or walkers. In addition, different surface materials contrast in color and texture (e.g., paved walkways, brick steps, wood porch) and pathway edges are defined by curbs, grass, or planting beds. There is adequate lighting operated by motion detectors or timers along the path to the home and at the doorway.

At the doorway, the entrance (Figure 5.21) is level with the exterior and interior landings, there is sufficient space to maneuver any travel aids,

Getting in and out of the home. (A,B,C) No-step entrances with contrasting textures and colors provide P1, Equitable Use; P2, Flexibility in Use; P4, Perceptible Information; P5, Tolerance for Error, P6, Low Physical Effort, P7, Size and Space for Approach and Use; P8, Social Integration; and P9, Contextual Integration (Photo A courtesy of Sheri Peifer and Erin Clay, Eskaton, Carmichael, CA; Photo B courtesy of Jean Yves Prodel, JYP Design, Choisy au Bac, France; Photo C courtesy of Charles Schwab, AIA, Moline, IL).

FIGURE 5.20

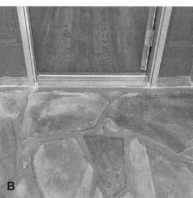

FIGURE 5.21

Getting in and out of the home. (A) Wide doors, (B) level thresholds, and (C) large interior door handles enable safe and easy movement through doorways by meeting principles P1, Equitable use; P2, Flexibility in Use; P3, Simple and Intuitive Use, P5, Tolerance for Error; P6, Low Physical Effort; P7, Size and Space for Approach and Use; and P9, Contextual Integration (Photo A courtesy of Andrea Hubbard, ASID, Bremen, GA; Photos B and C courtesy of Jean Yves Prodel, JYP Design, Choisy au Bac, France).

including mobility devices, strollers, or bicycles, and the doorway is wide enough for these devices to pass through easily. There is a place to place packages by the door, and the door has hands-free hardware on the exterior (at best an electronic lock and door opener, or at worst a lever handle that can operated with an elbow) to provide for ease of access if an individual cannot use his or her hands because of either a functional limitation or a situational one (e.g., carrying a package or a baby). On the interior side of the door, a large loop handle works well to pull a swinging door or sliding door open.

Moving Around the Home. Inside the home, circulation is free and unfettered by furniture, walls, level changes, or tight turns. Open spaces without hallways provide flexibility in creating clear circulation, and hallways are wide enough to accommodate two people, whether they are walking side by side or using mobility devices, such as two scooters (Figure 5.22) or a baby stroller for twins. Doorways are wide enough to accommodate individuals carrying packages, moving furniture, or using a wheelchair, and doors have handles that do not require grasping to operate. Transitions between spaces have smooth changes between flooring materials, and they contrast in color and texture. Lighting, in general, is even throughout, particularly between spaces, with as much natural light as possible and avoiding shadows and glare. Lighting is flexible, enabling users to highlight work surfaces and important

FIGURE 5.22

Moving around the home. (A,B) Eliminating level changes (unless mechanical means are used for vertical movement, see Figure 5.23) and providing open space or wide hallways enable P1, Equitable Use; P5, Tolerance for Error; P6, Low Physical Effort; P7, Size and Space for Approach and Use; P8, Social Integration (Photo B courtesy of Jean Yves Prodel, JYP Design, Choisy au Bac, France).

Moving around the home (between levels). Accessible design can become everyday design when it is integrated into the context, such as this stair lift, which through a simple transformation, is compatible with Asian décor, thus enabling P9, Contextual Integration as well as P1, Equitable Use; P5, Tolerance for Error; P6, Low Physical Effort; P7, Size and Space for Approach and Use; P8, Social Integration.

FIGURE 5.23

design features in the home when desired. If there is more than one level in the home, the slope of the stairs is as gradual as possible with handrails at multiple levels on each side and an elevator, vertical lift, or stair lift (Figure 5.23) that are integrated into the design of the home.

Performing Self-Care. Universal design bathrooms have spaces that are large enough and with sufficient space at each fixture (i.e., not a 5-ft AD turning diameter in a corner of the room) to enable all individuals, with or without a variety of assistive and health care technologies, to maneuver, access, and use each of the fixtures safely and easily. In addition, each fixture has sufficient supports integrated into the overall design to enable using the fixture easily and safely. Lighting is bright and adjustable through the use of different light sources (e.g., indirect or filtered natural light, down lighting, up lighting, tray lighting, track lighting) to compensate for different times of the day and needs of different users. All fixtures, support rails, and countertops contrast in color with the walls and flooring.

Toileting. First and foremost, a UD toilet minimizes effort getting on and off the fixture by facilitating sitting down and rising up. A comfort-height or wall-hung toilet (Figure 5.24) that is a few inches higher than a standard toilet with support rails integrated into the overall design permits safe and easy use without the need for add-on devices that are typically used for home modifications. In addition, the support rails are flexible enough to enable an individual to use both arms, if necessary, to maintain constant contact and a base of support throughout the transfer process.

Bathing/Showering. A UD tub or shower enables an individual to get in and out of the fixture easily and safely by minimizing lifting of one's legs and

FIGURE 5.24

Toilet height. (A,B) A wall-hung or comfort height toilet and grab bars that are residential in character, contrast from the floor and walls and integrated into the everyday design of the bathroom exemplify principles P1, Equitable Use; P2, Flexibility in Use; P3, Simple and Intuitive Use; P5, Tolerance for Error; P6, Low Physical Effort; P7, Size and Space for Approach and Use; and P9, Contextual Integration (Photo B courtesy of Jean Yves Prodel, JYP Design, Choisy au Bac, France).

stepping over the more than 12-in. sidewall of a bathtub or the more than 4-in. curb of a shower. In addition, like the toilet, a UD bathtub minimizes raising/lowering to get up and down from the bottom of the tub or to a seat in the shower. Walk-in (with 2–4-in. step) or slide-in tubs (Figure 5.25) minimize or eliminate stepping over the sidewall of a bathtub, whereas curbless showers (Figure 5.26) with integral seats (Figure 5.27) eliminate stepping over a shower curb and provide a place to sit, if needed to accommodate

FIGURE 5.25

Bathtub sidewalls. (A,B,C) Transfer tubs that have doors or retractable side walls enable users to slide directly in and out of the tub without having to step over the side wall and lower down to the tub bottom exhibit principles P1, Equitable Use; P2, Flexibility in Use; P5, Tolerance for Error; P6, Low Physical Effort; P7, Size and Space for Approach and Use; and P9, Contextual Integration.

balance problems. Integrated into the design of the fixture and/or bathroom, grab bars are provided at all points around the perimeter of the tub or shower and at multiple heights to enable changing positions within the fixture and from a standing to sitting position.

Grooming. A UD lavatory/vanity is placed at a height that will enable a variety of activities, including brushing teeth, washing face and hands, shaving, combing hair, and putting on makeup, from either a standing or seated position. At least part of the space is open underneath to accommodate a seated user with all parts of the countertop within easy reach, including the faucet controls (Figure 5.28), which can be brought forward toward the front of the sink to minimize reaching. Using electronic sensor faucets and soap dispensers eliminate grasping and handling altogether, although lever handle faucets and pump dispensers will at least eliminate grasping. Pullout drawers or shelves bring stored items to the user, rather

FIGURE 5.26

Shower curbs and controls. (A,B) Curbless showers eliminate the need for stepping over a curb, thus not only providing access for wheelchairs but also eliminating a tripping hazard for ambulatory individuals. These showers exemplify P1, Equitable Use; P5, Tolerance for Error; P6, Low Physical Effort; P7, Size and Space for Approach and Use; P8, Social Integration; and P9, Contextual Integration (Photo B courtesy of Charles Schwab, AIA, Moline, IL). (A) In addition, outboard lever faucet controls minimize reaching and grasping (not to mention getting wet and cold when the shower is first turned on), while the high contrast controls and flooring make the shower easier to differentiate from the rest of the bathroom. These characteristics further provide P3, Perceptible Information and P6, Low physical effort.

FIGURE 5.27

Shower seating. (A,B) Showers with integral seats and grab bars not only avoid creating clutter but also can be useful for people with and without mobility problems. These fixtures exhibit principles P1, Equitable Use; P2, Flexibility in Use; P3, Simple and Intuitive Use; P5, Tolerance for Error; P6, Low Physical Effort; P7, Size and Space for Approach and Use; and P9, Contextual Integration. They can also be useful for "showering with a friend," thus also promoting P8, Social Integration (Photo A courtesy of Jean Yves Prodel, JYP Design, Choisy au Bac, France).

FIGURE 5.28

Faucet handles and sink knee space. (A,B,C) Lever handles and open counters that can be used from a standing or seated position follow principles P1, Equitable Use; P2, Flexibility in Use; P3, Simple and Intuitive Use; P5, Tolerance for Error; P6, Low Physical Effort; and P9, Contextual Integration, and if truly universal there will be P7, Size and Space for Approach and Use, as well as P8, Social Integration (Photo B courtesy of Jean Yves Prodel, JYP Design, Choisy au Bac, France).

than the other way around, and swivel mirrors can be adjusted to enable users of varying stature to easily use them.

Preparing Meals. A UD kitchen, like the bathroom, provides flexible work spaces to enable a variety of activities to occur, including washing, cutting, mixing, cooking, and cleaning. Universal design kitchens have spaces that are large enough and with sufficient space at each appliance, fixture, and workstation (once again, not a 5-ft accessible design turning diameter in

FIGURE 5.29

Appliance attributes and positioning. (A) Refrigerator drawers, (B) french door, and (C) side-by-side refrigerators with through-the-door acess and sufficient maneuvering space can enable individuals to reach most items from either the left or right side in *both* the refrigerator and freezer compartments, whereas (D) a raised dishwasher (Photo courtesy of Andrea Hubbard, ASID, Bremen, GA) and (E) appropriately placed wall ovens (Photo courtesy of Sheri Peifer and Erin Clay, Eskaton, Carmichael, CA) limit bending for either a standing or seated user, demonstrating principles P1, Equitable Use; P2, Flexibility in Use; P5, Tolerance for Error; P6, Low Physical Effort; P8, Social Integration and P9, Contextual Integration.

FIGURE 5.30

Open space for seated users. Open space below (A,B) a sink at a lower than standard height (Photo A courtesy of Jean Yves Prodel, JYP Design, Choisy au Bac, France and Photo B courtesy of CATEA, GA Tech, Atlanta, GA), (C) two sinks at dual heights, or (D) counter workspaces with open space below (photo courtesy of Charles Schwab, AIA, Moline, IL) exemplify principles P1, Equitable Use; P2, Flexibility in Use; P6, Low Physical Effort; P8, Social Integration; and P9, Contextual Integration.

FIGURE 5.31

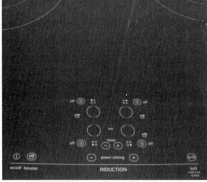

High contrast controls. Appliance controls that contrast from the background and are intuitive provide P3, Simple and Intuitive Use and P4, Perceptible Information, without sacrificing P9, Contextual Integration. Note that the flat, smooth surface also exhibits P6, Low physical effort by permitting a pot to be slid off the burner and onto the counter.

FIGURE 5.32

Storage options. Slide out full extension drawers and lazy Susan shelves at various heights in lower cabinets bring needed items to the user rather than the other way around, demonstrating principles P1, Equitable Use; P2, Flexibility in Use; P3, Simple and Intuitive Use; P6, Low Physical Effort, P8, Social Integration; and P9, Contextual Integration (photos courtesy of Andrea Hubbard, ASID, Bremen, GA and Sandra McGowan, FASID, Atlanta, GA).

some remote corner of the room) to enable all individuals, with or without a variety of assistive and health care technologies, to maneuver, access, and perform meal preparation tasks. Countertops at different workstations and built-in appliances (e.g., wall oven, cooktop, dishwasher, and refrigerator drawers) have a range of heights to provide the flexibility to perform the variety of tasks, including a lower-than-standard sink to reach the bottom, a higher-than-standard dishwasher, or dishwasher (as well as refrigerator drawers) just below the countertop to minimize bending and reaching (Figure 5.29). The space below the sink, cooktop, and adjacent to the wall oven are open (Figure 5.30) to accommodate a seated user, and all parts of the countertop are easy to reach, including the faucet controls, which can be brought forward toward the front of the sink to minimize reaching. Using electronic sensor faucets and soap dispensers eliminate reaching, grasping, and handling altogether, although lever handle faucets and pump dispensers will at least eliminate grasping. Similarly, cooktop controls, as well as all appliances, are located on the front to minimize reaching, especially over hot burners, and contrast in color from the appliance to be easily seen and read (Figure 5.31). Digital readouts (also on other appliances) not only are high contrast from the background but also provide auditory output. Heating elements are either staggered or induction (they are only hot to pots) to avoid reaching over hot burners. Burners are also flush with the masonry countertop to enable hot pots to slide across without grasping and lifting. Pullout drawers and shelves (Figure 5.32) bring stored items to the user or provide a convenient place to set down bowls and pots, whereas pull-down cabinets (Figure 5.33) minimize upward reach and bring stored items lower. Supports for balance and safety are integrated along the entire length of counters to enable users to maintain balance, reduce the risk of falling, and minimize demands of standing for periods at a time. Lighting is bright and adjustable through the use of different light sources (e.g., indirect or filtered natural light, down lighting, up lighting, tray lighting, under cabinet lighting, and track lighting) to compensate for different times of the day and needs of different users. All fixtures, support rails, and countertops contrast in color with the walls and flooring.

FIGURE 5.33

Movable cabinets. Mechanical or motorized pull-down cabinets (pictured at the Toto Showroom in Tokyo, JP) minimize reaching by bringing objects to user, demonstrating principles P1, Equitable Use; P2, Flexibility in Use; P3, Simple and Intuitive Use; P6, Low Physical Effort; and P9, Contextual Integration.

Universal Design to Improve Safety and Caregiver Supervision for People With Cognitive Loss

Unlike UD to support independent and assisted activity, UD to support individuals with cognitive loss takes on different meanings at different points in time. In the early stages of cognitive decline, it is important to promote independence and autonomy within the limits of an individual's physical abilities. This is familiar because it is the underlying presumption upon which all of the UD principles are based. However, as cognitive loss increases, caregiver intervention, supervision, and assistance are increasingly necessary, even if an individual is physically able to complete routine activities without assistance. For example, providing easy-to-use lever door handles that automatically unlock doors may enable or even encourage an individual to go outside. However, as cognitive decline progresses, often accompanied by increased physical frailty, UD principles can contradict the need to discourage independent activity because of the risk of injury or getting lost. At the same time, design must support the caregiver to maximize safety, and security of the individual by regulating independent access to objects, spaces, and controls may be paramount (Calkins, Sanford, & Proffitt, 2001).

To support individuals with cognitive loss, UD must be considered in the context of the caregiver/recipient dyad and, in fact, may be more for caregivers' use than for care recipients. To accomplish this, UD must be broadened to recognize that for certain users, usable to the greatest extent possible is often not an individual decision. Rather, it may be up to caregivers and/or family members to determine when independent activity is no longer safe activity. As a result, universal must accommodate independent use when possible, but also enable caregivers to regulate access and usability when necessary.

Regulated access, which is the degree to which the environment permits a caregiver to control, limit, or monitor access to potential hazards, clearly affects all seven of the activity/usability principles, because adhering to the principles can make it difficult to regulate access. Examples of controlled access include locked doors, complicated latches, or enclosed (e.g., fenced) outdoor spaces. Clearly, the easier something is for an individual with cognitive loss to use, the more difficult it is for a caregiver to regulate access. As a result, facilitating usability by adhering to the principles of equitability, flexibility, simple and intuitive, perceptibility, low effort, and size and space is often contradictory to regulated access.

Nonetheless, even tolerance for error is not completely compatible with regulating access. On paper, the guidelines for tolerance for error, which include cognitive processing and safety concerns through eliminating or shielding hazardous elements, providing warnings of hazards and errors, providing fail-safe features, and discouraging unconscious actions in tasks that require vigilance, would appear to be entirely supportive of promoting safe environments for people with cognitive loss. However, in practice, it is inconsistent with supporting caregiver/recipient dyads (Calkins et al., 2001).

First, tolerance for error advocates making the most used design features the most obvious and most accessible to avoid using the wrong feature. Unfortunately, many safety risks arise for people with cognitive problems from the design features that are most accessible, such as controls on the front of a stove. Second, tolerance for error frequently relies on cognitive processes (e.g., such as clearly signs or pictures to warn of features that can cause error) rather than on physical or sensory ones to deter error (such as locked doors and alarms). This strategy only works if an individual with cognitive loss recognizes the demarcation. (A skull and crossbones perhaps?) Finally, this principle presumes that error is inadvertent. For people with cognitive issues, even intended actions may cause error. For example, someone may leave the house to take a walk (intended) but not recognize the risk of getting lost (unintended consequences).

To accommodate activity from a level of independence to supervision, UD must meet the seven principles for independent use and the flexibility to be able to regulate access for controlled use. For example, a switch-operated power door openers or electronic door locks that require low physical effort can be turned off, thus making them effective means of regulating access. Similarly, timers and temperature-sensitive switches, such as those used on stoves, can regulate access while at the same time ensure safety. Ultimately, UD to accommodate individuals with cognitive loss will require careful consideration of an individual's initial needs for aging in place and planning for those of the caregiver in the future.

UNIVERSAL DESIGN FOR AGING IN PLACE: CASE STUDIES OF TOILETING AND BATHING

Supporting elders with toilet and bathing transfers is one area of concern that demonstrates the need for a more universal approach to design. Because difficulty with toileting and bathing at home is a frequent determinant of an older adult being relocated from the home to institutional care, facilitating these activities is particularly important for this population. Findings from a series of studies (Sanford & Megrew, 1995, 1999; Sanford, 2002; Sanford, Echt, & Malassigné, 1999) focusing on independent and assisted toileting and bathing demonstrated the need for a more UD approach to independent living. These studies reported that seniors transferred differently than younger adults, and as such, accessible designs, particularly those based on the *ADAAG*, caused difficulty for most older adults than designs that were more universal.

Elders Transfer Differently

As described in Chapter 4, the understanding of grab bar placement is based on removing barriers to independent transfers by wheelchair users who have the upper body strength to pull themselves onto a toilet or seat and back again. In contrast, older adults, who comprise the majority of wheelchair users today, generally do not have good upper body strength but can bear weight and stand for at least short periods. In addition, a large number of seniors who are ambulatory and use walking aids require grab bars at tubs and toilets because of difficulty lifting their legs, moving between sitting and standing positions, and getting up and down.

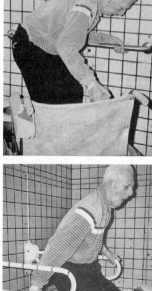

FIGURE 5.34

Grab bar configurations used in the laboratory study.

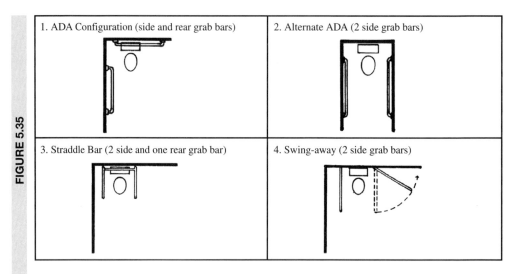

Four grab bar configuration evaluated in a national survey.

Contrary to assumptions embedded in accessible design strategies about who needs grab bars and how they are used, a survey of 717 older adults with mobility impairments found that half of those who needed grab bars did not use wheelchairs ($n = 362$). Even among those who used wheelchairs ($n = 355$), most (88.5%) transferred onto the toilet or into a tub from a standing rather than from a sitting position. Therefore, it is not surprising that almost two-thirds of the sample transferred from either the front (33.6%) or angled (32.8%) transfer position, which are the most commonly used positions to perform a standing transfer. Participants also reported that they had significantly less difficulty transferring from a front position than from any of the side transfer positions.

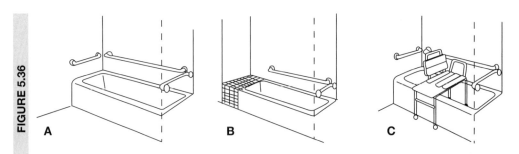

(A) Sketches of typical tub/shower with grab bars, (B) tub with rear transfer seat, and (C) tub with transfer bench (right) taken from a national survey.

Mismatch Between Accessible Toilet and Tub Design and Needs

Based on the way most older people get on and off a toilet, it is not surprising that older mobility aid users in a laboratory study reported significantly greater difficulty using the standard grab bar configuration based on the *ADAAG* (i.e., 18 in. to the centerline from an adjacent wall with grab bars a minimum of 42 in. in length located on walls adjacent to and behind the toilet) than grab bars better suited to standing transfers (i.e., located on both sides of the toilet). Standard accessible grab bars also had the lowest incidence of use (27.2%) among the four configurations tested (Figure 5.34), with the rear bar being used only slightly more than 10% of the time. In contrast, the configuration with swing-up grab bars on both sides of the toilet (i.e., better suited to front approach standing transfers) had the highest incidence of use at greater than 70%. Similarly, in a survey study of more than 700 older adults, significantly higher percentages of elder wheelchair ($p < .01$) and walking aid ($p < .001$) users reported greater difficulty with the standard ADAAG grab bar configuration than grab bars located on both sides of the toilet that would facilitate a standing transfer (Figure 5.35).

The survey study also found that 60% of the respondents reported that the typical residential bathtub/shower combination with grab bars (Figure 5.36), which also met the *ADAAG*, was the most difficult fixture to use. Surprising, however, an accessible bathtub with a rear transfer bench, which is also commonly used in residential settings and meets the *ADAAG*, was difficult to use for almost 50% of the respondents. In contrast, although significantly fewer respondents had difficulty using curbless showers, a larger percentage of respondents had difficulty using a curbless shower without a seat than a shower stall with a seat ($p < .001$), even when the latter had a 3 to 4 in. curb that required stepping over. Overall, respondents who used both wheeled mobility and walking aids had less difficulty using showers than bathtubs. However, they had less difficulty using fixtures with a seat than those without a seat. In fact, larger percentages of respondents reported that showers without seats, including the curbless shower without a seat (41%), were more difficult to use than either of the two bathtubs with seats.

These findings suggest that toilet and bathing fixtures intended for people who transfer directly from a wheelchair to a fixture may not support the abilities of older adults. More importantly, the reported levels of difficulty and patterns of grab bar use raise some important questions concerning the ability of accessible toilet and tub/shower designs to promote safe and, if possible, independent personal care activities by older adults.

In fact, it is likely that older adults need grab bars and in-fixture seats not because they cannot stand at all, but because they have difficulty standing for long periods or because they have difficulty getting up and down from a toilet seat or tub bottom. As a result, even toilets and curbless showers that meet the *ADAAG* and are commonly used for home modifications may create demands that exceed the competence of many older adults and may result in higher levels of dependency in toileting and bathing than those predicted by clinical assessments of functional capabilities. To reduce these "excess disabilities," designs that are more universal can better support the range of abilities of older adults.

Best Practices

The studies cited above focused only on independent transfer, which is the underlying presumption in accessibility codes and standards. Unfortunately, many older people lack the upper body strength to pull themselves out of a wheelchair, have difficulty stepping over the side of the tub, or have problems raising and lowering themselves onto a toilet even with the assistance of grab bars. However mechanical lifts, which are an alternative means of safely transferring an individual into a tub or onto a toilet, were generally discouraged, particularly among people with dementia because the experience of being lifted off the ground and lowered down can be unsettling. As a result, many individuals may require person-assisted transfers, regardless of the grab bar configuration.

To accommodate the largest number of individuals, toilet and bathing fixtures should have sufficient flexibility to promote independent use and assistance by as many as two care providers, when necessary. Therefore, designs should accommodate not only individuals who have the capability of supporting their own weight and pivoting on their feet during transfers but also those who cannot. Moreover, designs should prevent and/or reduce the risk of injuries to all users and permit ease of access by individuals with many types and levels of ability.

Research on best practices in assisted toileting and bathing suggests that several designs that radically depart from *ADAAG* specifications (e.g., swing-up grab bars) are not only intended to support greater safety and ease of independent transfer but also potentially provide greater flexibility in facilitating assisted transfers. Although the research was based on best practices in the design of long-term care facilities, alternative designs used to support and prevent and/or reduce injuries during independent or assisted toileting and bathing in long-term care provide

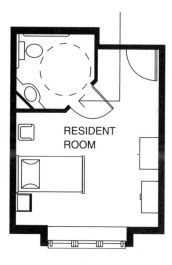

FIGURE 5.37

Toilet room door and configuration at *The Heritage* at Landis Homes Retirement Community, Lititz, PA (RLPS) has an outswinging door at a 45-degree angle that reduces 90-degree turns and creates a clear 5 ft space in the bathroom.

RESIDENT ROOM

a strong basis for UD for aging in place. Best practice designs include modifying the attributes of toilets and tub by adjusting the configuration of the bathroom, door swing, position and configuration of toilet grab bars, location of the toilet, position of toilet grab bars, location of the tub, bathtub design, position of shower grab bars, shower design, and bathroom as shower room.

Bathroom Configuration. The most common practice among the innovative designs was the placement of the bathroom room at a 45° angle (Figure 5.37). The angle facilitated maneuvering by eliminating the need for sharp turns in small spaces. In addition, the location of the door also permitted the toilet and lavatory to be located at right angles to each other. This configuration provided room for a 5-ft wheelchair turning radius and sufficient room for assistance on both sides of the toilet.

Door Swing. Orienting an out-swinging bathroom door at 45° (Figure 5.37) facilitated maneuvering by eliminating the need for sharp turns (typically) from a narrow hallway. Furthermore, the out-swinging door not only permitted a 5-ft turning radius in toilet room and space for assistance on both sides of the toilet but also facilitated entry by staff in the event of a resident fall or other incapacity inside the room that might block the door.

Toilet Grab Bar Type and Position. The *ADAAG* L-shaped grab bar configuration includes stationary grab bars on the sidewall and the rear wall behind

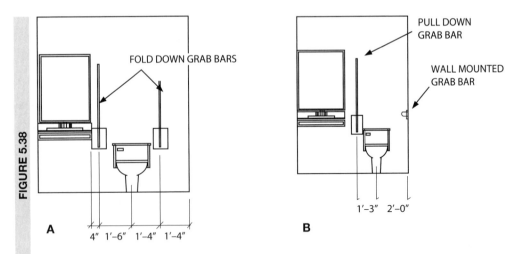

FIGURE 5.38

Grab bar type and location at (A) Memorial Hospital, Martinsville, VA (Ellerbe Becket), which has two fold down grab bars, allows the toilet to move 2'8" from the closest wall to the centerline, whereas (B) one wall-mounted grab bar at Memorial Hospital of Iowa County, Dodgeville, WI (Nelson Tremain Partnership) is 2'4" to the toilet centerline.

the toilet at the recommended accessible heights and distances from the toilet considered to be too high and too far away to meet the needs of either independent transfer or of people requiring assistance. In all cases, the rear grab bar was omitted, and in many cases, the sidewall grab bar was omitted as well. When the side grab bar was used, it was intended to be used as a support for a standing individual during dressing, and a swing-away grab bar was provided on the opposite side of the toilet. In place of accessible stationary grab bars, rear-mounted, swing-up (or fold-down) grab bars that pivot up and down were used on both sides of the toilet. These bars allowed the toilet to move away from a sidewall, thus providing sufficient space on both sides of the toilet to accommodate one- or two-person-assisted transfers as well as independent toileting (Figure 5.38).

With grab bars in the vertical or up position, sufficient space is provided for caregivers to stand next to the toilet on either (or both) side(s) to provide support getting on and of the toilet. In the horizontal or down position, grab bars on both sides of the toilet would permit individuals requiring assistance to maintain balance while clothing is being removed or replaced. Alternatively, for individuals capable of independent transfer, grab bars on both sides would enable them to pull up to a standing position and lower down to a sitting position. Whereas there is no data available to suggest the ideal length of grab bars, most designers tend to use

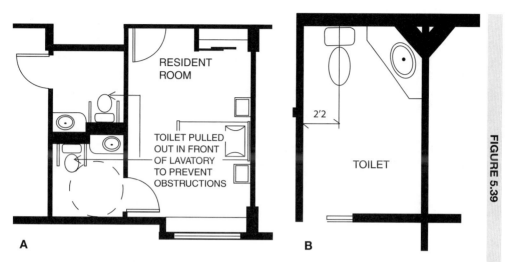

To create more space for assistance, toilet location at (A) Beechwood Home (Dorsky Hodgson and Partners) is pulled out from sink, whereas (B) the sink at Creekview at Evergreen Retirement Community, Oshkosh, WI (Nelson Tremain Partnership) is placed on a 45-degree angle.

swing-up grab bars that are considerably shorter (usually 24–30 in.) than the 42 in. minimum requirement for grab bars alongside the toilet. This approach minimizes ambulation for individuals who have unsteady gait and are at risk of falls.

Toilet Location. Moving the toilet away from obstructions, such as other fixtures and walls, increases clear floor space for maneuvering a mobility aid or for providing assistance. For example, the wet wall behind the lavatory and toilet was stepped so that the back of toilet was not in the same plane as the lavatory (Figure 5.39). This effectively pulled the toilet out in front of the lavatory, thus preventing the latter from interfering with assistance on that side of the toilet.

In addition, the use of swing-up grab bars frees the toilet from having to be located within reachable distance of a sidewall-mounted grab bar (Figure 5.38). Therefore, in contrast to the *ADAAG*, which specifies that the centerline of the toilet be located 18 in. from a sidewall, every innovative design located the toilet further away from the sidewall to provide space for caregivers to stand alongside one or both sides of the toilet as necessary to provide support and assistance with transfer and to help with the partial removal and replacement of clothing. Although 24 in. seemed to be the norm, the location of the toilet ranged from as little as 22 in. to as much as 30 in. from the sidewall. However, without research data upon which to determine how much space was adequate, side clearance varied; the general sentiment among designers was that more space is better, the amount of space, in the end, usually being dependent on the amount of space available within the overall design of the room or facility.

Tub Grab Bars Position. Accessible design for grab bars vary slightly for bathtubs with in-tub and head of tub seats (the latter having longer bars on the sidewall and no bar on the head wall). Nonetheless, in both conditions, grab bars are located to help individuals get into the tub and then to lower and raise themselves to and from a seated position. Because these positional changes were deemed safety risks for older adults, grab bars that would permit older adults to raise and lower themselves were not included in most bathtub designs. Rather, in most designs, grab bars were provided adjacent to the tub for temporary support to enable an individual to steady himself or herself while a care provider assisted with removal and replacement of clothing. In fact, in instances where local building authorities required bathing fixtures with the *ADAAG* compliant grab bar configurations, roll-in showers were installed instead because of safety concerns, even though the former were readily available from a number of manufacturers.

Tub Location and Clear Floor Space. The amount of clear floor space in front of a bathtub required for accessible design (30–48 in. minimum depth depending on the direction of travel by the length of the tub including a

FIGURE 5.40

Walk in tubs, which eliminate the need for a transfer bench or mechanical lift, are designed for individuals who can ambulate, but have difficulty lifting their legs (photos courtesy of Dara and Chuck McMillan, My Accessible Home, Alpharetta, GA).

seat at the head of the tub) is based on positioning a wheelchair alongside the fixture for a sliding transfer. However, because frail older adults do not perform sliding transfers, clear floor space was needed for one or more caregivers to be able to assist with getting in and out of a tub. This affected not only the size of the space but also where the space was needed. As a result, bathtubs were typically designed with one end against a wall and three open sides from which assistance could be provided. Because wheelchair maneuverability was not an issue, less space was needed on any one side. However, more space was needed overall to accommodate caregiver access from more than one side.

Bathtub Design. An alternative design that was for less frail, ambulatory individuals was a walk-in bathtub (Figure 5.40). These tubs have a non-institutional appearance, an integral seat, and a swinging side-entry door with a pressurized seal for ease of access. The walk-in capability makes this fixture suitable for either independent or assisted use by individuals with a reasonable level of mobility. In addition, the fixture is also taller (24 in. above the finished floor) than most typical bathtubs, which permits immersion in the water even when using the seat. Whereas the added height and side-entry features address the primary shortcomings of a traditional tub, they also create the two shortcomings.

First, the tub must be empty to open the door to get in or out of the fixture. As a result, an older individual who can only step through the door

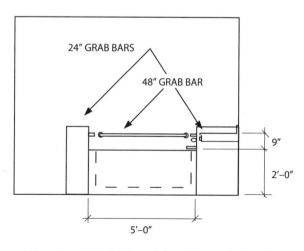

Location of bathtub grab bars in a walk-in tub.

FIGURE 5.41

must sit in the tub until it is filled or drained. Second, the tub does not meet the *ADAAG* grab bar guidelines. The 24 in. high sides make it impossible to install the two grab bars on the side wall in the manner prescribed in the *ADAAG*. As a result, in facilities where this fixture was used, one of the grab bars on the side wall was eliminated (Figure 5.41) to comply with the distance of 9 in. from the rim of the tub and 33–36 in. from the floor to the grab bar.

Shower Grab Bars Position. Accessible grab bars on the three walls of a roll-in shower stall are located at 33–36 in. above the floor. This was deemed insufficient for independent use of the shower. As a result, more bars, particularly vertical ones and in different configurations than specified in the *ADAAG*, were often installed. However, the location and orientation of grab bars were dependent on the type and size of shower provided.

Shower Design. To accommodate caregiver assistance, all showers were curbless and exceeded minimum accessible guidelines of 48 in. square. In fact, showers were made as big as space would allow. In addition, a half height wall was sometimes incorporated on one side to enable a caregiver using a handheld shower to stay dry while standing behind a resident seated in a shower chair.

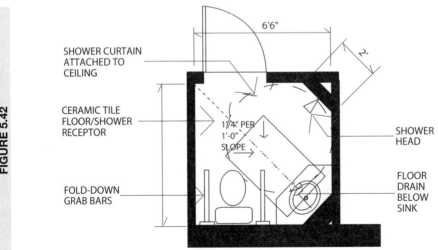

FIGURE 5.42

Wet area bathroom at Covenant Oaks at Oakwood Village, Madison, WI (OWP&P).

Wet Area Bathroom. The "bathroom as a shower room" (Figure 5.42) is a concept adapted from the common European residential model as an alternative for including a shower in every resident bathroom. Having a shower close to the resident room was particularly important to allow for impromptu cleanups in the event of incontinent episodes without the indignity of leading residents down a corridor to a central bathing facility. As a result, each resident bathroom was designed as a shower room that permitted either independent or assisted showering. The latter is facilitated by use of a handheld shower wand, which can be manipulated by the caregiver standing outside the area enclosed by the shower curtain. The bathroom-as-a-shower-room design requires more space than a typical toilet room and special considerations for drainage, doorway design, and waterproofing of other fixtures in the space. However, it affords an enhanced opportunity for assisted showering without the caregiver getting drenched in the process as well as permitting individuals to shower independently.

Universal Design Attributes for Toileting and Bathing

Based on the studies reviewed, there are a number of design attributes that can be applied to universal design of toilet and bathing fixtures to supports a wider range of needs and abilities. These include the following:

1. A minimum of 24-in. clearance between any obstruction (e.g., sidewall) and the side of the toilet seat to provide space on both sides of the fixture for one or more caregivers to stand alongside.
2. Rear or floor mounted swing-up/fold-down grab bars on both sides of the toilet to facilitate independent or assisted transfers.
3. Grab bars with a maximum length of 36 in. to permit ambulatory individuals to stand and sit without having to step to the toilet.
4. Walk-in bathtubs with a single horizontal grab bar on all sides to provide support for getting up and down from the integral seat.
5. Grab bars on the outside of the bathtub or shower to permit the individual maintain balance while disrobing or drying off.
6. Swing-up/fold-down grab bars in and adjacent to tubs and showers to add flexibility.
7. Curbless showers that are as large as possible, incorporating a seat and horizontal and vertical grab bars surrounding the enclosure to enable use by ambulatory and non-ambulatory individuals
8. A half wall on one side of the shower to facilitate assistance from the outside.

SIX

Work Environments:
Universal Design as a Rehabilitation Strategy
for Aging in the Workplace

Work is an essential life activity. The average adult spends much of his or her life working. Other than sleep, work is the activity that takes up the most amount of time in an individual's life (Bernspang & Fisher, 1995; Sandqvist & Henriksson, 2004). From a practical standpoint, work is an important part of living independently, having economic independence, achieving status and recognition, acquiring income, and developing relationships. From a health perspective, it is the basis for feelings of psychological well-being, identity, self-worth, and life satisfaction (Campbell, Converse, & Rogers, 1976; Christie, 2008; Clutterbuck & McKay, 1984; Judge, & Bono, 2001; National Council on Disability, 2007; Schermerhorn, 2009; Sook, 2007; Winter-Collins & McDaniel, 2000). It has also been suggested that the work environment can represent the most significant group membership and concentration of time as well as a source of structure, meaning, and support for an individual. From a social perspective, it is important for all individuals to be productive members and participate in society to the greatest extent possible.

Almost two-thirds (21.3 million) of the 33 million working-age adults with disabilities (ages 16–64 years) in the United States have chronic conditions that restrict their ability to work and participate in the workforce (Waldrop & Stern, 2003). Nonetheless, just as with the general population of workers, persons with disabilities desire and need to work. Participation in work leads to positive perceptions of self-efficacy and self-concept (Strong, 1998) and is believed to be essential to the recovery process by enabling individuals with disabilities to gain a new sense of self and purpose (Deegan, 1988).

However, when an employee is unable to adapt to the needs of the task and/or there are deficiencies in workplace equipment or design, environmental demands can exceed a worker's abilities rendering work tasks difficult, if not impossible to complete. As a result, despite the desire to work, adults with disabilities have the highest unemployment rate of any cohort in the United States. Moreover, data indicate that almost 8 of 10 people with disabilities did not obtain their impairment until after age of 20 years and 50% became disabled after age of 40 years (Hinton, 2003). This suggests that people with disabilities are just as likely to have the knowledge, skills, and motivation necessary to be productive in a variety of job areas. Further, 63% of individuals with disabilities who are not working would prefer to be working (NOD, 2004), and 25% of workers with disabilities who are employed part-time would like to work full time (Shur & Kruse, 2002). These statistics suggest that work disability, rather than a lack of desire to work, is the problem.

Chronic conditions are the most frequent cause of work disability. Based on the 1994 National Health Interview Survey data (LaPlante & Carlson, 1996), almost 4 million people experience work limitations due to back disorders (including orthopedic impairments and disc disorders), which accounts for 21.1% disability due to all conditions. Other causes include heart disease (2.1 million people or 10.9% of all conditions), osteoarthritis and related disorders (1.6 million people or 8.3% of all conditions), diseases of the respiratory system (1.1 million or 5.6% of all conditions), mental disorders (925,000 or 4.9% of all conditions), orthopedic impairments of lower extremities (861,000 or 4.5% of all conditions), and diabetes (624,000 or 3.3% of all conditions). In addition, work disability can also be attributed to occupational injuries and illnesses; and although the incidence of injuries and illnesses has steadily declined since the latter part of the 20th century, the number of work days lost and the cost of medical payments have greatly increased (Stoddard, Jans, Ripple, & Kraus, 1998).

To further compound the problem, the number of workers with disabling and chronic conditions is also expected to grow as the workforce ages. The United States has one of the highest labor force participation rates for persons 65 years and older in the developed world. Moreover, all indications are that this trend will only increase as workers choose to stay in the workforce longer, viewing retirement age as a time for "midcourse corrections" (Moen, 2003) rather than a time to leave the workforce. In fact, the AARP surveys have reported that two-thirds of workers older than 45 years plan to continue working past age 65 years (Rix, 2004), and even in retirement, most have reported that they would prefer to be engaged in some type of employment (AARP, 2002). However, for all practical purposes, disability in old age typically results in retirement from the workforce, as census data indicate that older adults with disabilities have lower workforce participation rates and higher unemployment rates than either younger adults with a disability or older adults without a disability.

PROSTHETIC AND THERAPEUTIC ROLES OF THE WORK ENVIRONMENT

Like the fit between housing environments and the people who live in them, work environments can have a significant impact on the work performance and the well-being of individuals who work in them. As a prosthetic environment, activity performance and health are the result of the fit between the worker's abilities and the demands of the work environment (Edwards, Caplan, & Van Harrison, 1998; French, Caplan, & Van Harrison, 1982). When demands exceed or fall below the worker's abilities, the environment hinders performance and the misfit results in negative health and performance outcomes. In contrast, when demands match ability, the environment facilitates worker productivity and well-being. As a therapeutic environment, job performance and well-being are associated with the behavioral, cognitive, and health outcomes of a worker's feelings and perceptions of the workplace (Isen, 1987; Warr, 1999). As a result, environments that do not engage the worker will result in negative emotional states, poor performance, and low productivity. In contrast, work environments that engender positive feelings at work and high job satisfaction are associated with better job performance and productivity.

Also similar to housing, workplaces are not typically designed to meet either the prosthetic or therapeutic needs of workers, particularly employees with limited abilities. Physical, organizational, and social environmental barriers are the primary sources of misfit between the rehabilitation and the work needs of these employees. Nonetheless, prosthetic work environments, and particularly those that are universally designed, can help promote aging and diversity in the workplace by supporting the inclusion of workers with diverse abilities, thus enabling individuals with disabilities to gain and maintain employment (Gamble, Dowler, & Orslene, 2006; Inge, Wehman, Strobel, Powell, & Todd, 1998). In addition, prosthetic work environments can reduce the risk of injury (Zwerling et al., 2003), enable retention of productive and qualified employees (Blanck, 1994; Unger & Kregel, 2003), and facilitate job performance of coworkers without disabilities (Blanck, 1998; Pitt-Catsouphes & Butterworth, 1995).

Although aging and the increase in chronic conditions have led to public concerns about health care costs and the growth of home health care, similar concerns about work environments have been lacking. Nonetheless, the workplace is a therapeutic environment that is inextricably tied to both psychological health and the maintenance of health. Work contributes to the psychological health of individuals by contributing to a sense of being as individuals and confidence in one's abilities, a sense of belonging to a larger community, and a sense of group identity through forming bonds with the work, people, place, and organization. These psychological needs require the provision of both private and community space (Strong & Rebiero, 2003). Private space is important for a sense of being, whereas the opportunity to visit others and to meet in more public spaces is important for needs for social interaction.

At the same time, there is increasing concern about health and safety because of the changing nature of work tasks that have resulted in a range of new occupational injuries, including computer-related repetitive stress disorders, back pain, and psychological stress. Such issues have important implications for workers' compensation costs, medical payments, and downtime due to lost workdays, which affect almost 6 million workers or 6.1% of the workforce and account for over $225 billion in costs to public and private insurers (DOL, 2001).

Contextual Factors

Whereas ergonomic guidelines developed by the Occupational Safety and Health Administration (1999) have significantly increased workplace safety and reduced the cost of workplace accidents, they do not accommodate workers across the full range and types of abilities. To promote aging in the workplace, the impact of workplace demands on the work and productivity of people with diverse abilities must be minimized. This requires an understanding of the organizational, social, and physical contextual factors in the workplace, including the interests of the organization, its employees, and their interactions with each other, colleagues, and customers. The organizational context refers to the policies, procedures, safety and security, economics, and resources that create an enabling and productive workplace. The social context refers to the workplace culture and attitudes of employers and other employees. The physical context refers to the places and the physical spaces where work occurs, including individual and shared workspaces. Whereas rehabilitation professionals must be cognizant of all three contextual factors, this chapter will focus on the latter.

To further complicate aging in the workplace, a number of societal trends, including the diversity of the workforce and the increasing importance of the social nature of work, are also redefining the physical context of the 21st century workplace.

Diversity in the Workplace. The American workforce is changing because of current economic and demographic trends. Not only are people living longer and healthier lives but also because of economic and psychological needs, baby boomers are planning to work longer. In addition, people older than 65 years are still in the workplace, Gen X is now in the workplace, and Gen Y is just entering. These trends are creating and will continue to create a workforce that is more diverse than ever before, including people of all ages, genders, ethnic backgrounds, and abilities.

Of equal importance is the effect of aging in the workplace from the standpoint of older workers continuing to work and those retiring from work. The Bureau of Labor Statistics data reveal that one out of five people aged 65–74 years was working at the beginning the 21st century. However, as baby boomers age, the annual growth rate of persons 55 years and older in the U.S. labor force is expected to increase from 26 million in 2010 to 33 million people in 2025 (Czaja & Moen, 2004). With the direct correlation between age and disability, the number of people with disabilities in the workforce will rise dramatically as the U.S. workforce continues to age.

Yet, how employers and employees define disability and aging, or think about the relationship between the two, is unknown. In other words, if an older worker has difficulty performing work tasks because of a functional limitation, then is it considered to be a disability that requires accommodation or the result of natural aging that does not require accommodation?

The question is important, not only because it will determine whether changes to the physical workplace environment are required to accommodate an older worker but also because older adults may decline from requesting accommodations because of the stigma associated with disability and the fear of being forced out of the workforce. In either case, older employees may be pushed out of the workplace—for employers/supervisors' perceptions that they cannot do the job on the one hand and for having difficulty or not being able to do it on the other.

Second, the number of jobs in the United States is projected to increase by mid-decade despite the current economy. Although the number of jobs might be considerably less than the 19 million projected to increase from 2004 and 2014 (Hecker, 2005), it should nonetheless increase significantly. Despite the intergenerational nature of the workplace, if older workers retire, there will not be enough workers to replace all of the retirees resulting in a drastic shortage of workers. To make up for the shortfall of workers, employers will have to adopt new strategies that will enable them to draw on untapped sources of labor, such as people with disabilities. In this scenario, the workplace will have to accommodate not only people as their abilities change across their life span but also the increase in the number of workers with differing abilities across different life spans. This will require an understanding of the needs of this diverse working community and how we can make the workplace, work tools, and work technologies easier to use.

Changing the Nature of Work. Whereas work has traditionally focused on the individual performing a set of tasks in a fixed space, it is increasingly centered on teamwork, collaborative group work, communication, and interactions between coworkers. To accommodate these activities, the workplace is being transformed from a single defined space to anyplace where work can be done most effectively, including airports, airplanes, hotels, coffee shops, customer sites, or anywhere there is a wireless hotspot. However, this changing nature of work is creating a need for workplaces to enable workers to share knowledge physically and virtually. As virtual workspaces increase, physical workplaces where coworkers can come together face to face to share knowledge and ideas are becoming increasingly important.

To facilitate communication and knowledge sharing, information and communication technology, which links people and places together, has become ubiquitous, providing flexibility and mobility and enabling seamless movement within and across physical workplaces and virtual workspaces. Information and communication technologies are not only changing the nature of work from a physical place where the required task is completed to a space where it gets done but also changing the nature of workplace design, often making it difficult to distinguish between the physical workplace and the virtual workspace.

These changes have created a greater need for a flexible physical layout that provides greater functional opportunities. Traditional private offices lining the exterior walls of double-loaded corridors are giving way to open spaces filled with workstations that are unassigned and used on a first-come-first-serve basis and quiet rooms and team spaces. As work is increasingly done in nondedicated, shared environments, there is greater need for workstations and spaces that can be adjusted to accommodate different physical sizes and abilities of employees. Similarly, there is a need for furniture and equipment that can be adjusted and used in the most suitable position to relieve discomfort and accommodate various body sizes, heights, and postures.

With the need for flexibility and sharing of spaces among such a wide range of ages and abilities, universal design is a logical approach to workplace design. It can provide prosthetic support to alleviate the stigma associated with specialized accommodations and ameliorate disability and it can reduce accidents, cut compensation costs, and lessen the risk of lawsuits. For those who have accidents or injuries, universal design can facilitate their return to work. It can also provide therapeutic support for employee mental health and medical devices that might be necessary for employment. This chapter explores the prosthetic and therapeutic roles of workplace accommodations and universal design, in particular, as a rehabilitation strategy that can promote aging in the workplace through facilitating improved health, increased diversity, and changing nature of work.

ACCOMMODATING ACTIVITY: SPECIALIZED DESIGN AS A PROSTHETIC INTERVENTION

Among those individuals with disabilities who are employed, adapting the work environment and providing assistive technologies are common prosthetic accommodations to compensate for unsupportive work settings. Unlike home modifications, which carry neither legal definition nor mandate, workplace accommodations are mandated and defined by both the Rehabilitation Act of 1973 and the Americans with Disabilities Act. Section 504 of the Rehabilitation Act granted federal employees and employees of federal contractors (i.e., any agency or activity that receives federal financial assistance) the right to reasonable accommodations. In addition, Section 508 requires that commonly used electronic and information technology (e.g., telephones, copiers, fax machines) used by the federal government be accessible to people with disabilities. Although this legislation is applicable only to the federal government, it has had far-reaching impacts, setting the precedent, if not the standard, for all electronic and information technology developed in the past three decades.

Title I of the ADA of 1990 prohibits employers with 15 or more employees from discriminating against a qualified applicant or worker who has a physical or mental impairment that substantially limits a major life activity; has a history of such disability; or is regarded as having such disability, even if he or she does not. In addition, it extended the right to reasonable accommodation mandated under Section 508 of the Rehabilitation

Act to most other employees in public, for-profit, and nonprofit sectors unless doing so creates undo hardships for the employer. Under Title I of the ADA, employers must provide "reasonable accommodations" for a qualified applicant or worker with a disability to enable that individual to perform the essential functions or fundamental job duties (Equal Employment Opportunity Commission, 1992).

Accommodations are broadly defined as "any change in the work environment or in the way things are customarily done that enables an individual with a disability to enjoy equal employment opportunities" (ADA, 1991). More specifically, the Equal Employment Opportunity Commission (1992) defines workplace accommodations as modifications or adjustments that enable (a) a job applicant with a disability to be considered for a job (such as providing application forms in alternative formats like large print or Braille); (b) a qualified individual with a disability to perform the essential functions of the job (such as providing assistive technology or sign language interpreters); and (c) employees with disabilities to enjoy equal benefits and privileges of employment (such as removing assistive technology or barriers to performing job tasks). It should also be noted that because the ADAAG (Title III of the ADA) covers public environments, the technical requirements mandated under Title III are not necessarily reasonable under Title I. For example, a ramp with a 1:12 gradient, which is the typical (yet, maximum) slope allowed for ramps in public spaces, might not be a reasonable accommodation in an employee area if it is too steep given a worker's abilities and the demands of the context.

Based on the objectives stated in Title III, a variety of rehabilitation strategies might potentially be used to provide workplace accommodations, including improving access to facilities and spaces within a workplace, restructuring a job, modifying work schedules, reassigning qualified employees to an open position that may be better suited for them, acquiring new or specialized equipment, modifying existing equipment, reworking training materials, and modifying workstations. The choice of accommodations for any client should be the intervention(s) that best fit the client's needs. Furthermore, this fit should be based on an assessment and analysis of the relationship between the client, work environment, and occupational performance in work tasks. The accommodation should meet the most salient needs for the situation and produce the best functional outcomes within the context of application. Unfortunately, accommodations that meet the needs of the situation may not be the same as those that attain the best functional outcomes.

In work environments, the reasonableness of an accommodation is a compromise that weighs the cost of the accommodation against the benefit that might be achieved. In other words, the law requires that architectural barriers be removed when their removal can be easily accomplished and able to be carried out without undo difficulty or expense. What is considered reasonable will vary from organization to organization depending on the type and cost of the interventions, technical feasibility, size of organization and resources, type of job tasks, and hierarchy of priorities, including access to the facility, goods and services, and restrooms. As a result, the most functional accommodation may not be the most reasonable.

Evidence Base for Workplace Accommodations

Although workplace accommodations can help people with disabilities find and remain employed, there is little empirical evidence about their costs, benefits, and effectiveness with which to inform the practice providing them. In fact, workplace accommodation is better described as a field that is driven by practice-based evidence rather than the other way around (Sanford & Milchus, 2006). The field is relatively immature, dominated, out of necessity, by practice. Accommodations and the process that provides them are generally idiosyncratic. Although accommodations are typically individualized for each employee, the degree to which a common set of effective accommodations are used to address similar problems across individuals is dependent on the expertise and experience of those who are involved in the accommodation process.

To date, much of the evidence for workplace accommodations is practice based. The aggregate knowledge base is characterized by anecdotal case studies that describe specific accommodations made for specific individuals. In their review article of workplace accommodation findings, Butterfield and Ramseur (2004) noted that 19 of the 30 articles were single-subject case studies. Case study evidence is useful for setting precedents and, ultimately, if enough case studies are reported, for suggesting trends.

In the decade following the passage of the ADA (1990), researchers began to investigate the incidence of workplace accommodations in the workplace, both those that were made by employers (Bruyere, 2000; Condrey & Brudney, 1998; McFarlin, Song, & Sonntag, 1991) and those received by employees (Chirikos, 2000; Daly & Bound, 1996; Harlan & Robert, 1998; MacDonald-Wilson, Rogers, Massaro, Lyass, & Crean, 2002). Driven by concerns with ADA compliance, most of these studies focused on the provision of accommodations for any employee with disabilities and factors related to the likelihood of receiving any type of accommodation, without differentiating between disabilities, types of accommodation, or context. Yet, although accommodations are clearly neither equal nor interchangeable, few studies examined the specific types of barriers to work that employees encountered; the types of accommodations that were actually received, by whom and for what; or performance outcomes associated with the accommodations.

More recently, a number of descriptive studies have documented and compared the types of accommodations used by employees within a particular disability group, such as people with psychiatric disabilities (MacDonald-Wilson et al., 2002), who are deaf or hard of hearing (Scherich, 1996), with mobility disabilities (Balser, 2007; Zolna, Sanford, Sabata, & Goldwaithe, 2007), with dexterity limitations (Zolna et al., 2007), and with musculoskeletal conditions (Yelin, Sonneborn, & Trupin, 2000), or across disability groups (Williams, Sabata, Zolna, 2006; Zwerling et al., 2003).

Despite the increase in the number of large-scale descriptive studies of accommodations, only a few published studies have systematically evaluated the effectiveness of specific types of accommodations in meeting needs of workers with disabilities (e.g., Yeager, Kaye, Reed, & Doe, 2006; Yelin et al., 2000) or the cost–benefits of accommodations (e.g., Shartz, Hendricks, & Blanck, 2006). The lack of large-scale outcome studies leaves a significant gap in our general understanding of what works, for whom, and at what cost across individuals, job tasks, and work environments. Such information is vital to making more informed decisions about workplace accommodations in practice.

Accommodation Strategies

By definition, workplace accommodation strategies are varied, including specialized and universal design to change the work site, workstation, equipment, and/or tools; adaptive strategies that change the way work tasks are done; and organizational approaches that change policies and procedures about the way work is performed, scheduling, job assignments, and location of work (e.g., telework or work at home). This chapter will focus specifically on those strategies aimed at changing the physical environment of the workplace. Although this includes both specialized and universal design strategies, in everyday practice the barrier-removal, activity-begets-participation mentality of the ADA and the mandate for individualized interventions promoted by U.S. reimbursement policy and tax incentives has tended to favor specialized design strategies and assistive technology

(AT) interventions in particular. In fact, the term *workplace accommodation* is often used interchangeably with AT.

Workplace accommodations can be simple modifications, such as placing blocks under the legs of a desk to raise the height to enable a wheelchair to roll up under, or it can be complex, such as using screen reading or voice recognition software so that a person who is blind can manage documents. They range in scale from small assistive technologies such as a wrist support for a keyboard to reduce the effects of repetitive stress disorders and a track ball to facilitate mousing on a computer to environmental control units that provide remote-controlled access via wiring, ultrasound, infrared, radio frequency, or speech recognition to typical workplace devices (e.g., computers, intercoms, phones, projectors, lights, thermostat, security systems, and elevators) to larger accessible designs such as a ramp at an employee entrance, grab bars in employee bathrooms, or an ergonomic chair to alleviate back pain.

Although the *ADAAG* covers public (i.e., nonemployee) areas of a facility, where these areas overlap with employee areas, *ADAAG* requirements might also be reasonable accommodations. Then again, they might not be, particularly for scoping and location requirements. For example, requirements for number and location of accessible parking spaces based on public use of a facility will not provide any spaces for employees who require accessible parking. Moreover, the location of those spaces might not be on the shortest route to the employee entrances if those entrances do not coincide with those used by the public. However, reasonable accommodation works both ways. As a result, not all employees with disabilities require or desire the level of accessible design required in the *ADAAG*. For example, an employee who can ambulate but uses a scooter may not need an accessible parking space at all. Nonetheless, technical requirements in the *ADAAG* for accessible parking, vehicular drop-offs, and accessible exterior route of travel from parking or public transit and accessible route from the entrance that connects all accessible features (e.g., bathrooms and drinking fountains) provide reasonable guidance, not mandated requirements, for parking and other accessible accommodations.

In using the *ADAAG* for guidance, it is important to note that technical requirements in *ADAAG* pertain to all areas of a facility used by the public, regardless of how frequently anyone with a disability uses that space. In contrast, employee areas are not required to be accessible if an employee with a disability does not use that space to perform essential job tasks. Moreover, where public areas of a building are fixed, spaces where essential job tasks are performed are variable and can be changed. For example, an employee whose workstation is on the second floor in a building that has no elevator could be moved to an accessible route on the entry level to eliminate the need to climb stairs, rather than having to install an elevator to make the workstation accessible.

Whereas the *ADAAG* may be used for guidance to overcome architectural barriers, a number of other strategies are typically used to overcome product-related barriers (e.g., workstation, seating, and communications technologies) to essential job tasks. These include use of adjustable or accessible design products, standard options or accessories from product manufacturers that are accessible, use of assistive devices, and customized accommodations. It should be noted that these strategies are not mutually exclusive and that it is often necessary to use a combination of approaches to ensure that the accommodations meet the specific needs of the individual employee and the needs of the organization.

Accommodations to Improve Performance of Essential Job Tasks

Although similar specialized design strategies may be used to facilitate aging in place and aging in the workplace, federal policies governing workplace accommodations account for considerable differences in where and what specific interventions are used. In addition, unlike home settings that are composed of predictable activities and generic set of environmental demands, the complexity of the environment, including physical spaces where individual or group work occurs, safety and security issues, personal relationships, organizational policies, and the diversity of activities that vary by type of work and job classification, can exert a variety of unpredictable context-specific demands on workers.

For example, in a sample of 4,000 workers with vision impairments, in a sample of 4,000 workers with vision impairments, the Job Accommodation Network (JAN) reported 76 different job functions that crossed a wide variety of job types (e.g., clerical, sales, professional, administrative, government, education) (Gamble et al., 2004). Among job functions, read text or graphics from computer screen (15%), read text or graphics from print material (12%), read from instrument or control board (10%), travel to/ from work (8%), access worksite, travel away from office, keyboard, communicate with others (4%), and repair construct pieces and take notes (3%) were the tasks that most often required accommodation. However, a variety of other activities pose demands on other abilities as well, including cognitive abilities (e.g., computing, discriminating objects), motor abilities (e.g., access information materials, access office equipment, gripping tools, manipulating controls, mousing, and reaching objects), and sensory abilities (e.g., respond to emergency signals, respond to vehicles, communicate using telephone, and transcribe dictation).

Common Barriers and Accommodations

Despite the broad range of essential job tasks, research suggests that workplace accommodations can be categorized by a key set of generic work-specific activities that are common across work settings. In a meta-analysis of workplace accommodations, Zolna et al. (2007) reported that the most commonly reported barrier to employment was *access to the physical work environment*. Ten articles focused on barriers faced by people with a variety of functional limitations becasue of the design of furnishings and workstations. The *design of furnishings and workstations* led to problems such as having to hold their hands above the chest, stand on a hard surface, and repeatedly bend their back, as well as problems with sitting in a chair, lack of workspace, and getting up from their desk. *Computer-related difficulties* were also common. These included holding arms outstretched, having wrists bent, and repetitive movements.

Environmental modifications to common spaces outside of the personal workstation were important accommodations. Although many of these accommodations, including accessible parking and transportation, access to meeting rooms, bathroom, and lunch areas, did not directly impact performance of job tasks; they were necessary for "activities of daily work." Many of the environmental changes reported were accommodations for people with mobility and vision limitations that affected their ability to climb stairs, walk long distances, find their way, or operate heavy doors or gates. Examples of such accommodations included ramps, elevators, parking, floor surface changes, environmental control, signage, evacuation routes, low-wattage overhead lights, task lighting, and adjustments to entrances.

Workstation accommodations for individuals with mobility and dexterity issues included not only changes to chairs, back supports, arm rests, foot rests, desks, and modified workspace layout but also better ergonomics, such as bringing frequently used items closer, lowering work surfaces, raising the height of the desk, creating handles on hanging files, relocating power switches, rearranging furniture and desk items, or using adjustable chairs, tables, and shelves. Workstation tasks, including reading print materials, computer monitor, and peripheral equipment, as a JAN study reported (Gamble et al., 2004), are among the most common accommodations for people with visual limitations. Whereas task lighting is common for workstations, most accommodations for these tasks tend to be more technology oriented such as closed-circuit televisions (CCTVs), computer screen readers, speech-to-text software, and low-vision magnifiers. Accommodations for workers with hearing and communication limitations include amplified telephones and use of text-based communication systems (e.g., e-mail, online chat, short message service messaging) to compensate for auditory peripheral communication equipment. For people who have difficulty remembering, a range of memory aids from simple desk calendars to electronic and computer-based reminders are generally available.

Finally, a variety of assistive technologies were the most common types of accommodations to aid people with disabilities perform *computing tasks*. These technologies included speech recognition software and alternative input devices, such as a mouthstick, trackball, head-controlled mouse, and ergonomic keyboard.

Based on these findings, and with an intentional focus on work-specific activities (i.e., not personal hygiene), this chapter will focus on accommodations to remove barriers to getting in and out of the worksite, moving around the worksite, and using the workstation (including using computer and peripheral equipment and engaging in interpersonal communication).

Getting In and Out of the Workplace. To be able to perform essential functions of the job, an employee must be able to get the in and out of the workplace, including all exterior routes on the site from the parking or vehicular drop-offs (e.g., public transit) to the employee entrance. To enable an employee to get in and out of the worksite, technical requirements in the *ADAAG* for the site (i.e., accessible parking, vehicular drop-offs, and accessible exterior route of travel from parking or public transit) provide reasonable guidance for accessing the designated employee entrance. In addition, to improve general safety, common exterior accommodations to remove barriers to getting in and out of the workplace include replacing walkways so they have smooth surfaces, repairing broken steps, adding handrails on both sides and using contrasting nosings, and adding adequate lighting operated by motion detectors or timers.

■ *Lower Extremity Limitations.* For workers with lower extremity limitations, problems getting in and out of the worksite are caused by decreased range of motion, strength, speed, and accuracy, which manifest in travel difficulties such as walking on surfaces that are uneven or in poor condition, using stairs, and getting through doorways. For employees with these limitations, common workplace accommodation strategies to remove barriers to getting in and out of the employee entrance include the following:

1. *Removing barriers on exterior paths of travel* (e.g., uneven surfaces, curbs) by providing accessible parking as close as possible to the employee entrance; installing curb cuts/ramps; widening paths; installing firm, smooth, slip-resistant path surfaces; having transitions of no more than ¼ inch high and ½ inch wide between pavers or two surfaces; and repairing or rebuilding steps (with standard 7:11 tread/riser ratio or 4:24 ratio for walker users).
2. *Eliminating demands of stairs or level changes* (greater than ½ inch) by constructing curb ramps, ramps, sloping walkways, mechanical lifts (e.g., stair or vertical power lift), or wide tread/low riser stairs or moving the employee entrance to a location that does not have stairs or level changes (Figure 6.1).
3. *Reducing demands of stairs or level changes* by constructing stairs with uniform riser and tread dimensions or wide-tread/low-riser stairs.
4. *Providing or changing the location of supports* by installing handrails at a convenient height on both sides of a stair.
5. *Removing obstructions at the door* by reducing the threshold, eliminating revolving doors and turnstiles, widening swinging doors, changing the door swing, providing latch-side clearance, creating space to maneuver on both sides of the door, reducing mechanical force to open the door, or installing an electronic/electromechanical door opener.

■ *Upper Extremity Limitations.* For employees with upper extremity impairments, problems getting in and out of the workplace are caused by decreased range of motion, strength, speed, and coordination. These functional limitations are manifest in difficulties using handrails to climb stairs or ramps, operating door handles, and using keys. Common workplace accommodation strategies to remove barriers to getting to the employee entrance for workers with upper extremity impairments and mobility problems include the following:

1. *Changing the attributes of gripping surfaces* (e.g., handrails, door handles, and keys) by altering size, shape, and texture to facilitate gripping, pushing, and pulling and eliminate pinching and turning.

FIGURE 6.1

Accessible designs to reduce the demands of steps are typically accomplished by constructing a ramp in addition at the step. This can be achieved through ramps of various shapes and sizes from (A) a small threshold ramp to (B) a short, shallow ramp on a low-riser, wide-tread stair to (C, D) very long ramps for elevation changes of 3' or more.

2. *Changing the location of gripping surfaces* (particularly handrails) by installing handrails at a convenient height on both sides of a stair to minimize reaching.
3. *Reducing mechanical force to open the door* by installing a lighter door; changing the resistance on the door closer; or installing a power-assisted door opening.
4. *Changing hardware to be operable without grasping or twisting* by installing lever or large loop handles and combination locks.
5. *Using alternative or automatic opening systems* by installing electric or automatic doors (Figure 6.2); electronic or remote-controlled locks; door handles; or keypads that eliminate reaching and handling.

FIGURE 6.2

Power-assisted door openers are added-on to permit a door to be opened either manually or by electricity. This accessible design enables an employee with lower or upper extremity limitations who can operate a large button (pictured on the pole in front of the doors) to open a single-entry door that is designated by the "handicapped" symbol (located on the righthand door).

■ *Vision Limitations.* Employees with vision limitations not only have difficulty finding their way because of problems seeing the route of travel but also are at risk for injury because of an inability to see pathways, obstructions, or drop-offs in the path of travel (e.g., stairs and curbs). Common workplace accommodation strategies to remove barriers for these employees getting to and from the entrance include the following:

1. *Increasing light levels* by adding enough light where it is most needed, including light (preferably equipped with a motion sensor or dusk-to-dawn photo cell) at the employee entrance, along the exterior path of travel, and wherever there are steps or a change in grade.
2. *Increasing visual contrast* by painting or using natural materials to make doors, gates, and stair nosings a contrasting color so that they are visually distinctive.
3. *Decreasing unnecessary pattern* by paving walks in solid colors or muted patterns to eliminate visual ambiguity.
4. *Eliminating hazards in the path of travel* by providing visual contrast and tactile warnings at drop-offs and other obstacles, and audible signals at crosswalks.
5. *Enhancing way finding and orientation* by providing high-contrast and tactile cues on or along walkways, tactile and audible signs, high-contrast signage with large text, tactile maps, or tactile markings on handrails (Figure 6.3).

FIGURE 6.3

High contrast and tactile cues (A) applied to or (B) integrated into walkways leading up to buildings and (C) located at transition spaces on interior routes are commonplace in Japan to provide wayfinding information.

Moving Around the Worksite. Once inside the worksite, interior paths of travel within the facility must enable employees to get to and from their individual workstations and essential common spaces (e.g., restroom). In addition, employees may also need to be able to get to other spaces, such as coworkers' workstations, common spaces (e.g., meeting rooms), and equipment (e.g., copy machines), to the extent that they are part of an individual's essential job tasks. To enable employees to move around the worksite, technical requirements in the *ADAAG* for the facility (i.e., accessible interior routes) can be used as a guide for accommodations to ensure that there is an accessible route from the entrance to an employee's workstation.

■ *Lower Extremity Limitations.* For individuals with lower extremity impairments, typical barriers to accessing their workstations are created by obstacles in the path of travel; level changes or handrails (or lack of) that do not provide support for ascending and descending stairs; and doorways that are too narrow or have high thresholds. Common workplace accommodation strategies to remove these barriers include the following:

   1. Removing barriers on interior paths of travel by widening hallways and doorways; eliminating stairs or level changes; installing smooth, nonskid surfaces; or moving furniture.

2. *Providing or changing the location of supports* by installing handrails at a convenient height on both sides of a stair or locating handrails or supports (e.g., furniture) at strategic places in workplace.
3. *Removing obstructions at doorways* by reducing thresholds, widening doorway, changing door swing, or creating space to maneuver.
4. *Eliminating stairs or level changes* (Figure 6.4) by constructing ramps or installing mechanical lifts (e.g., stair or inclined stair lift) or elevators, or moving essential job tasks to the accessible entry level.
5. *Eliminating the need to use the stairs* by moving essential job functions to an accessible level (Figure 6.4).

■ *Upper Extremity Limitations.* For employees with upper extremity impairments, common barriers from the employee entrance to their designated workstation are the result of handrail designs that make stairs difficult to use and door handles and keys that are difficult to grasp to open doors. Typical accommodations to remove these barriers include the following:

1. *Changing the attributes of gripping surfaces* (e.g., handrails, door handles, and keys) by altering size, shape, and texture to facilitate gripping, pushing, and pulling and eliminate pinching and turning.
2. *Changing the location of support surfaces* (particularly handrails) by installing handrails at a convenient height on both sides of a stair to minimize reaching.

FIGURE 6.4

(A, B) Mechanical stair lifts are added onto stairs to enable employees who have difficulty walking on stairs to negotiate level changes. (C) Elevators provide a more integrated strategy unless special handicapped call buttons (lower buttons to the left of the elevator) are added (photos A and C courtesy of Carrie Bruce, CATEA, Georgia Tech, Atlanta, GA).

3. *Using alternative or automatic opening systems* by installing electronic or motion-activated doors, remote-controlled locks, door handles, or keypads that eliminate reaching and handling.

■ *Vision Limitations.* Like getting to the entrance, employees with vision limitations have difficulty finding their way and avoiding hazardous situations. Accommodations to remove barriers to individuals with vision loss from the employee entrance to their designated workstations include the following:

1. *Increasing light levels* by adding lighting or increasing wattage of bulb light levels in hallways, in circulation spaces, and at the top and bottom of stairs.
2. *Increasing contrast* by painting or using materials for doors and adjacent walls or thresholds and surrounding floor that contrast in color; changing a doorknob to contrast with the door; using decals on glass doors; marking the edges of steps with contrasting colored tape or other materials; painting the handrail to contrast with the wall; using carpet or other contrasting material at top and bottom stair landings.
3. *Decreasing unnecessary pattern* by replacing patterned carpet or floor coverings with solid colors or muted patterns to eliminate visual ambiguity.
4. *Controlling glare* by using sheer curtains or translucent shades (as opposed to metal mini-blinds that reflect light) to buffer bright sunlight.
5. *Reducing dark/light transitions* from inside to outside or between hallways and rooms by adding light to dark areas or shading to bright outside areas (e.g., canopy) to create more similar lighting levels between areas.
6. *Eliminating hazards in the path of travel* by removing or providing high-contrast and tactile warnings at edges or obstacles that contrast in color and texture with the background walking surface.
7. *Enhancing way finding and orientation* by providing high-contrast informational and directional signage with large text and tactile letters, illuminated routes (e.g., nightlights or string lights), or handrails with tactile markings (Figure 6.5).

■ *Cognitive Limitations.* Workers with cognitive limitations typically encounter barriers finding their way from the employee entrance to their designated workstation because of lack of reinforcing cues and repetitive information in the environment. Accommodations help these employees

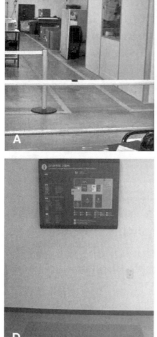

(A) Tactile markers on rails (CATEA file photo) provide directional or orientation information, whereas those on the floor, such as raised bars and domes, indicate (B) decision points, (C) transitions from horizontal to vertical circulation, or (D) location of important information, such as a building directory.

focus on *accentuating important design features*, such as hallways, routes to specific destinations, and doorways, by providing prompts and reminders, including accent or string lights, contrasting colors, labels and signs.

Using the Workstation. A workstation is a designated space in which many, if not all, of an individual's essential work tasks are performed. Workstations are found in almost all workplaces, including office buildings, retail stores, manufacturing plants, repair shops, and even construction sites, creating a wide variety of workstation types from a traditional desk to a drafting table to a workbench to large machinery. Performing work tasks at a workstation typically requires (a) using some type of work surface, (b) maintaining position and postural stability during work task performance, (c) reading printed material, (d) using a computer, and (e) communicating through either face-to-face interactions or communication technologies.

Using the Work Surface

The work surface not only contains much of the equipment and materials used to conduct work tasks but also those items must be positioned so they can be easily accessed by the worker. Such requirements have implications for people with motor limitations that affect mobility, positioning, and reach.

■ *Lower Extremity Limitations.* Workers with lower extremity motor limitations who use wheeled mobility aids typically have difficulty pulling under work surfaces that are designed for chairs with lower seat heights. Accommodations to assist employees who use wheelchairs access their work surfaces include the following:

   1. *Raising the height of the work surface* by putting the desk or table on blocks, as suggested above, or by using an adjustable height work surface that allows variable positioning to match the height of the user and/or the seat in which he or she is sitting. This not only allows an individual to roll under but also enables multiple people with varying abilities to use the same workstation.
   2. *Removing obstacles* by taking out drawers or cutting out a part of the work surface to enable a wheelchair to roll under the work surface.

■ *Reaching limitations.* The design and layout of the work surface can also make it difficult for workers with limited reaching ability (e.g., those who use wheelchairs and who have upper extremity motor limitations) to reach and grasp equipment or other items necessary to perform work tasks or the work itself. Accommodations to remove barriers to reaching all areas of a work surface include the following:

   1. *Changing the slope of the work surface* to bring the back of the surface closer to the worker by using an adjustable table such as a drafting table that integrates both adjustable height and slope or by adding a sloping tray to the work surface.
   2. *Relocating items on the work surface within reach* (i.e., forward, side, upward, and downward) and that promote arm movements that pivot about the elbow rather than the shoulder to avoid stress on the shoulder, neck, and upper back by moving items closer to the employee's location (Figure 6.6) or using a revolving lazy Susan system to store items.
   3. *Enabling horizontal movement* along the workstation by providing a horizontal rail along which the wheelchair can slide sideways.

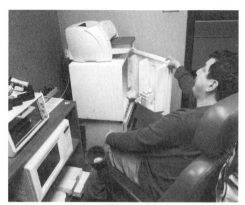

FIGURE 6.6

Arrangement of objects on work surface within reach (i.e., forward, side, upward, and downward) avoids stress on the shoulder, neck, and upper back by moving items closer to the employee's location (CATEA file photos).

4. *Eliminating reaching* by using mechanical reachers or mouthsticks with special ends can help retrieve items that are out of reach.
5. *Customizing the work surface* by providing fittings designed to hold work in place (Figure 6.7).

Maintaining Support and Position

To minimize fatigue, pain, and risk of injury, the worker and the work tasks should be properly positioned, and postural stability should be maintained during the performance of work tasks. Maintaining support is also

FIGURE 6.7

CATEA designed this workstation to bring the work surface closer to an art frame restorer with chronic back pain so the worker could sit upright rather than standing (CATEA file photo).

important to enable a worker to adjust his or her position such that equipment and job-related materials are within reach, as well as for jobs that require standing.

■ *Upper and Lower Extremity Limitations.* For employees with back pain or motor limitations who require long-term comfort, *providing adjustable seating* by using standard office ergonomic chairs allows the employee to be supported in the right position; adjust seat height and tilt to distribute body weight between feet, legs, and buttocks; change back height and tilt to spine; and alter armrests to position the arms and hands for the task at hand.

For other workers who require additional support, such as workers who have limited hip flexion on one side, *providing postural or positioning support* by using specialized chairs can enable them to lean forward safely and easily to ensure that work tasks can be performed.

A workstation that is higher than a typical desk, such as a retail checkout stand, requires a standing posture to complete job tasks. For employees with lower extremity limitations, *eliminating the need to sit or stand* for long periods by providing a stool of the appropriate height or a sit-to-stand stool will allow them to alternate between sitting and standing at a workstation without interrupting work tasks (Figure 6.8).

Reading Print Materials
Difficulty reading printed materials is experienced not only by workers with visual limitations who cannot see the printed materials or have problems with visual fatigue but also by those with upper extremity motor limi-

FIGURE 6.8

CATEA designed this customized support system to enable a cook with lower extremity limitations alternate between sitting and standing at a workstation as well as to move between different locations within the workstation (CATEA file photo).

tations for whom turning pages of books and manipulating paper can be difficult.

■ *Vision Limitations.* Typical accommodations to remove barriers to reading print materials for workers with vision limitations include the following:

1. *Increasing the amount of light* by increasing the wattage or changing the type of light bulbs or adding task lighting.
2. *Enlarging print and graphics* by printing a document in a larger font (usually 18–22 pt), enlarging it on a copier, or using a magnifier such as a desktop magnifier, portable magnifier, or a CCTV video magnifier (Figure 6.9).
3. *Using audio output* by recording documents and printed materials on tape digital media (although linear audio formats make it difficult to skip or jump to a specific section and graphic information needs to be

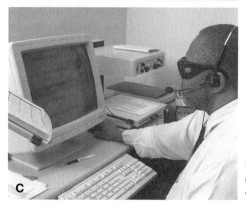

FIGURE 6.9

Printed material can be enlarged by using (A) a simple magnifier or (B, C) a CCTV video magnifier (CATEA file photos).

described) or by converting text into an electronic format then using a screen reader (described below).

4. *Using tactile formats* by obtaining or printing Braille documents, which will be useful for a small percentage of workers who are blind, although it is unlikely that many older adults with new vision limitations will be able to read Braille.

5. *Creating electronic documents* by downloading materials from the Internet or scanning printed materials that can be read through Optical Character Recognition (OCR) software, which permits color, contrast, and magnification to be changed or voice output by text-to-speech software and screen readers (see Computing below).

■ *Upper Extremity Limitations.* For workers who can see text but have upper extremity motor limitations that make it difficult to hold or turn pages, common accommodations to overcome barriers to reading include the following:

1. *Using adaptive devices* such as mouthsticks with rubber tips and powered page turners to turn the pages.

2. *Creating electronic documents* by downloading documents from the Internet or scanning printed materials that can be read through OCR software or voice output by text-to-speech software and screen readers (see Computing below).

Computing

Computers are ubiquitous in today's workplace. On the one hand, an assortment of multimedia input and output hardware devices and an array of software are used in virtually every workplace to train employees, perform individual job tasks, and exchange and store information. On the other hand, the plethora of devices and applications also ensures that computers almost universally create task difficulties for workers with all types and levels of abilities. The most typical tasks include (a) *seeing text and images on the monitor*, which exerts strong demands primarily on workers with visual limitations; (b) *keyboarding*, which exerts strong demands primarily on workers with upper extremity motor limitations; and (c) *mousing*, which also exerts strong demands on workers with upper extremity motor limitations.

   A. *Seeing text and images on a computer monitor* is the primary barrier to computer use encountered by workers with vision limitations. For many of these individuals, enhancing the visibility of the information can be accommodated with basic strategies including the following:

FIGURE 6.10

A screen that fits over an old CRT monitor is used to control glare (photo courtesy of Carrie Bruce, CATEA, Georgia Tech, Atlanta, GA).

1. *Reducing glare* by using a glare screen or a low-glare monitor (Figure 6.10).
2. *Increasing contrast* by using a high-quality computer monitor, contrast enhancement that is resident in Windows and Mac OS operating systems, and highly contrasting foreground (text) and background colors (Figure 6.11).
3. *Enlarging objects on the screen* by placing a screen magnifier in front of the display, using one or even two of the largest monitors possible (Figure

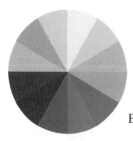

Black Text/White Background – standard, good contrast

White Text/Black Background—reverse colors, good contrast

Yellow Text/Blue Background—good contrast

Yellow Text/Gray Background—poor contrast

FIGURE 6.11

Increasing contrast can be accomplished by exaggerating value (lightness–darkness) differences between foreground and background colors and using colors that are dissimilar in hue and saturation (i.e., as far apart as possible on a color wheel such as dark hues from the bottom half of this hue circle against light colors from the top half of the circle).

FIGURE 6.12

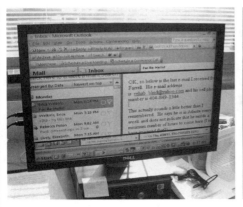 

Using one or two large monitors permits enlargement of text and objects for workers with low vision.

6.12), selecting larger fonts in a document, using zoom settings in software applications to provide low-level magnification, using resident screen magnification software built into computer operating systems, or using specialized add-on screen magnification software that enlarges anything that appears on the screen.

4. *Eliminating reading* by using synthesized speech applications to provide voice output (Figure 6.13), including text-to-speech software that translates typed information into synthesized speech and screen reader software that converts text (or embedded text on tagged images) in menus, dialog boxes, documents, e-mails, and Web pages to synthesized speech.

B. Keyboarding requires reach, repetitive hand function, fine motor control, and touch sensitivity and seeing the keys. As a result, workers with

FIGURE 6.13

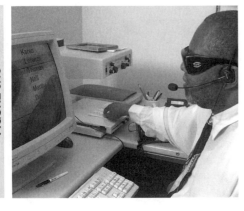

Headsets work with speech-to-text applications to provide hands-free input for workers with vision loss as well as enabling audio output without disturbing others for workers.

upper extremity motor may fatigue quickly and have difficulty reaching all of the keys on a standard QWERTY keyboard, pressing down on keys, or pressing the right key. In addition, many workers with vision or cognitive limitations may have difficulty picking out the right keys.

■ *Upper Extremity Limitations.* For workers who do not have sufficient motor function to use a standard keyboard, keyboarding difficulty can be addressed by using hardware that is a different size, shape, layout, or sensitivity to reduce stress on the arms or enhance sensitivity of keys. Depending on the abilities and needs of the worker, accommodations to overcome barriers to keyboarding typically include a range of strategies that employ alternative keyboards, adaptive devices, and adaptive software for the following:

1. *Reducing reaching distance* by using an adjustable keyboard tray (Figure 6.14) that integrates both adjustable height and slope.
2. *Reducing finger travel* by using compact or mini-keyboards that have smaller keys and/or arrange the keys so they are closer together; keyboards with frequency of use layout, which position the most-used letter and function keys in more familiar and more efficient locations in the center; one-handed keyboards that use DVORAK layouts where the letters are repositioned to take up only the right or left half of a keyboard (Figure 6.15); articulating, curved, and multiplane keyboards, which can be adjusted in various positions to reduce reach by positioning the keys closer to the user's resting hand position;

FIGURE 6.14

(A) Adjustable keyboard trays and (B) wrist rests (CATEA file photo) minimize reaching distance and provide support for people with upper extremity limitations.

FIGURE 6.15

A one-handed keyboard that uses a DVORAK layout where the letters are repositioned to take up only the right or left half of a keyboard reduces finger travel by workers with dexterity problems (photo courtesy of Carrie Bruce, CATEA, Georgia Tech, Atlanta, GA).

and Chordic keyboards, which use different combinations of keys, similar to musical chords on a piano, to type each letter.

3. *Reducing the force required to activate a key* by using a light-touch or membrane keyboards that are touch rather than pressure sensitive so they are less painful for individuals with finger pad sensitivity and may be easier for individuals using an alternative pointing device (e.g., headstick or mouthstick); using software to adjust the sensitivity of the keyboard so that only intentional keystrokes are registered and only the desired number of times, such as applications that require a key to be held down for a period before it registers as an intentional keystroke or that prevents a string of letters from typing when an individual does not lift his or her finger from the key fast enough; or using an onscreen keyboard that uses a mouse or other input device to select the appropriate key.

4. *Minimizing precision* by enhancing targets (i.e., keys) through the use of large-button or expanded keyboards, which use a series of overlays to provide larger targets; by adding a key guard (Figure 6.16), which is an overlay with finger holes that fits over a standard keyboard to isolate keys and reduce the chance of accidentally hitting neighboring keys; or increasing spacing between targets.

5. *Minimizing hand travel* by using keyboards that are split in half and angled to promote left and right hand use in a more ergonomic position help reduce hand travel, shoulder discomfort, and/or wrist pain (Figure 6.17), or adaptive devices, such as wrist rests and mobile arm supports, can be used for better positioning to reduce fatigue, ease pain, and minimize the possibility of further distress.

6. *Eliminating sustained effort* that requires the user to hold down two or more keys simultaneously (e.g., capitalization or keyboard commands)

FIGURE 6.16

A keyguard minimizes precision for workers with upper extremity and dexterity limitations by isolating targets (photos courtesy of Carrie Bruce, CATEA, Georgia Tech, Atlanta, GA).

by using the StickyKeys feature in the Macintosh and Windows operating systems, which allows the computer user to press a key (Shift, Ctrl, or Alt) and subsequently press another letter (in the case of capitalization), rather than pressing both at the same time.

7. *Reducing repetitive efforts* by using macros to automate text, such the autotext feature in Microsoft Word, which enables the user to substitute a two- or three-letter combination for blocks of frequently used text.

8. *Eliminating hand and finger travel* by using speech recognition software, such as *Dragon Naturally Speaking*, which converts voice to text files and enables an employee to dictate rather than type.

FIGURE 6.17

Alternative ergonomic keyboards minimize reach for workers with upper extremity limitations by reducing hand travel (photos courtesy of Carrie Bruce, CATEA, Georgia Tech, Atlanta, GA).

■ *Vision, Cognitive, and Sensation Limitations.* For workers with limitations in vision, cognition, or sensation that make it difficult to select the right key, accommodation strategies to overcome barriers to keyboarding are typically aimed at changing the input and feedback and include the following:

1. *Increasing visual and tactile contrast* can be accomplished by using high-contrast (Figure 6.18), Braille, or tactile keyboards or adding Velcro or other tactile stimuli on location keys that make it easier to feel and identify specific keys.
2. *Providing auditory feedback* by using an onscreen keyboard built into the operating system that makes an audible click (or provides voice output with screen reader) when a key is selected using the mouse or other pointing device.
3. *Eliminating the keyboard* by using speech recognition software, such as *Dragon Naturally Speaking*, which converts voice to text files and enables an employee to dictate rather than type.

C. *Mousing*, which requires eye–hand coordination, grasping, fingering, fine motor control, and range of motion for cursor movement and control, can also be difficult for workers with vision and upper extremity impairments.

■ *Upper Extremity Limitations.* For workers with upper extremity limitations, barriers to cursor movement can be removed by simple hardware input devices or adaptive software to work in conjunction with hardware.

FIGURE 6.18

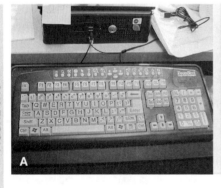 

(A, B) Black text on light (e.g., white or yellow) keys with dark or light backgrounds create high contrast that enable keys to be easily seen by employees with vision limitations (Photo B courtesy of Carrie Bruce, CATEA, Georgia Tech, Atlanta, GA).

Common accommodation strategies to remove barriers to mousing for workers with upper extremity limitations include the following:

1. *Reducing hand travel distance* by using stationary input devices that require a small range of motion (Figure 6.14), such as a touchpad, trackball, or joystick, which translate the user's hand or finger movement into cursor movements rather than using the movement of the mouse, or adaptive software applications, such as MouseKeys, which is built into operating systems and converts the arrow keys on the keyboard number pad into cursor control mouse keys.
2. *Eliminating grasp* by using a touchpad, trackball, or MouseKeys that can be operated with open-hand or finger movements.
3. *Enhancing targets* (i.e., keys) by using large trackballs or adding a key guard to a trackball or joystick (Figure 6.19).
4. *Eliminating hand operation* by using alternative means of physical input, such as a mouthstick or and head pointer, which uses a reflective surface mounted to the person's head and tracked by an IR sensor mounted to the computer monitor; a head-tracking device, which converts head movements recorded from a head-mounted sensor or a reflective dot into cursor movements; and, for individuals who have very little movement in their limbs or torso, eye gaze or eye tracking, which uses a specialized camera mounted on the computer monitor to convert eye movement to cursor movement or voice input systems that include options for mouse control.

FIGURE 6.19

Input devices such as (A) a joystick and (B) a trackball limit grasping and are operable with a small range of motion (photos courtesy of Carrie Bruce, CATEA, Georgia Tech, Atlanta, GA).

■ *Vision Limitations.* For workers with vision limitations, barriers to cursor movement are the result of an inability to see the cursor on the screen. Common accommodation strategies to remove barriers to mousing for workers who are blind or have vision loss include the following:

1. *Changing the characteristics of the cursor* by using add-on software that increases the size or can change the shape, color, and animations of the cursor.
2. *Providing tactile feedback* by using a gesture interface (e.g., touchpad) that provides vibration feedback or the Virtual Reality Mouse, which identifies, operates, and navigates icons and menu items, buttons, and Internet hyperlinks in a Windows environment.
3. *Eliminating the mouse* by using voice commands to control cursor movement.

Communicating

Employees with limitations in hearing and speech are likely to have difficulty with interpersonal verbal communication through both face-to-face interactions, whereas workers with hearing, speech, vision, motor, and cognitive limitations are likely to have more difficulty communicating though the use of technologies (e.g., telephone or Skype).

■ *Hearing and Speech Limitations.* For workers with hearing and speech limitations, barriers to using electronic telecommunications are often the result of too much ambient noise that can be distracting or muffle human speech. Accommodation strategies to remove barriers to communication include the following:

1. *Providing a good acoustical environment* by minimizing reflective surfaces and using sound-absorbing materials on walls, floors, and ceilings to ensure that important information is audible or covering large expanses of glass with shades/curtains.
2. *Controlling/minimizing/eliminating background noise* by using a headset; maintaining or replacing sources of noise, such as window air-conditioners, appliances, copy machines, and printers with quieter ones; increasing the distance between the worker and the sound source by moving the source or worker; or isolating sources of noise by enclosing them.
3. *Amplifying telecommunications* by using an external amplifier, amplified telephone, speakerphone or headset; or using a computer for videoconferencing or voice over Internet protocol.

4. *Amplifying face-to-face communication* by using a personal amplification system that uses a microphone to amplify sound and direct it to the ears through the ear buds, headphones, or neck loop for those with T-coils in their hearing aids.

5. *Providing appropriate visual access* by removing obstructions and providing a clear line of sight to ensure that communication partners can clearly see each other and any visual information in the work environment.

6. *Conveying information by alternative means* by using visual signals such as flashing lights (e.g., telephone strobe) or vibration supplement auditory signals of an incoming call; or by using a code (e.g., number of flashes or vibrations) to identify a specific signal.

7. *Eliminating the need for speaking and/or hearing* by using text communications via a teletypewriter (Figure 6.20), voice-to-text phone (Figure 6.21A), e-mail, or Web, telephone, or mobile communication system short message service instead of speech; captioning of streaming video conferences; or video transcription software.

■ *Vision, Cognition, and Upper Extremity Motor Limitations.* For workers who have difficulty seeing, manipulating/fingering, and remembering, dialing the right telephone number and removing, holding, and replacing the handset are common barriers to electronic communication. To remove these barriers to electronic communication for workers, common accommodation strategies include the following:

1. *Enhancing targets* by using a large-button telephone (Figure 6.21B) or a picture telephone that associates pictures of the person with a pre-programmed speed dial number.

FIGURE 6.20

(A) TTYs and (B) captioning are useful for employees with speech and hearing limitations by eliminating the need to communicate using speech or hearing.

FIGURE 6.21

Modified phones that use (A) voice-to-text output eliminates the need for employees with hearing loss to communicate verbally and (B) large buttons, make them more visible to individuals with low vision and provide larger targets for employees with dexterity limitations (CATEA file photos).

2. *Eliminating hand operation or the need for seeing the equipment* by using an automatic dialing system or voice-activated speakerphone that automatically dials the preprogrammed number.

Implications of Specialized Design for Aging in the Workplace

Clearly, the Rehabilitation Act of 1973 and the ADA of 1990 are the most significant pieces of federal legislation enacted to ensure that people with disabilities have equal opportunities to engage in work tasks and promote participation of people with disabilities in the workforce. Despite these goals, employees with disabilities continue to have lower levels of job satisfaction and productivity than those without disabilities (McAfee & McNaughton, 1997a; McAfee & McNaughton, 1997b; Shur, et al., 2009; Uppal, 2005; Yelin & Trupin, 2003). A major reason for this disparity in work outcomes is the way in which workplace accommodations are understood and implemented under the ADA.

First, like other rehabilitation strategies embedded in federal disability legislation, the intent of workplace accommodations is to remove social and/or physical barriers to activities and task performance by people with disabilities. The removal of barriers affords people with disabilities with a greater opportunity to engage in work, live independently, and participate in society. However, barrier removal, as discussed in Part I, is a symptom-focused approach that is achieved through disability-specific specialized design or assistive technologies individualized for each client. As a result, accommodations are targeted at the person rather than the work environment, in general.

Second, accommodations are activity based (i.e., "to perform the essential functions or fundamental job duties"). In this case, essential functions are the basic duties that an employee must be able to perform, with or without an accommodation. However, unlike Title III (as will be discussed in the following chapter), which mandates technical requirements for accessible design for all individuals in all public settings, accommodations are determined on a case-by-case basis based on the worker's abilities and the context. They are usually made as a collaborative effort among the employee, employer, and other individuals, such as a rehabilitation counselor, human resource personnel, and union representative, as the situation requires. The main issues considered are the job tasks that must be accomplished, the functional limitations of the employee, and whether the proposed accommodation will pose an undue hardship to the employer. Thus, for accommodation purposes, activity in the workplace is typically operationalized as the execution of individual tasks without face-to-face interactions with another person, such as e-mail, writing, and talking on the telephone.

Third, work is inherently social in nature. In fact, the majority of work requires some degree of cooperation and interaction with others (Kraut et al., 1990). Depending on job type, between 25% and 70% of the work time is estimated to be spent in face-to-face interactions (Kraut et al., 1990; Panko, 1992). Yet, despite the social nature of work, workplace accommodations have focused almost entirely on the individual tasks associated with getting to and using an employee's individual workspace. Unfortunately, work is not just a "space" in which a series of tasks occur in isolation. It is also a "place" where a sense of belonging is fostered by employee engagement and work toward a common goal.

This distinction between workspace and workplace is crucial because it reflects *ICF* based differences between activity and participation, both of which are necessary to ensure positive work outcomes for workers with disabilities. On the one hand, space is passive, providing the physical context in which work activities occur. On the other hand, place is dynamic, providing social foundation for participation. Place is space that is vested with social meaning and cultural understandings of role (Harrison & Dourish, 1996). As such, the workplace must support not only individual activity but also the social roles (e.g., role in a work team), interpersonal relationships (e.g., ties with coworkers)m and activity interdependence (e.g., support among coworkers) that are necessary to achieve a sense of belonging and well-being (Berkman & Glass, 2000; Marshall, Michaels, & Mulki, 2007; Pearce & Randel, 2004).

WORKPLACE WELL-BEING: SOCIOPETAL SPACE AS A THERAPEUTIC INTERVENTION

Whereas the work environment serves a prosthetic role in facilitating job performance, it is also inextricably linked to health. Traditionally, the connection between work and health has largely been concerned with protection from injury in the work environment. As a result, safety concerns have typically focused on ergonomic fit (e.g., seating, workstation, and computer) and hazard mitigation (e.g., noise, dust, chemical exposure, burns, and falls). However, also inherent in the nature of any workplace is the wide-ranging impact that the environment, including the organization, social fabric, and physical space, has on a worker's emotional and psychological well-being. It is this aspect of health that is of most concern here.

Well-being is linked to collaboration and social interactions in the workplace, as well as obtaining greater meaning and personal development from one's work and having work as enjoyable, fulfilling, and socially useful (Avolio & Soski, 1999; Wrzesniewski, McCauley, Rozin, & Schwartz, 1997). Together, these participation aspects of work act to foster a sense of belonging, which is crucial not only to an employee's emotional health, well-being, and participation outcomes but also to his or her job satisfaction and job performance.

Correlates of Well-being

Belonging, defined as a "sense of personal involvement in a social system so that persons feel themselves to be an indispensible and integral part of the system" (Anant, 1966, p. 21), has long been viewed as an important human need, ranking third on Maslow's (1954) hierarchy of basic human needs. Most importantly, sense of belonging in the workplace, defined by Shermerhorn (2009) as the degree to which an employee relates to, feels an integral part of, experiences personal involvement in, and has a connectedness to an organization., is also perceived as a basic human work-related (Baumeister & Leary, 1995) and the most important element of job satisfaction (Schermerhorn, 2009).

Job satisfaction of employees is, in turn, highly correlated with well-being and life satisfaction, (Judge & Watanbe, 1993, 1994; Lustig & Strauser, 2002; Spector, 1997). It is also closely linked to job performance and productivity in a variety of professions and environments (Christen, Lyer, & Soberman, 2006; Cohrs, Abele, & Dette, 2006; Iaffaldano & Muchinsky, 1985; Judge Thoresen, Bono, & Patton, 2001; Rayton, 2006). For example, research has included nurses (Christie, 2008; Hagarty et al., 1992; Winter-

Collins & McDaniel, 2000), physicians (Konrad et al., 1999) adjunct college faculty (Merriman, 2010), grocery store workers (Orisatoki & Oguntibeju, 2010), and informational technology workers (Lim, 2007, 2008). In addition, employees who have a sense of belonging and high job satisfaction exhibit other participation outcomes that benefit both the employee and organization, including a greater willingness to help others, higher morale and levels commitment, lower absenteeism and turnover rates, effective coordination of group activities, transmission of office culture, team building, and group performance (Fish Kraut, Root, & Rice, 1993; Guthrie, 2001; Kraut, Fish, Root, & Chalfonte, 2002; Randel & Ranft, 2007; Whitaker, Frohlich, & Daly-Jones, 1994). Ultimately, these participation-based outcomes are good for business because they typically result in higher profits for organizations (Harter, Schmidt, & Keyes, 2002).

Sociopetal Space and Workplace Well-being

To promote a sense of belonging and well-being, the work environment must support the formal (e.g., planned meetings, trainings or group work) and informal (e.g., spontaneous hallway conversations or social activities such as lunch) face-to-face interactions (Lueg, 2001; Yang, Harris & Sanford, 2010). Although some social activities, such as e-mailing or using a telephone, can be carried out without workers being physically collocated, these types of interactions do not foster a sense of inclusion and belonging (Abel, 1990; Fish et al., 1993; Whitaker et al., 1994). Similarly, employees with disabilities who are only able to access those areas of the workplace that are necessary to do their essential job tasks lack face-to-face social interactions. As a result, they can be just as isolated as those working from remote locations (Kraut et al., 2002; Paul, 2003). Moreover, workers who do not have direct access to their coworkers have lower job satisfaction, productivity, and workplace well-being than those who have direct access (Bailey, 2002).

For interaction to occur, people need to be in the same place at the same time. For people with disabilities, this copresence is aided by ADA-mandated reasonable accommodations that provide opportunities for interaction through providing physical access to areas that are essential to an individual's job tasks and other spaces that are essential to an employee's health and function (e.g., restroom). However, access alone neither encourages nor ensures that workers will be in close physical proximity for interaction to take place.

To promote social interaction, workplaces typically have sociopetal spaces (Osmond, 1959) that intentionally or unintentionally draw workers together. These include coworkers offices/workspaces and conference rooms that support formal interaction, as well as corridors, lunchrooms, or lounges that support informal ones. Sociopetal spaces foster proximity by allowing workers to encounter each other frequently (e.g., corridor or break room), supporting visual channels to induce access and readiness for communication and facilitating highly interactive communication. Proximate colleagues have more opportunity for intended, opportunistic, serendipitous, and spontaneous conversations.

Implications of Sociopetal Space for Aging in the Workplace. For employees with disabilities, like other workers, positive health, activity, and participation outcomes are linked to their ability to engage in the social aspects of work through formal and informal interactions with coworkers. To accomplish this, an ADA paradigm that focuses on essential work tasks needs to be superceded by an *ICF* model, in which all aspects of the work environment that are essential to an employee's well-being—that is, those that are essential to perform work activities and those that enable participation in the social aspects of the work—should be reasonably accommodated. Such a need goes beyond mere specialized design to accommodate of activity but necessitates the design of universal sociopetal spaces—spaces that not only are accessible to workers with disabilities but also are designed to bring workers together and promote interactions among employees with a broad range of abilities.

> An ADA paradigm that focuses on accommodating an individual's essential work tasks can be transformed by adopting an ICF approach that focuses on accommodating an individual's essential work needs.

ACCOMMODATING ACTIVITY AND PROMOTING PARTICIPATION: UNIVERSAL DESIGN AS EVERYDAY INTERVENTIONS FOR AGING IN THE WORKPLACE

To date, workplace accommodation policy has adopted a traditional approach that focuses removal of barriers to work activity as a series of individual tasks. However, the barrier removal approach does not comprehensively take into consideration the role of work and the level of engagement that it involves in people's lives. Although individualized accommodations are vital, a more inclusive approach to address the needs of employees across the range of what they do and need to do on a daily basis and across their working lives is lacking. More specifically, the accommodation approach has not taken into account an individual's need to participate in the cooperative work group that is manifest in the interactive social nature of work and that is crucial for successful work outcomes (Gates, 2000). Thus, despite the success of accommodations in enabling employees with disabilities to perform in *individual* work tasks (Butterfield & Ramseur, 2004; JAN, 2010; Mendelsohn et al., 2008), employees with disabilities consistently report lower job satisfaction than those without disabilities (McAfee & McNaughton, 1997a, 1997b; Uppal, 2005).

Whereas prosthetic barrier-removal interventions promote activity and traditional therapeutic interventions (e.g., workplace safety) promote environmental health, neither promotes participation. What is lacking in the workplace is a rehabilitation strategy that promotes participation plus activity and emotional health. Clearly, just as in the home, the provision of such a rehabilitative strategy to support aging in the workplace will have a profound impact on the work environment that goes well beyond just adding ramps and computer access.

Evidence Base for Universal Design

The need to accommodate work tasks is undeniable. However, evidence suggests that many workers and particularly older workers nearing retirement are not receiving the accommodations they need. In addition, research suggests that decisions to request accommodations and the impact of accommodations are often related to coworker attitudes and feelings of jealousy and resentment. Finally, recent studies have begun to demonstrate that ADA task-based accommodations alone are not sufficient to promote satisfaction or improve productivity of employees with disabilities in the workplace without consideration of social interactions. These findings suggest that the effects of aging and social interactions in the workplace have important implications for universal design.

Effects of Aging in the Workplace. There are more than 16 million Americans older than 55 years who are either working or seeking work in the United States. Over the next several years, the number of workers 55 years and older is expected to grow twice as fast as the total workforce as the "baby boom" population matures and life expectancy increases. In addition, research on work and disability indicate that people between the ages of 55 and 64 years (the oldest cohort included) experience work disability at nearly double the rates of those aged 45–54 years and at rates two and half times of those aged 35–44 years. Despite the demographic shifts and increasing disability, the percentage of older workers aged 50–60 years receiving accommodations declined from 31% the mid-1990s to 22% in 2000 (Lightfoot & Lum, 2001).

Research (McMullin & Shuey, 2006) suggests that older workers, particularly those approaching retirement age, are less likely than younger workers aged 20–39 years to acknowledge a need for workplace accommodations to do their job. Older employees who attributed their functional limitations to the normal aging process were twice as likely to have an unmet need for accommodation as those who attributed their condition to another cause. Moreover, when older workers attributed their limitation to aging, they were less likely to receive accommodations than younger workers. Together, these findings suggest that both employees and employers view aging as a natural process that produces functional limitations that are not perceived as disabilities and therefore do not necessitate being accommodated.

Like McMullin and Shuey (2006), a recent survey by Williams et al. (2006) found that older workers, regardless of their functional limitation, often received no workplace accommodations, even though most of the respondents reported that their functional limitations prevented them from performing job tasks and that accommodations were essential for task performance. In addition, the researchers found that there were differences in the types of accommodations used by older and younger workers who had the same functional limitation. For example, among workers with hearing loss, younger workers used sign language more frequently, whereas preretirement and retirement-age workers used more hearing aids. Working age adults with vision impairments used electronic documents, Braille, and CCTVs more than preretirement or retirement-age workers.

Together, the high rate of functional limitation associated with aging, lack of accommodations, and the likelihood that one's place of work is designed for younger, able-bodied workers can compromise the ability of older workers to remain productive and may lead to premature retirement. However, with the decline in birth rates after the baby boom, there are not enough younger workers to make up for the labor shortage that mass retirement of older workers would create. Even if there were enough new workers to fill the gap, they could not replace the cumulative knowledge and experience that older workers possess. As a result, keeping older workers on the job is becoming increasingly important to many organizations. Ironically, rising health care costs and inadequate retirement income are working in their favor because these factors may make it necessary for many workers to remain in the workforce longer than they anticipated.

Older adults who continue to work beyond traditional retirement age represent the changing face of aging in the workplace. As this population grows, so does the need for accommodations to support changes in abilities across the life span. Universal design, which promotes maximum productivity for all workers throughout their working lives without the need for special accommodations, is a logical approach to rehabilitation interventions in the workplace.

Effects of Coworker Attitudes. Although workplace accommodations are intended to enable an employee with a disability to perform essential work tasks, accommodations, particularly those for an individual's workstation, often create negative feelings and resentment among coworkers who believe that an accommodated worker is receiving preferential treatment (Collela, 2001; Stoddard, 2006). First, coworkers may perceive an accommodation as unfair because it increases the levels of the accommodated person's rewards or outcomes, particularly when the accommodation is viewed as valuable or a perk that they do not have, such as a special chair, being able to sit while at work, flexible hours, rest periods, working at home, and exemption from stressful tasks (Colella, 2001). In addition, employees may believe that an accommodation gives an unfair advantage to a coworker with a disability by making nonessential and essential work tasks easier (e.g., excusing them from expected but not required work-related duties; Borman & Motowidlo, 1993). Finally, it may be perceived that the accommodation will use up valuable resources, thus reducing the coworkers' own rewards and making their jobs less desirable or as causing them to lose competitive rewards (Colella, 2001).

In fact, the way in which an employee with a disability expects coworkers to react to an accommodation may influence not only his or her own decision to request one (Florey, 1998) but also a supervisor's decision to grant a request (Cleveland, Barnes-Farrell, & Ratz, 1997). Even if a request is granted, coworkers' reactions, morale, and productivity may be considered as a factor that enters into the "cost" of accommodation (Colella, 2001).

Effects of Social Interactions in the Workplace. Contrary to assumptions about essential work tasks that are embedded in the ADA, a considerable body of research suggests that job performance (and its correlates including well-being, job satisfaction, and productivity) is a function of both activity and participation outcomes. In fact, among employees with disabilities, lower job satisfaction and productivity outcomes have been linked primarily to *poor social interactions* in the workplace (Uppal, 2005).

A survey of workers with and without disabilities by the Rehabilitation Engineering Research Center on Workplace Accommodation, which is part of the Center for Assistive Technology and Environmental Access at Georgia Tech, found that accommodations made for individual job tasks failed to include inclusive features that would promote formal and informal social interactions (Yang, Harris, & Sanford, 2011). As a result, employees with disabilities had significantly more unmet accommodation needs for *participation* than those for individual work tasks. Not surprisingly, these employees reported lower levels of inclusion and lower participation (i.e., less inclusive social activities with coworkers and lower participation in decisions) than employees without disabilities (Yang et al., 2010). Compared with employees with met needs, those with unmet needs in shared workspace reported lower satisfaction in meetings/group projects; greater difficulty in participating in informal social events; and decreased opportunity to participate at work. However, when controlling for unmet participation needs, there were no significant differences in any of the participation domains between employees with and without disabilities, suggesting that meeting participation needs of people with disabilities is critical to creating equality in the workplace.

Accommodating Health, Activity, and Participation in the Workplace

Clearly, positive performance outcomes and well-being cannot be achieved without consideration of both activity-based interventions aimed at job tasks and participation-based interventions aimed at integrating all workers into the social milieu of the workplace. To achieve these aims, the workplace, like housing, must support all three constructs in the *ICF*: health, activity, and participation. In contrast to everyday and specialized design, which only accommodates activity, universal design as rehabilitation strategy for aging in the workplace not only supports function of people with a wide range of abilities and health conditions but also is a rehabilitation strategy that introduces a seamless, integrated system of everyday design (i.e., all employees have the same workstations such that accommodations are not needed) that facilitates work and promotes participation among all employees, regardless of ability. By considering the collective needs of a group, as well as those of the individual, universal design enables all workers to engage in work and the workplace.

However, whereas logic suggests that universal design provides cost–benefits by being functional for all users across their work life and the life of the job, like housing, there is a dearth of outcomes-based evidence for universal design as a rehabilitation intervention for aging in workplace. This is perhaps less surprising than housing, as there is less of an evidence base for accommodation outcomes than there is for home modifications. Nonetheless, universal design in the workplace suffers from a similar set of factors, including the lack of measurable criteria for universal design, difficulty of studying universal design as an intervention in situ, and lack of naturally occurring opportunities to conduct outcomes research. Therefore, on the basis of the existing evidence on the effectiveness of workplace accommodations, universal design as a more comprehensive strategy to implement workplace accommodations makes pretty good sense.

Universal Design Features to Enable Activity and Participation

Like housing, universal design in the workplace is everyday design at all scales of design that is usable by all individuals within the context. As such, it eliminates the need for special accommodations or extensive remodeling of worksites and workspaces to make them suitable for individuals to age in the workplace. In addition, because it is everyday design, it is compatible with the workplace in both scale and character, thus avoiding the stigma of specialized design. Logically, universal design as a rehabilitation intervention for aging in the workplace provides cost–benefits by being functional for all users across their working life and across the life span of the work environment.

The amount and configuration of space, the location of products, technology and other equipment in that space, or the design of the products and equipment themselves can achieve universal design. In addition, like housing, universal design features can be standard building products, hardware, technology, or equipment that have been placed differently, such as standard electrical outlets that are located higher above the floor than usual to minimize bending and reaching, whereas switches and other controls can be lowered down to minimize reaching and enable viewing of displays. Alternatively, features can be selected for specific attributes that have both function and functionality, such as communication systems that have large buttons and both audio and text output.

Table 6.1
Design Features Included in the Workplace Ergonomics Workbook
(Based on Mueller, 1992)

1. Workplace accessibility
    a. Accessible routes of travel
    b. Accessible doorways and door hardware
    c. Changes in level
    d. Flooring
    e. Navigation
    f. Emergency evacuation

2. Visual and auditory information
    a. Positioning and lighting
    b. Typeface selection
    c. Ambient noise and auditory signals
    d. Sound attenuation

3. Lighting
    a. Illumination without glare
    b. Materials and positioning to reduce glare
    c. Orientation to natural and artificial light
    d. Personal measures for reducing eye fatigue

4. Storage
    a. Easy access at the workstation
    b. Appropriate containers
    c. Identification of materials
    d. Safe handling and transport

5. Seating
    a. Adequate support and stability
    b. Adjustability features
    c. How to adjust seat, back, and arm support

6. Work space layout
    a. Adequate space
    b. Work surface materials and adjustments
    c. Air quality

7. Computer displays
    a. Monitor placement
    b. Minimizing glare
    c. Locating source documents

8. Computer inputs
    a. Keyboard and mouse positioning
    b. Hand and wrist support
    c. Software options

9. Telephones and other office equipment
    a. Electrical supply
    b. Equipment controls
    c. Telephone location
    d. Telephone peripheral options

(continued)

Table 6.1
Design Features Included in the Workplace Ergonomics Workbook
(continued)

10. Work practices
    a. Maintaining a neutral posture
    b. Minimizing repetitive and cumulative stresses
    c. Maintaining general health and productivity

Although many universal design features for the workplace are similar to those in housing, unlike housing, lists of such features, such as the one presented in Chapter 5, are nonexistent for the workplace. In fact, very little has been written about universal design features in the workplace with the exception of the *Workplace Workbook* by J. L. Mueller (Mueller, 1992) and a chapter in *Universal Design New York* from the IDEA Center at SUNY Buffalo (Levine, 2003). Interestingly, both publications are affiliated with authors of the Principles of Universal Design. However, neither publication links universal design in the workplace to principles of universal design. The former (Table 6.1), which was published 5 years prior to the principles, is organized around accessibility features and ergonomics to enable individuals with disabilities to perform essential work tasks. The latter, which was published a little more than 5 years after the principles, focuses on everyday design features of a workplace to facilitate work for all employees (e.g., partitions and doors, lighting, electrical controls, thermal environment, acoustics, social interaction and workstations). Although the principles were described in the IDEA Center publication, they were not used as a rationale for selecting universal design features for the workplace.

Although the evidence base for universal design is limited, the knowledge base of accommodations contains a wealth of information about the needs, functional abilities, and criteria for successful intervention. Aggregated, these data can be crucial in informing the application of universal design in the workplace. This information can be used to incorporate successful specialized design concepts into products and workspaces, thus reducing the need to retrofit the workplace with additional accommodations.

Based on general *worksite* accommodations, worksites should provide better lighting, clear travel paths, more room to maneuver, and no-step entrances; such workplaces will be more accessible to all individuals regardless of their ability to ambulate and reduce the need for individualized accommodations. Personal *workstations* should include adjustable furniture and ergonomically designed workstations so that employees can make adjustments as needed to provide themselves easy access to tools necessary to perform their job. As standard workstation equipment, individual issues with access to work tools will not require special office furniture accommodations. Finally, *assistive technology for computing,* such as speech recognition software, trackballs, ergonomic keyboards, and mouthsticks, were also common accommodations for people with all ranges of impairment. Universal design might eliminate the need for some of these accommodations by including similar alternative inputs in computers used to perform job functions.

Getting In and Out of the Workplace. Unlike accessible design, universal design solutions enable all employees to enter and exit in the same manner. As a result, there is direct access from all potential drop-off points (e.g., parking, public transit, and sidewalk) to the entrance(s) used by employees.

Sloping walkways (i.e., less than 1:20 slope) are the most advantageous entry feature because they enable all individuals to get to an entrance in the same manner, with low effort, while at the same time being integrated with the overall context of the worksite and community

FIGURE 6.22

Sloping walkways that are integrated into landscape and have well-defined edges (e.g., low walls and planters) enable all users to get to the entrance in the same manner, such as (A) the entrance to the Atlanta VA Medical Center, Decatur, GA, or (B) the entry plaza at the Georgia World Congress Center, Atlanta, GA. These features exemplify principles P1, Equitable Use; P2, Flexibility in Use; P4, Perceptible Information; P6, Low Physical Effort; P7, Size and Space for Approach and Use; P8, Social Integration; and P9, Contextual Integration.

(Figure 6.22). In the absence of one point of access/egress for all users, flexibility is increased by providing multiple means of getting to the entrance, such as wide-tread/low-riser steps in addition to a ramp or lift that are integrated into the overall design. Paths to the entrance, including changes in level (e.g., stairs and ramps), are smooth, hard, slip-resistant surfaces to minimize obstructions or falls risk and are wide enough along the entire length (given the expected volume of traffic) to accommodate at least two people side by side, whether they are walking or using mobility devices, such as bicycles, wheelchairs, or personal transports (e.g., Segway).

To identify specific routes and places along the routes, different surface materials and pathway edges contrast in color and texture (e.g., paved walkways, brick steps); edges are clearly defined by grass or planting beds, curbs, walls, fences, bollards, railings, or planters; landmarks, such as fountains, statues, and signs are strategically located; and there is a comprehensive, multisensory information system with high-contrast, large-text directional signs, tactile maps, and talking signs. Paths are evenly illuminated by lighting operated by motion detectors or timers; emergency communications and video surveillance equipment are at strategic locations along the route; and railings or low walls guard against falls at all edges of drop-offs (e.g., platforms and pools).

The employee entrance(s) is/are well marked and clearly visible from the route(s). The doorway is differentiated from the rest of the building by higher lighting levels, materials (e.g., glass vs. masonry or vice versa), color, and/or form to make it easier to identify from the path to the building. At the doorway, the entrance is level with the exterior and interior surfaces, and there is sufficient space to maneuver any travel aids, including

Wide doorways with no step entrances and smooth transitions between interior and exterior surfaces, such as the sloped entrance to Le Place D'Armas, Montreal, Quebec, CA, enable all users to enter and exit safely and easily by demonstrating principles P1, Equitable Use; P2, Flexibility in Use; P6, Low Physical Effort; P7, Size and Space for Approach and Use; P8, Social Integration; and P9, Contextual Integration.

FIGURE 6.23

For buildings that do not require controlled access (i.e., are not locked), motion sensor entrance doors enable hands-free access/egress to/from a workplace. (A) Doors can be sliding, such as Meridian Mark Plaza, Atlanta, GA, and (B) Tokyo International Forum, Tokyo, Japan; or (C, D) swinging, such as the Atlanta VA Medical Center, Decatur, GA, and when double sets of doors are used, like at the VA, space between interior and exterior doors allows for the expected number of users and their mobility devices. These types of features enable P1, Equitable Use; P3, Simple and Intuitive Use; P5, Tolerance for Error; P6, Low Physical Effort; P7, Size and Space for Approach and Use; P8, Social Integration; and P9, Contextual Integration.

mobility devices, strollers, or bicycles (Figure 6.23). An automatic door operated by a pressure switch on the ground, motion sensor, or RFID reader provides hands-free operation (Figures 6.24 and 6.25). The sliding, revolving, or hinged door opens wide enough for employees to pass through easily while carrying backpacks, briefcases, packages, and other work materials or using mobility devices.

For buildings that have controlled access, keycards with embedded RFID tags permit hands-free access if the reader is located in the path of travel and at a height that will enable a keycard located on a wheelchair or in an employee's purse/pocket to be read, such as the one at the entrance to CATEA on the Georgia Tech campus, Atlanta, GA. The RFID reader demonstrates principles P1, Equitable Use; P2, Flexibility in Use; P3, Simple and Intuitive Use; P5, Tolerance for Error; P6, Low Physical Effort; P7, Size and Space for Approach and Use; P8, Social Integration; and P9, Contextual Integration.

FIGURE 6.25

Moving Around the Worksite. Inside the worksite, layout of the spaces and circulation is consistent with employees' expectations. Circulation, both horizontal (i.e., hallways) and vertical (i.e., stairs, ramps, elevators and lifts), is clearly visible from the entrance, uncluttered with furniture and free of level changes in the direct path of travel. When level changes occur in a corridor, tactile and visual warnings are provided at the top, and when possible, ramps rather than using stairs are used so that traffic can continue to flow in the direction of travel. Corridors are wide enough to accommodate two people side by side, whether they are walking or using mobility devices.

Corridors and paths of travel across open spaces are differentiated by changes in flooring materials, textures, and color (Figures 6.26 and 6.27). Continuous handrails along corridors assist individuals with balance and gait limitations, and tactile information on the handrails identify specific rooms along the corridor for employees who have difficulty seeing or are just not paying attention to where they are going (Figure 6.26). The multisensory signage system includes high-contrast, large-text signs; tactile signs, audio signs, and landmarks, such as statues or columns that are strategically located to identify different hallways, places along the hallway, and other key destinations (Figure 6.28).

Lighting, in all corridors, is even, and there is a gradual transition between different spaces, such as the hallway and workspaces or stairwells. Transitions between spaces have smooth changes between flooring materials and contrast in color and texture. Walls are made of different material and with different color and texture than flooring to reflect sound differently and provide way-finding information.

FIGURE 6.26

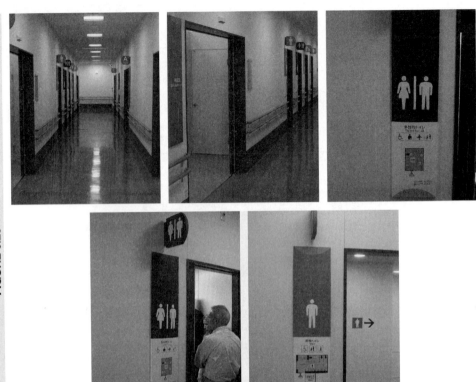

Redundant and multisensory wayfinding systems, including color changes in signs and floor colorings at different rooms, as well as tactile information on wall and handrail signs are used at the Toto Universal Design Research Center for Advanced Science and Technology in Tokyo, Japan. This system exemplifies principles P1, Equitable Use; P2, Flexibility in Use; P3, Simple and Intuitive Use; P4, Perceptible Information; P5, Tolerance for Error; P8, Social Integration; and P9, Contextual Integration.

In buildings that have more than one level, the slope of stairs between levels is as gradual as possible with handrails at multiple levels on both sides. Stairs, as well as an elevator or vertical lift, are located in convenient places to minimize the distance that any employee has to travel. Elevator call buttons and controls are located at a convenient height, have large easy-to-use buttons, and provide redundant visual, tactile, and auditory feedback for all employees (Figure 6.29).

FIGURE 6.27

Changing everyday flooring materials and colors as exemplified by the College of Architecture, Georgia Tech, Atlanta, GA, provides visual and tactile orientation cues by demonstrating principles P1, Equitable Use; P4, Perceptible Information; P5, Tolerance for Error; and P9, Contextual Integration.

FIGURE 6.28

(A) High-contrast, large-text signage are common in Tokyo, Japan, to identify building elements and provide direction, whereas (B) landmarks, including sculpture (CATEA file photo) and (C) columns, such as those in the College of Architecture, GA Tech, Atlanta, GA, can also help distinguish routes, identify specific locations, and differentiate corridors in a workplace. These features employ principles P1, Equitable Use; P2, Flexibility in Use; P3, Simple and Intuitive Use; P4, Perceptible Information; P5, Tolerance for Error; P8, Social Integration; and P9, Contextual Integration.

FIGURE 6.29

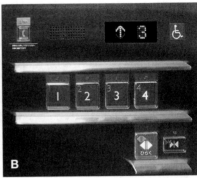

(A) Elevators are usable by everyone but should be located to minimize travel distances and should have (B) large button, tactile controls for multimodal feedback, such as the control panel at the Toto Universal Design Research Center for Advanced Science and Technology in Tokyo, Japan, making the handicapped sign totally unnecessary. These features illustrate principles P1, Equitable Use; P3, Simple and Intuitive Use; P4, Perceptible Information; P5, Tolerance for Error; P6, Low Physical Effort; P7, Size and Space for Approach and Use; P8, Social Integration; and P9, Contextual Integration.

Using the Workstation. Workstations (Figure 6.30) are designed for optimal performance of specific work tasks by focusing on a number of key characteristics (Figure 6.31) that support worker's abilities to perform those tasks across his or her work life and for other workers to perform those specific tasks across the life of the tasks. Rather than large open areas, where job tasks permit, individual workspaces have high sound-resistant walls to minimize ambient noise levels and enable each worker to control the noise levels in his or her own workspace. Workstations are arranged and oriented to enable employees to have visual access to coworkers to communicate effectively.

Controls on equipment and drawer hardware are large, contrast from the background, enable operation by multiple modalities or methods, do not require grasping or simultaneous actions (e.g., push and turn), and minimize dexterity and operating forces. Alternative input mechanisms, such as remote controls and speech recognition, are provided to minimize reaching or to eliminate manipulation altogether.

Using the Work Surface
Every workstation provides sufficient knee space and toe clearance below the work surface to enable employees of any stature and chairs with a

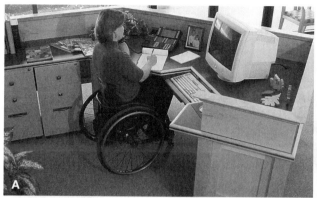

FIGURE 6.30

Universal design features that provide flexibility, such as large workspaces that (A) locate all objects within reach (CATEA file photo), (B, C) provide convenient heights for standing or seated individuals or for different tasks, and (D) enable easy access to all parts of a workstation and facilitate work tasks for individual workers and teams. These features illustrate principles P1, Equitable Use; P2, Flexibility in Use; P3, Simple and Intuitive Use; P4, Perceptible Information; P5, Tolerance for Error; P6, Low Physical Effort; P7, Size and Space for Approach and Use; P8, Social Integration; and P9, Contextual Integration.

range of seat heights (including wheelchairs) to be as close to the workstation as possible.

Work surfaces provide sufficient space and locations for work items, controls, keyboards, and other work objects within easy reach, thus enabling their use by the maximum number of workers. Those items that are used most frequently are located in the closest positions to the user as possible. In most cases, employees can reach and use controls and work items with the least change in body position; however, a chair that slides along

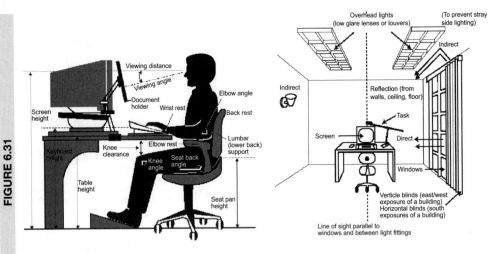

FIGURE 6.31

Like all design features, workstations are composed of a number of important characteristics that determine the range of abilities that will be enabled. Characteristics include
(A) heights, distances, and viewing angles of various elements, as well as (B) position
of lighting sources (Source: U.S. Occupational Safety and Health Administration, www.
osha.gov/Publications/videoDisplay/videoDisplay.html)

the entire length of the work surface enables workers to also adjust their
position for all work items, equipment, and controls to be within reach.

Work surfaces are of matte finish to minimize glare. The amount of
light necessary depends on the requirements of the task, so a combination
of natural and artificial light sources that can be adjusted through the use
of motorized blinds to minimize reaching and grasping, overhead lights,
and task lights with touch controls directly on the work surface are used.
This flexibility enables employees to adjust the lighting to fit the requirements of their tasks and individual abilities.

Maintaining Support and Position

For tasks that require standard work surfaces, adjustable ergonomic chairs
enable employees to be supported in the right position; adjust seat height
and tilt to distribute body weight between feet, legs, and buttocks; change
back height and tilt to spine; and alter armrests to position the arms and
hands for the task at hand. On the other hand, some job tasks, such as grocery store checkouts and many types of equipment repair, have traditionally been performed standing. However, not all employees can sit or stand
for long periods, if at all. As a result, regardless of the tasks to be performed,
all workstations, within the limits of the tasks to be performed, provide
flexibility to enable either seated or standing use by as many employees as

FIGURE 6.32

Universal Retail Checkout Stand. A prototype for a universal design grocery store retail checkout stand permits use by standing and seated workers. (Designed by Camillo Vargas, MID in fulfillment of the requirements for his Master's thesis in Industrial Design at Georgia Tech).

possible for as long as possible. To do so, adjustable workstations have work surfaces that raise, lower, and pivot to enable employees to change positions as needed to minimize effort and maximize abilities (Figure 6.32).

Computing

Most computer equipment is plug-and-play. As a result, most workplace accommodations for computing are, in fact, universal design. A variety of alternative input devices, including ergonomic keyboards, keyboards, and voice input, are available depending on employee preferences and needs. Input devices are wireless to provide flexibility, independent placement, and ease of use, and keyboards have tilt-adjustable supports to increase comfort and reduce fatigue. All workstations are equipped with a high-contrast, large-screen monitor on a tilt-adjustable stand that raise, lower, and tilt to reduce eye, neck, and back strain. In addition, all computer systems are capable of having dual monitors, and a second monitor is available for those who desire one. To complement the large monitors, employees are encouraged to use screen enlargement and contrast enhancement options that are built into the computer's operating system. Finally, the workspace is configured to enable employees to access computer drives and other peripherals (e.g., printers and scanners) with either hand.

Interacting. To enable face-to-face communication, all communal spaces and individual workspaces are usable by any employee, regardless of ability. Informal communal spaces, such as hallways and break rooms, are designed to encourage social interaction, whereas formal ones, such as meeting rooms and cafeterias, provide opportunities for planned and impromptu meetings. Social spaces are AT and ability friendly to enable all workers to benefit equally from workplace interactions. Meeting spaces are located near workstations and have a clear, simple path of travel to make spaces easy to find and to minimize travel time. In addition, routes to meeting spaces are continuous routes that do not require the use of stairs; use contrasting colors and floor materials; and provide high-contrast, large-text, iconographic, and tactile information to identify spaces and aid way finding.

Informal meeting spaces are intentionally and strategically located, with extra space and casual seating provided where employees have the opportunity for serendipitous encounters, such as at a copy machine, a coffee pot, water cooler, stair, elevator lobby, or hallway intersection. Meeting spaces have sufficient space and are equipped with chairs and tables to facilitate social interaction between all employees and groups of employees regardless of ability or use of assistive devices to interact. Furniture is arranged in clusters to facilitate interaction among employees. Tables have movable chairs and can be arranged in different configurations to enable use by differing size groups and employees with and without mobility aids. There are no obstructions to enable clear lines of sight so that communication partners can clearly see each other and any visual information in the work environment. There is a good acoustical environment to ensure that important information is intelligible, and reverberation time and characteristics are optimized by minimizing hard reflective surfaces and using sound-absorbing materials on walls, floors, and ceilings or covering windows with shades/curtains. Background noise is minimized to ensure that unwanted noise is not distracting and does not mask speech and other important information. Formal meeting spaces are equipped with assistive listening system (e.g., transmitter and receiver) to amplify sound to enable individuals who benefit from amplification to focus directly on the sound source.

SEVEN

Barriers to Adoption of Universal Design as a Rehabilitation Strategy

*A*s the the population ages and the work force becomes increasingly diverse, universal design as a rehabilitation strategy for aging in place and the workplace has the potential for enabling individuals of all ages and abilities to participate equally and productively throughout their lives. Universal design potentially eliminates or, at least, reduces the need for specialized accommodations, thus saving resources that might otherwise be required to accommodate other individuals and enabling everyone to use and share the same resources. In the workplace, this can increase the pool of potential employees for any job and lower the cost of hiring new employees and the promotion of long-term employees. Most importantly, universal design strategies can enhance sense of inclusion, belonging, and participation. These are not only critical to increasing well-being, life satisfaction, and productivity but also enable employers to attract and retain a competitive workforce—ultimately resulting in increased profitability and success.

Simply put, universal design (UD) makes good sense—for individuals living and working in the community, for employers, and for society. This problem is not inherent in universal design itself, but rather results from a variety of policy (including U.S. civil rights and health care policies) and practice (including lack of awareness and misunderstanding of universal design) barriers that have limited its use as a rehabilitation strategy. Nor are these barriers limited to the workplace. Similar policy and practice limitations have restricted the use of universal design as a rehabilitation strategy for aging in place. Chapter 7 will describe these barriers and propose a set of strategies for overcoming them. Yet, despite its potential as a rehabilitation strategy for aging in place and the workplace, UD has not yet been widely adopted by rehabilitation providers. Although the barriers to UD are numerous and varied, including misperceptions about UD by rehabilitation professionals themselves (which, at a minimum, should be assuaged by this text), there has been an almost "perfect storm" of policies, practices, and perceptions that have affected both the supply and demand sides of the UD equation.

Overt barriers to UD as a rehabilitation strategy can be traced back to U.S. public policies, including civil rights and disability policies and those that shape federally funded health, housing, and employment entitlements and subsidies, which were designed to operate as separate systems, each achieving separate "public goods." As a result, the systems not only have different regulations but also deliver separate services, performance measurements, and implementation guidelines, which often conflict with each other and impede coordination. Not surprisingly, therefore, there is a general lack of a clear, coordinated, and comprehensive system of services that would expand housing options and employment opportunities to support self-sufficiency, independence, health, and well-being. Rather, we have a fragmented system of services provided by various public and private health care and social service organizations (Lau et al., 2007; Pynoos, Liebig, Overton, & Calvert, 1997) that are hampered by lack of information, experience, funding, and resources. Similarly, consumers are often uninformed or harbor misperceptions about environmental innovations. Together, these factors have resulted in both a poor supply of and limited demand for UD interventions.

PUBLIC POLICY DISINCENTIVES FOR UD

This text has repeatedly pointed out that the Americans with Disabilities Act (ADA), civil rights/disability policies in general, and health reimbursement policies under the Department of Health and Human Services and Centers for Medicare/Medicaid Services (CMS) have provided policy disincentives, and a maze of funding resources are major barriers to implementing UD interventions. To compound the problem, overlapping interests intended to promote positive outcomes in housing provision under the Department of Housing and Urban Development (HUD) and employment under the Department of Labor and the Office of Disability Employment Policy are disconnected in policy decisions and resource allocation. Add to that mix, model building codes, please write out in all cases, which focus on building rather than people outcomes, and the policy climate is cool for implementing UD as a rehabilitation outcome.

If-We-Build-It-They-Will-Come Disability Policies

Promoting activity has generally fallen under the purview of civil rights legislation to provide access to public facilities and places of employment (although the latter does not have specified technical requirements), not private single-family housing. As a result, there are few accessibility-focused regulations that cover residential facilities and even fewer that comprehensively regulate the design of private housing specifically for people who have functional or health limitations (Hyde, Talbert, & Grayson, 1997).

Nonetheless, U.S. disability and civil rights legislation, which promulgates specifications for accessible design (AD) interventions, is perhaps the largest impediment to the adoption of UD. In housing, these policies either dictate (i.e., in multifamily dwelling units) or provide a reference (i.e., in single-family residences) for AD through guidelines and standards (e.g., *Americans with Disabilities Act Accessibility Guidelines*, *Fair Housing Amendments Accessibility Guidelines*). In the workplace, the Internal Revenue Service (IRS) uses AD requirements (i.e., Title III *ADAAG*) to dictate specifications for AD accommodations that are eligible for tax incentives to overcome financial challenges faced by small businesses in implementing reasonable accommodations to remove environmental barriers to employment of and workers with disabilities. This, despite the purpose of ADAAG to provide basic access for the general public, not specific job tasks by individual workers.

Disability policies are based on an outdated "if-we-build-it-they-will-come" paradigm that is, itself, predicated on the premise that removing barriers to independence in activities through AD will beget participation in social roles. This 20th century linear thinking from activity to participation is clearly antithetical to the *International Classification of Functioning, Disability, and Health* (*ICF's*) 21st century model of health, activity, and participation, which suggest that although the three constructs are interconnected, they require their own environmental responses. Clearly, UD is a rehabilitation intervention that is a means to achieve these positive ends. Although removing barriers are specific to an individual rehabilitation client, UD interventions not only benefit the individual client but also have the potential to also benefit others, including family members, coworkers, employers, and others who share social environments and who also encounter usability and inclusivity difficulties because of their own functional (dis)abilities, even if these abilities do not "qualify" as disabilities. In doing so, UD can also have economic benefits as everyday housing and workplace design to support health, activity, and participation needs of all individuals without the need for (potentially expensive) specialized interventions.

Hands-off-Housing Health Care Policy

Like most disability policies, the U.S. health care reimbursement system is also person-centric, focused on meeting the specific needs individual rehabilitation clients. As such, health care policy provides economic disincentives for UD by supporting quick-fix specialized assistive technology (AT) and (to a lesser extent) AD solutions, which may (although not always) have lower initial costs but far less long-term benefits to families, organizations, or society.

The key barrier to UD in housing is that the U.S. health care system does not recognize the home as a health care environment and, as such, does not include UD as a reimbursable rehabilitation strategy. Unlike Sweden and other countries with socialized medicine that include home modifications as an option to support independent and healthy living, our reimbursement system does not. The CMS reimbursement policy, which is based on a person-centric, rather than social-centric, medical model, is focused on improving health and activity outcomes of individual clients. As such, it will pay for rehabilitation interventions, such as personal assistance and assistive and medical technologies, and, depending on the state, some limited home modifications that have direct benefit to the health and activity of individual clients. It will not cover interventions that provide additional benefits to the client or to others, such as participation in social roles, reducing the cost of health care, or helping to ensure that caregiving and technology interventions are effective.

In a 2009 article in the *New York Times*, Ashlee Vance (Vance, 2009) painted a grim picture of our reimbursement system as a process so invested in the medical model that specialized medical devices and equipment are preferred over universal everyday designs even when the latter are less expensive, work better, and preferred by the user. Although the article is based on reimbursement for an AT device, the same policies hold true for home modifications and workplace accommodations. Regardless of the type of intervention, policies that support specialized technologies over everyday designs may result in increased costs, decreased effectiveness, and poor outcomes. Vance wrote:

> *Kara Lynn has . . . A.L.S . . . A couple of years ago, she spent more than $8,000 to buy a computer . . . that turns typed words into speech . . . Under*

*government insurance requirements, the maker of the PC, which ran ordi-
nary Microsoft Windows software, had to block any nonspeech functions, like
sending e-mail or browsing the Web . . . Dismayed by the PC's limitations
and clunky design, Ms. Lynn turned to a $300 iPhone 3G from Apple run-
ning $150 text-to-speech software.*

*Medicare and private health insurers decline to cover cheap devices like
iPhones and netbook PCs . . . despite their usefulness and lower cost. Instead
. . . if Ms. Lynn and others like her want insurance to pay, they must spend
10 to 20 times as much for dedicated, proprietary devices that can do far less.
The logic: Insurance is supposed to cover medical devices . . .*
*"We would not cover the iPhones and netbooks with speech-generating soft-
ware capabilities because they are useful in the absence of an illness or injury," said Peter Ashkenaz, a spokesman for the federal Centers for Medicare
and Medicaid Services.*

Overall, the medical model mentality has contributed to a general
hands-off-housing policy that rejects reimbursement for interventions that
might potentially enhance the value of a private residence. At the public
level, paying for changes to private residences can give the appearance of
spending taxpayer dollars on unnecessary remodeling that increases the
comfort and wealth of individuals, even if homeowners themselves do not
perceive that these changes will increase value. At the private level, third-
party payers are reluctant to spend money on environmental interventions
that may increase the value of property that they do not own and could be
sold by the owner for profit at any time. Such reluctance to invest taxpayer
or investor dollars in permanent changes to one's home for the potential of
private benefit is a major barrier to UD as a rehabilitation strategy.

Where Is Health in the Health, Safety, and Welfare of Building Code Policy?

Model and local building codes, which regulate construction of housing,
work environments, and other public buildings, are intended to protect
health, safety, and welfare of the general public. However, despite the
health implications in building codes, as we have seen, environmental interventions in housing and work settings are not considered to be medical
interventions under our medical model approach to health care.

Historically, this has not always been the case. If we examine the
earliest examples of building codes in the United States, the New York
City Tenement House Act of 1867 was precisely a means of manipulating

health outcomes to effect social policy (Davis, 1997). This law was intended to protect society from squalid living conditions that were associated with smallpox and tuberculosis epidemics. The legislation included not only policies to protect the health of New York's citizens but also enforceable building regulations that mandated design features for cleaner, safer, and better built housing and the designation of public agencies to carry out those regulations. Similarly, the *ICF* and the social model of medicine upon which it is based, reinforce the link between home environment and health. As a consequence, the *ICF* provides the impetus and rationale for incorporating environmental interventions for supportive housing into building codes.

> Building codes are intended to protect health, safety, and welfare, yet AD and UD interventions to support these goals are not reimbursed under U.S. health policy. Conversely, AD and UD are intended to promote aging in place, yet does not come under the BC mandate of protecting health, safety, and welfare.

Conversely, AD does not fall under the mandate of health, safety, and welfare. As a result, local building codes do not specifically regulate accessibility in private housing or work settings. Although they do not include specific requirements for AD or UD in housing or work environments, they do use accessibility standards (i.e., *ADAAG*) to regulate safety of features such as handrails, stairs, and ramps. Moreover, in adopting ADA specifications for some building code requirements, AD under the *ADAAG* has become the de facto model for home modifications and workplace accommodations, although it is based on civil rights, not health, safety, and welfare concerns, and although the specific requirements are intended for public, not housing or work environments. More importantly, as noted above, AD under the *ADAAG* does not foster UD interventions.

Following Funding Through A-mazing Government Programs

Although CMS does not recognize the home as a health care environment or UD as a reimbursable expense, funding for rehabilitation interventions is distributed across a maze of federal and state agencies and programs. The separation of housing and health care in different governmental agencies has created various systems of public subsidies that make it difficult for individuals to find or receive adequate funding. Housing dollars are distributed as a limited subsidy by HUD, which sets income restrictions on who qualifies for housing assistance. In contrast, Medicare distributes health dollars as an entitlement at the federal level and by Medicaid at the state level.

Within the federal government alone, there are at least seven departments that have programs where funds can be used for home modifications, including Agriculture, Energy, Education, Health and Human Services, HUD, Treasury, and Veterans Affairs. Accordingly, each has its own regulations and guidelines that dictate the types of home modifications that are eligible for funding. However, despite differences in eligibility criteria, most government programs are based on barrier removal, thus minimizing the potential for UD as a viable intervention strategy.

In the workplace, employees who are eligible to be clients of their state department of vocational rehabilitation receive many of their accommodations through Rehabilitation Services Administration funding. Alternatively, the IRS has two provisions to assist businesses cover the cost of workplace accommodations. First, the *Disabled Access Tax Credit* is available to small businesses in the amount of 50% of "eligible access expenditures" for a taxable year for the purpose of enabling the business to comply with the applicable requirements of the ADA. Second, the *Tax Deduction to Remove Architectural and Transportation Barriers to People with Disabilities and Elderly Individuals* allows businesses to deduct up to $15,000 of the costs incurred each year for "qualified architectural and transportation barrier removal expenses." To be eligible for the tax credit, a business must remove barriers or provide services, modifications, materials, or equipment that prevent a business from being accessible to, or usable by, individuals with disabilities and acquiring or modifying equipment or devices for individuals with disabilities. These accommodations are required to meet technical standards of the *ADAAG* that implement Title III of the ADA. To be eligible for the deduction, modifications must meet the requirements of standards established by the IRS regulations with the concurrence of the U.S. Architectural and Transportation Barriers Compliance Board (U.S. Access Board). Although the latter does not specifically state that *ADAAG* will be used to determine eligibility, since the Access Board promulgates the *ADAAG*, the presumption is that similar guidelines will be used to determine tax deductions. Clearly, programs based on barrier removal and accessibility guidelines specifically for employees with disabilities will not promote UD interventions that may go beyond ADA requirements.

PROVIDER PERCEPTIONS AND PRACTICES

Despite the widespread acknowledgment and acceptance of the UD principles across many professions, application of the principles by builders, manufacturers, rehabilitation professionals, and service providers to the construction and retrofit of housing and the design of consumer products and technologies has been slow to occur. A major reason for the underutilization of UD in the home and workplace to enable positive health, activity, and participation outcomes is the lack of specialists who are familiar with the basic principles and guidelines. Most providers tend to rely on what they already know rather than try something new (Belser & Weber, 1995). As a result, not only do providers who lack familiarity with UD have biases that create a reluctance to use it as a rehabilitation strategy but also these biases result in misperceptions about UD that become self-fulfilling prophesies.

Builders' Bluffs

Home builders are most familiar with everyday design. Not surprisingly, that is the way many home builders prefer to build. When confronted with a request to use a UD feature, such as putting in a sloping walkway, a builder, who would rather construct the same step he or she has done hundreds of times before or does not want to be bothered with doing something new, may bluff a client into doing just that. A typical approach is to invoke the *BC Rule*, where the builder claims that the desired feature is in violation of the building code, which in this case requires a step to the house, even if the house is constructed slab-on-grade and has a porch protecting the door from the elements (Figure 7.1). Because builders are usually much more familiar with building codes than clients, this rationale generally puts an immediate end to the discussion.

In other cases, builders may be familiar with AD, but not with UD. As a result, it is not uncommon to find that they misuse the term *universal design* as a synonym for AD. This is especially evident when housing that is advertised as UD is also marketed as meeting the *ADAAG* or fully ADA compliant and highlights the AD features that have been included.

Finally, many builders and manufacturers have the misperception that UD adds cost to a project and are therefore reluctant to use it as a design strategy. Whereas this might be true in a retrofit situation, the same can be said for AD interventions. However, if introduced at the beginning of a project, additional costs might be negligible, if any at all. For example, the cost of a wider doorway is offset by the diminished costs of the wall around it.

Professional Perspective

Home and workplace rehabilitation services are delivered by a wide variety of professions. Home assessments are primarily undertaken by occupational therapists, rehabilitation engineers, and other rehabilitation professionals, and, to a lesser extent, professionals in the construction

FIGURE 7.1

Despite the slab-on-grade construction (i.e., there are no steps) and a screen porch protecting the front door from rain, the builder convinced my parents that building code required a step up to the entrance. As a result, the 2-in. high brick step not only creates a barrier to my mother's wheelchair and wheeled walker but also is a trip hazard for everyone.

industry. Conversely, constructional professionals, and to a lesser extent, rehabilitation professionals, are primarily responsible for the implementation of the interventions in the home.

Nevertheless, intervention decisions often vary by familiarity with environmental interventions based on discipline and level of expertise of the individual delivering the services. Each profession tends to have its own disciplinary perspective that influences the understanding of needs and intervention solutions. By virtue of their training and driven by reimbursement systems, rehabilitation health professionals are understandably more familiar and concerned with impairment and activity performance of the client than with environmental factors, residential construction, or even the range of potential environmental modifications (Pynoos, 1993; Pynoos et al., 1997). As a result, these individuals often underestimate the physical aspects of the environment and may not recommend environmental interventions at all. On the other hand, rehabilitation engineers may focus more on AT interventions, whereas construction professionals, who know less about activity and ability than environmental attributes, may overestimate the need for AD interventions.

Similarly, agencies that pay for modifications and accommodations often introduce system bias by requiring assessments that adhere to their guidelines and result in recommending only interventions that will be reimbursed. This is clearly the case with vocational rehabilitation funding and IRS tax incentives for workplace accommodations. In addition, the plethora of funding sources for home modifications, including federal, state, and local governments; private insurers; workers compensation; service organizations, such as Area Agencies on Aging, Centers for Independent Living, State Tech Act Programs, and Naturally Occurring Retirement Community

Initiatives; and nonprofit volunteer organizations, such as Rebuilding Together, each has their own bias and approach to home modification and their own way of prioritizing what is most important.

Targeted Training

Unfortunately, no single discipline or systematic program provides training that encompasses a comprehensive understanding of UD. Although some disciplines, such as occupational therapy (OT) and architecture, include college-level courses on home modifications or environmental interventions, these are typically isolated efforts of individual faculty members, rather than promoted by the program or a particular profession.

It is important to recognize that there are no standards or licensure requirements for provision of either AD or UD interventions in the home or workplace (other than general professional licensure required by a particular state). Anyone can provide the service, regardless of certification or licensure, although the scope of services that an individual can provide may be restricted by their professional licensure and reimbursement restrictions. For example, OTs can perform home assessments, modify products, and provide off-the-shelf products in states in which they are licensed but are not permitted to engage in home remodeling as an OT. In contrast, home remodelers are not restricted from providing any of those services, including assessments. Whether those services are as effective as other professionals is another debate.

Despite the lack of standards, there are a variety of certifications associated with home modifications. However, none are legally binding and are not affiliated with any professional licensure. For example, the National Association of Home Builders offers a Certified Aging in Place certification; the American Occupational Therapy Association offers a specialty certification in environmental modifications; and the Rehabilitation Engineering and Assistive Technology Society of North America offers assistive technology professional and rehabilitation engineering technologist certifications. None of these certifications are required to engage in home modification or workplace accommodation practice, although assistive technology professional and rehabilitation engineering technologist (which do not specifically focus on either home or workplace interventions) are eligible for reimbursement as clinical services. In addition, several universities including the University of Southern California, SUNY Buffalo, and Georgia Tech offer certificates for online programs. However, these programs are not intended to specifically target either UD or particular environments. As a result, none are sufficiently focused to ensure comprehensive knowledge of either UD in the home or workplace.

PERSONAL PERCEPTIONS

On the demand side, the maze of government programs and service providers ensures that consumers are as equally uninformed as providers about the benefits and costs of UD. Whereas individuals with trauma or chronic illness who are automatically placed into the rehabilitation system through their health care provider are exposed to home or work interventions, those interventions will more often than not be specialized designs to remove existing environmental barriers. At the same time, individuals, such as seniors with declining abilities, who have not had a catastrophic injury or a chronic health condition but who are in need of more enabling environments, are likely to be on their own to find out about UD interventions.

Buyer Be Aware

A major reason for the large numbers of individuals with unmet needs for home and workplace interventions is the lack of awareness of either the interventions themselves or their benefits. Moreover, because UD and other environmental intervention strategies are the exceptions to everyday home or workplace design, rather than the norm, there are few traditional marketing strategies (e.g., TV advertisements) to inform consumers about their benefits. Even the few advertisements that feature modifications are often promoting the contractors who specialize in them, rather than for the modifications themselves, and few include UD features. As a result, consumers may only be familiar with "ADA" accessibility features that they have seen in public settings or "handicapped" features (e.g., ramps and stainless steel grab bars) in their friends' homes.

CONSUMER CONFIDENCE

Consumers often associate prosthetic and therapeutic interventions with the stigma of disability and institutional care (Pynoos et al., 1997; Wolford, 2000). As such, these interventions are not perceived to be compatible with the everyday design of housing or work environments and will most likely reduce the market value of their property (Gilderbloom & Markham, 1996) or further exclude them from workplace interactions. As a result, consumers may only accept environmental interventions as a last resort when there is a perceived need, they have increasing restrictions in activities, or they experience a disabling condition that threatens independence (Pynoos et al., 1987, 1997).

Whereas these perceptions have a firm basis in the many assistive and health care technologies and AD solutions that have an institutional or medical appearance, bathroom equipment in particular, there are many UD interventions that heave been developed specifically for the home and workplace that have become available. Despite this, UD and home modifications continue to carry the stigma of disability and institutionalization (Pynoos et al., 1997; Wolford, 2000).

Assistive technology and medical equipment, in contrast to AD and UD, are not only institutional looking but also routinely accepted as devices that promote activity independence and health. Nonetheless, these devices are either accepted or rejected by users based on perceived benefit versus social judgments. Assistive technology may be viewed positively as a mechanism by which to regain independent performance or negatively as a symbol of lost function and abilities. The individual may therefore need to adjust to using an assistive device by relinquishing previously valued and preferred ways of carrying out basic living tasks.

Unfortunately, even when consumers know the benefits of UD, they believe that the costs of implementing it are prohibitive. In fact, cost seems to trump information about the benefits of home modifications. For example, one recent study (Sanford et al., 2007) found that only 42% of home modification recommendations were implemented by a sample of self-payers even when additional information about the benefits of home modifications was provided. In another study (Sohn, 1997), older consumers' perceptions of the usefulness and attractiveness of residential UD features increased after they tried out the features and products. However, consumers' new positive views failed to overcome their perceptions that the products were too expensive.

REFERENCES FOR PART II

AARP. (2000). *Fixing to stay: A national survey of housing and home modification issues.* Washington, DC: Author.

Abel, M. J. (1990). Experiences in an exploratory distributed organization. In R. K. J. Galagher & C. Egido (Eds.), *Intellectual teamwork* (pp. 489–510). Norwood, NJ: Lawrence Erlbaum Associates.

Anant, S. S. (1966). The need to belong. *Canada's Mental Health, 14,* 21–21.

Avolio, B. J., & Sosik, J. J. (1999). A life-span framework for assessing the impact of work on white-collar workers. In S. L. Willis & J. D. Reid (Eds.), *Life in the middle: Psychological and social development in middle age* (pp. 251–274). San Diego, CA: Academic Press.

Allen, S., & Resnik, L. (2006). Promoting independence for wheelchair users who live alone: The role of home accommodations. *The Gerontologist, 46*(1), 115–123.

Bailey, D. E., & Kurland, N. B. (2002). A review of telework research: Findings, new directions, and lessons for the study of modern work. *Journal of Organizational Behavior, 23*(4), 383–400.

Balser, D. B. (2007). Predictors of workplace accommodations for employees with mobility-related disabilities. *Administration & Society, 39*(5), 656–683.

Baumeister, R. F., & Leary, M. F. (1995). The need to belong: Desire for interpersonal attachments as a fundamental human motivation. *Psychological Bulletin, 117*(3), 497.

Binstock, R. H., & Cluff, L. E. (2000). *Home care advances: Essential research and policy issues.* New York, NY: Springer Publishing.

Berkman, L. E., & Glass, T. (2000). Social integration, social networks, social support, and health. In L. F. Berkman & I. Kawachi (Eds.), *Social epidemiology* (pp. 137–173). New York, NY: Oxford University Press.

Bernspang, B., & Fisher, A. G. (1995). Differences between persons with right or left cerebral vascular accident on the assessment of motor and process skills. *Archives of Physical Medicine and Rehabilitation, 76*(12), 1144–1151.

Blanck, P. D. (1994). *Communicating the Americans with Disabilities Act, transcending compliance: A case report on Sears, Roebuck and Co.* Iowa City, IA: Annenberg Washington Program.

Blanck, P. D. (1998). *The Americans with Disabilities Act and the emerging workforce: Employment of people with mental retardation.* Washington, DC: American Association of Mental Retardation.

Bruyere, S. M. (2000). *Disability employment policies and practices in private and federal sector organizations.* Ithaca, NY: Cornell University, School of Industrial and Labor Relations Extension Division, Program on Employment and Disability.

Bureau of Labor Statistics, U.S. Department of Labor. (2006). *Career guide to in-dustries, 2006–2007 edition.* Retrieved April 12, 2008, from http://www.bls.gov/oco/cg/cgs035.htm

Butterfield, T., & Ramseur, H. (2004). Research and case study findings in the area of workplace accommodations including provisions for assistive technology: A literature review. *Technology and Disability, 16*(4), 201–210.

Calkins, M., Sanford, J. A., & Proffitt, M. (2001). Universal design and dementia design. In W. F. E. Preiser & E. Ostroff (Eds.), *Manual of universal design* (pp. 22.1–22.24). New York, NY: McGraw-Hill.

Campbell, A., Converse, P. E., & Rogers, W. L. (1976). *The quality of American life: Perceptions, evaluations and satisfactions.* New York, NY: Russell Sage.

Carter, S. E., Campbell, E. M., Sanson-Fisher, R. W., Redman, S., & Gillespie, W. J. (1997). Environmental hazards in the homes of older people. *Age and Ageing, 26,* 195–202.

Centers for Disease Control and Prevention. (2011). *Falls among older adults: An overview.* Retrieved June 5, 2011, from http://www.cdc.gov/Homeand RecreationalSafety/Falls/adultfalls.html

Center for Universal Design. (2006). *Universal design in housing.* Raleigh, NC: Author.

Chirikos, T. N. (2000). Employer accommodation of older workers with disabilities. In P. D. Blanck (Ed.), *Employment, disability, and the Americans with Disabilities Act* (pp. 228–257). Evanston, IL: Northwestern University Press.

Christen, M., Lyer, G., & Soberman, D. (2006). Job satisfaction, job performance, and effort: A reexamination using agency theory. *Journal of Marketing, 70*(1), 137–150.

Christie, T. (2008). Nurses' perception of job satisfaction and sense of belonging in a critical care environment. Master's thesis presented to Laurentian University.

Clemson, L., Roland, M., & Cumming, R. G. (1997). Types of hazards in the homes of elderly people. *Occupational Therapy Journal of Research, 17*(3), 200–213.

Clutterbuck, P., & McKay, S. (1984). *Work and well being, the changing realities of employment.* Toronto, Canada: Canadian Mental Health Association.

Cohrs, J. C., Abele, A. E., & Dette, D. A. (2006). Integrating situational and dispositional determinants of job satisfaction: Findings from three samples of professionals. *The Journal of Psychology, 140*(4), 363–395.

Commission on Affordable Housing and Health Facility Needs for Seniors in the 21st Century. (2002, June 28). *Seniors Commission report. Final report to congress.* Retrieved September 18, 2009, from http://govinfo.library.unt.edu/seniors commission/pages/final_report/sencomrep.html

Condrey, S. E., & Brudney, J. L. (1998). The Americans with Disabilities Act of 1990: Assessing its implementation in America's largest cities. *American Review of Public Administration, 28*(1), 26–42.

Connell, B. R., & Sanford, J. A. (1997). Housing needs of older people to facilitate in-dependence and safety. In S. Lanspery & J. Hyde (Eds.), *Staying put: Adapting the places instead of the people* (pp. 113–148). Amityville, NY: Baywood Publishing.

Connell, B. R., & Sanford, J. A. (2001). Difficulty, dependence, and housing accessibility for people aging with a disability. *Journal of Architectural and Planning Research, 18*(1), 234–242.

Cumming, R. G., Thomas, M., Szonyi, G., Frampton, G., Salkeld, G., & Clemson, L. (2001). Adherence to occupational therapist recommendations for home modifications for falls prevention. *American Journal of Occupational Therapy, 55*, 641–648.

Cumming, R. G., Thomas, M., Szonyi, G., Salkeld, G., O'Neill, E., Westbury, C., & Frampton, G. (1999). Home visits by an occupational therapist for assessment and modification of environmental hazards: A randomized trial of falls prevention. *Journal of the American Geriatrics Society, 47*, 1397–1402.

Czaja, S. J., & Moen, P. (2004). Technology and employment. In R. Pew & S. Van Hemmel (Eds.), *Technology for adaptive aging*. Washington, DC: National Academies Press.

Daly, M. C., & Bound, J. (1996). Worker adaptation and employer accommodation following the onset of a health impairment. *Journal of Gerontology, 51B*(2), S53–S60.

DHHS. (1999). *Mental health: A report of the surgeon general*. Rockville, MD: U.S. Department of Health and Human Services.

DOL. (2001, December 18). *Workplace injuries and illnesses in 2000*. Washington, DC: U.S. Department of Labor, Bureau of Labor Statistics,. Retrieved July 26, 2002, from http://stats.bls.gov/iif/oshwc/osh/os/osnr0013.pdf, or http://www.bls.gov/iif/home.htm

Deegan P. (1988). Recovery: The lived experience. *Psychoscial Rehabilitation Journal, 11*(4), 11–19.

Edwards, J. R., Caplan, R. D., & Van Harrison, R. (1998). Person–environment fit theory: Conceptual foundations, empirical evidence and directions for future research, In C. L. Cooper (Ed.), *Theories of organizational stress* (pp. 29–67). New York, NY: Oxford University Press.

EEOC, Equal Employment Opportunity Commission. (1992). *A technical assistance manual on the employment provisions (Title I) of the Americans with Disabilities Act*. Annapolis Junction, MD: Author.

Fange, A., & Iwarsson, S. (2003). Accessibility and usability in housing—Construct validity and implications for research and practice. *Disability and Rehabilitation, 25*, 1316–1325.

Feinberg, L., Reinhard, S. C., Houser, A., & Choula, R. (2011). *Valuing the invaluable: 2011 update the growing contributions and costs of family caregiving*. Washington, DC: AARP.

Fish, R., Kraut, R., Root, R., & Rice, R. (1993). Video as a technology for informal communication. *Communications of the ACM, 36*, 48–61.

Freedman, V. A. (2011). Disability, functioning and aging. In R. Binstock & L. George (Eds.), *Handbook of aging and the social sciences* (7th ed.). Ann Arbor, MI: Institute for Social Research.

Freedman, V. A., Martin, L. G., & Schoeni, R. F. (2002). Recent trends in disability and functioning among older adults in the United States. *Journal of the American Medical Association, 288,* 3137–3146.

French, J. R. P., Caplan, R. D., & Van Harrison, R. (1982). *The mechanisms of job stress and strain.* New York, NY: Wiley.

Galinsky, T., Waters, T., & Malit, B. (2001). Overexertion injuries in home health care workers and the need for ergonomics. *Home Health Care Serv Quarterly, 20,* 57–73.

Gamble, M. J., Dowler, D. D., & Hirsh, A. E. (2004). Informed decision making on assistive technology workplace accommodations for people with visual impairments. *Work, 23,* 123–130.

Gamble, M., Dowler, D., & Orslene, L. (2006). Assistive technology: Choosing the right tool for the right job. *Journal of Vocational Rehabilitation, 24*(2), 73–80.

Gates, L. B. (2000). Workplace accommodation as a social process. *Journal of Occupational Rehabilitation, 10*(1), 85–98.

Gershon, R. M., Pogorzelska, M. T., Qureshi, K. A., Stone, P. W., Canton, A. N., Samar, S. M. Sherman, M. (2008). *Home health care patients and safety hazards in the home: Preliminary findings.* Retrieved September 15, 2009, from http://www.ahrq.gov/downloads/pub/advances2/vol1/Advances-Gershon_88.pdf

Gill, T. M., Robison, J. T., Williams, C. S., & Tinetti, M. E. (1999). Mismatches between the home environment and physical capabilities among community-living older persons. *Journal of the American Geriatrics Society, 47,* 88–92.

Gitlin, L. N. (2001). Assistive technology in the home and community for older people: Psychological and social considerations. In M. Scherer (Ed.), *Assistive technology and rehabilitation psychology: Shaping an alliance* (pp. 109–122). Washington DC: American Psychological Association.

Gitlin, L. N., Mann, W., Tomita, M., & Marcus, S. (2001). Factors associated with home environmental problems among community-living elders. *Disability and Rehabilitation, 23,* 777–787.

Gitlin, L. N. (2003). Conducting research on home environments: Lessons learned and new directions. *The Gerontologist, 43,* 628–637.

Gitlin, L. N., Corcoran, M. A., Winter, L., Boyce, A., & Hauck, W. W. (2001). A randomized, controlled trial of a home environmental intervention to enhance self-efficacy and reduce upset in family caregivers of persons with dementia. *The Gerontologist, 41,* 15–30.

Gitlin, L. N., Liebman, J., & Winter, L. (2003). Are environmental interventions effective in the management of Alzheimer's disease and related disorders? A synthesis of the evidence. *Alzheimer's Care Quarterly, 4,* 85–107.

Gitlin, L. N., Winter, L., Corcoran, M., Dennis, M. P., Shinfeld, S., & Hauck, W. (2003). Effects of the home environmental sill-building program on the caregiver–care recipient dyad: Six-month outcomes from the Philadelphia REACH initiative. *The Gerontologist, 43,* 532–546.

Gitlin, L. N. (2007). The impact of housing on quality of life: Does the home environment matter now and into the future? In H.-W. Wahl & C. Tesch-Rorner (Eds.), *New dynamics in old age: Individual, environmental and societal perspectives.* Amityville, NY: Baywood Publishing.

Guthrie, J. P. (2001). High involvement work practices, turnover and productivity: Evidence from New Zealand. *Academy of Management Journal, 44*(1), 11.

Hagerty, B. M. K., Lynch-Sauer, J., Patusky, K. L., Bouwsema, M., & Collier, P. (1992). Sense of belonging: A vital mental health concept. *Archives of Psychiatric Nursing, VI*(3), 172–177.

Hare, P. (1992, Spring). Frail elders and the suburbs. *Generations, Journal of the American Society on Aging, 16,* 35–39.

Harlan, S. L., & Robert, P. M. (1998). The social construction of disability in organizations: Why employers resist reasonable accommodation. *Work and Occupations, 25*(4), 397–435.

Harrison, S., & Dourish, P. (1996). Re-placing space: The roles of place and space in collaborative systems. *Proceedings of the ACM Conference on Computer Supported Cooperative Work '96.* Cambridge, MA.

Harter, J. K., Schmidt, F. L., & Keyes, C. L. (2002). Well-being in the workplace and its relationship to business outcomes: A review of the Gallup studies. In C. L. Keyes & J. Haidt (Eds.), *Flourishing: The positive person and the good life* (pp. 205–224). Washington, DC: American Psychological Association.

Hecker, D. E. (2005). Occupational employment projections to 2014. *Monthly Labor Review, 128*(11), 70–101.

Hinton, C. A. (2003). The perceptions of people with disabilities as to the effectiveness of the Americans with Disabilities Act. *Journal of Disability Policy Studies, 13*(4), 210–220.

Hughes, J., Randall, D., & Shapiro, D. (1991). CSCW: Discipline or paradigm? A sociological perspective. *Proceedings of the Second European Conference on Computer-Supported Cooperative Work,* Amsterdam, Netherlands, pp. 309–323.

Hyde, J., Talbert, R., & Grayson, P. J. (1997). Fostering adaptive housing: An overview of funding sources, laws and policies. In S. Lanspery & J. Hyde (Eds.), *Staying put: Adapting the places instead of the people* (pp. 223–236). Amityville, NY: Baywood Publishing.

Holt-Lunstad, J., Smith, T. B., & Layton, J. B. (2010). Social relationships and mortality risk: A meta-analytic review." *PLoS Medicine, 7*(7): e1000316. doi:10.1371/journal.pmed.1000316

Iaffaldano, M. T., & Muchinsky, P. M. (1985). Job satisfaction and job performance: A meta-analysis. *Psychological Bulletin, 97,* 251–273.

Inge, K., Wehman, P., Strobel, W., Powell, D., & Todd, J. (1998). Supported employment and assistive technology for persons with spinal cord injury: Three illustrations of successful work supports. *Journal of Vocational Rehabilitation, 10,* 141–152.

Isen, A. M. (1987). Positive affect, cognitive processes, and social behavior. In L. Berkowitz (Ed.). *Advances in experimental social psychology* (pp. 203–253). San Diego, CA: Academic Press.

Iwarsson, S. (2005). A long-term perspective on person–environment fit and ADL dependence among older Swedish adults. *The Gerontologist, 45,* 327–336.

JAN. (2010). *Workplace accommodations: Low cost, high impact.* Morgantown, WV: Job Accommodation Network.

Judge, T. A., & Bono, J. E. (2001, February). Relationship of core self-evaluations traits—self-esteem, generalized self-efficacy, locus of control, and emotional stability—with job satisfaction and job performance: A meta-analysis. *Journal of Applied Psychology, 86*(1), 80–92.

Judge, T. A., Thoresen, C. J., Bono, J. E., & Patton, G. K. (2001). The job satisfaction-job performance relationship: A qualitative and quantitative review. *Psychological Bulletin, 127,* 376–407.

Judge, T. A., & Watanabe, S. (1993). Another look at the job satisfaction–life satisfaction relationship. *Journal of Applied Psychology, 78*(6), 939–948.

Judge, T. A., & Watanabe, S. (1994). Individual differences in the nature of the relationship between job and life satisfaction. *Journal of Occupational and Organizational Psychology, 67*(2), 101–107.

Kendra, M. A., Weiker, A., Simon, S., Grant, A., & Shullick, D. (1996). Safety concerns affecting delivery of home health care. *Public Health Nursing, 13,* 83–89.

Kochera, A. (2002, March 1). *Falls among older persons and the role of the home: An analysis of cost, incidence and potential savings from home modification.* AARP Public Policy Institute. Retrieved September 23, 2009, from http://www.aarp.org/research/ppi/liv-com/housing/articles/aresearch-import-797-inb49.html

Konrad, T. R. Williams, E. S., Linzer, M., McMurray, J., Pathman, D. E., Gerrity, M., & Schwartz, M. D. (1999). Measuring physician job satisfaction in a changing workplace and a challenging environment. *Medical Care-Philadelphia, 37*(11), 1174–1182.

Kraut, R., Fish, R. S., Root, R. W., & Chalfonte, B. L. (2002). Informal communication in organizations: Form, function and technology. In I. S. Oskamp & S. Spacapan (Eds.), *Human reactions to technology: The Claremont Symposium on Applied Social Psychology.* Beverly Hills, CA: Sage Publications.

LaPlante, M., & Carlson, D. (1996). *Disability in the United States: Prevalence and causes, 1992.* Disability Statistics Report No. 7. Washington, DC: U.S. Department of Education, National Institute on Disability and Rehabilitation Research.

Lau, D. T., Scandrett, K., Jarzebowski, M., Holman, K., & Emanuel, L. (2007). Health-related safety: A framework to address aging in place. *The Gerontologist, 47*(6), 830–837.

Lawler, K. (2001). *Aging in place: Coordinating housing and health care provision for America's growing elderly population.* Cambridge, MA: Joint Center for Housing Studies of Harvard University Neighborhood Reinvestment Corporation.

Lesser, E., & Prusak, L. (1999). *Communities of practice, social capital and organizational knowledge*. Retrieved July 9, 2008, from http://www.providersedge.com/docs/km-articles/Cop_-_Social_Capital_-_Org_k.pdf

Levine, D. (2003). *Universal design New York*. Buffalo, NY: IDEA Publications, Center for Inclusive Design and Environmental Access.

Lightfoot, E., & Lum, T. (2006, January). *An analysis of work accommodation rates for older adults since the implementation of the Americans with Disabilities Act*. Fairfax, VA: Society for Social Work and Research.

Lim, S. (2007). Library informational technology workers: their sense of belonging, role, job autonomy and job satisfaction. *Journal of Academic Librarianship, 33*(4), 492–500.

Lim, S. (2008). Job satisfaction of information technology workers in academic libraries. *Library & Information Science Research, 30*(2), 115–121.

Lustig, D. C., & Strauser, D. R. (2002). The relationship between sense of coherence and career thoughts. *The Career Development Quarterly, 51*(1), 2–11.

Lueg, C. (2001). Where is the action in virtual communities of practice. Retrieved July 9, 2008, from http://www-staff.it.uts.edu.au/~lueg/paper/commdc scw00.pdf

MacDonald-Wilson, K. L., Sally Rogers, E., Massaro, J. M., Lyass, A., & Crean, T. (2002). An investigation of reasonable workplace accommodations for people with psychiatric disabilities: Quantitative findings from a multi-site study. *Community Mental Health Journal, 38*(1), 35–50.

Maisel, J. (2010). Vistability, International Encyclopedia of Rehabilitation, Center for International Rehabilitation Research Information and Exchange. Retrieved April 5, 2010, from http://cirrie.buffalo.edu/encyclopedia/pdf/en/visitability.pdf

Maisel, J. R., Smith, E., & Steinfeld, E. (2008). *Increasing home access: Design for visitability*. AARP Public Policy Institute. Retrieved July 4, 2009, from http://assets.aarp.org/rgcenter/il/2008_14_access.pdf.

Mann, W. C., Ottenbacher, K. J., Fraas, L., Tomita, M., & Granger, C. V. (1999). Effectiveness of assistive technology and environmental interventions in maintaining independence and reducing home care costs for frail elderly: A randomized controlled trial. *Archives of Family Medicine, 8*, 210–217.

Mann, W. C., Hurren, D., Tomita, M., Bengali, M., & Steinfeld, E. (1994). Environmental problems in homes of elders with disabilities. *Occupational Therapy Journal of Research, 14*, 191–211.

Manton, K. G., Corder, L., & Stallard, E. (1993). Changes in the use of personal assistance and special equipment from 1982 to 1989: Results from the 1982–1989 NLTCS. *The Gerontologist, 33*, 168–176.

Marshall, G. W., Michaels, C. E., & Mulki, J. P. (2007). Workplace isolation: Exploring the construct and its measurement. *Psychology & Marketing, 24*(3), 29.

Maslow, A. (1954). *Motivation and personality*. New York, NY: Harper.

McAfee, J. K., & McNaughton, D. (1997a). Transitional outcomes: Job satisfaction of workers with disabilities—Part two: Satisfaction with promotions, pay, co-workers, superision, and work conditions. *Journal of Vocational Rehabilitation, 8*, 243–251.

McAfee, J. K., & McNaughton, D. (1997b). Transitional outcomes: Job satisfaction of workers with disabilities—Part one: General job satisfaction. *Journal of Vocational Rehabilitation, 8*, 135–142.

McFarlin, D. B., Song, J., & Sonntag, M. (1991). Integrating the disabled into the work force: A survey of Fortune 500 company attitudes and practices. *Employee Responsibilities and Rights Journal, 4*(2), 107–123.

McMullin, J. A., & Shuey, K. M. (2006). Ageing, disability and workplace accommodations. *Ageing and Society, 26*, 831–847.

Mendelsohn, S., Edyburn, D. L., Rust, K. L., Schwanke, T. D., & Smith, R. O. (2008). Using assistive technology outcomes research to inform policy related to the employment of individuals with disabilities. *Assistive Technology, 20*(3), 10.

Merriman, C. L. (2010). *Adjunct faculty organizational sense of belonging and affective organizational commitment*. Doctoral dissertation presented to faculty at Old Dominion University.

Moen, P. (2003). Midcourse: Navigating retirement and a new life stage. In J. Mortimer & M. J. Shanahan (Eds.), *Handbook of the life course* (pp. 269–291). New York, NY: Plenum Press.

Mueller, J. L. (1992). *The workplace workbook 2.0*. Chantilly, VA: JL Mueller.

Myers, A., Jensen, R. C., Nestor, D., & Rattiner, J. (1993). Low back injuries among home health aides compared with hospital nursing aides. *Home Health Care Services Quarterly, 14*, 149–155.

National Council on Disability. (2007). *Empowerment for Americans with disabilities: Breaking barriers to careers and full employment*. Washington, DC: Author.

NOD. (2004). *Landmark disability survey finds pervasive disadvantages*. Washington, DC: National Organization on Disability.

Orisatoki, R. O., & Oguntibeju, O. O. (2010). Job satisfaction among selected workers in St Lucia, West Indies. *Scientific Research and Essays, 5*(12), 1436–1441.

OSHA. (1999). The benefits of participating in VVP. OSHA Voluntary Protection Programs. Washington, DC: Occupational Safety and Health Administration.

Osmond, H. (1959). The relationship between architect and psychiatrist. In C. Goshen (Ed.), *Psychiatric architecture*. Washington, DC: American Psychiatric Association.

Oswald, F., Wahl, H.-W., Schilling, O., Nygren, C., Fange, A., Sixsmith, A., Sixsmith, J., Szeman, Z., Tomsone, S., & Iwarsson, S. (2007). Relationships between housing and healthy aging in very old age. *The Gerontologist, 47*, 96–107.

Panko, R. (1992). Managerial communication patterns. *Journal of Organizational Computing, 2*(1), 95–122.

Paul, W. (2003). Workplace inclusion: Persons with disabilities and coworkers working together. *Journal of Vocational Rehabilitation, 18*(2), 131–141.

Pearce, J. L., & Randel, A. E. (2004). Expectations of organizational mobility, workplace social inclusion, and employee job performance. *Journal of Organizational Behavior, 25*(1), 81–98.

Pinquart, M., & Sorensen, S. (2003). Differences between caregivers and noncaregivers in psychological health and physical health: A meta-analysis. *Psychology and Aging, 18*(2), 250–267.

Pitt-Catsouphes, M., & Butterworth, J. (1995). *Different perspectives: Workplace experience with the employment of individuals with disabilities.* Rehabilitation Research and Training Center: Promoting the employment of individuals with disabilities. Institute for Community Inclusion at Children's Hospital. Center on Work and Family at Boston University.

Pynoos, J., Liebig, P., Overton, J., & Calvert, E. (1997). The delivery of home modification and repair services. In S. Lanspery & J. Hyde (Eds.), *Staying put: Adapting the places instead of the people* (pp. 171–191). Amityville, NY: Baywood Publishing.

Pynoos, J., & Nishita, C. M. (2006). *Elders and the right to housing.* In R. Bratt, M. Stone, & C. Hartman (Eds.), *A right to housing: Foundation for a new social agenda.* Philadelphia, PA: Temple University Press.

Pynoos, J., Steinman, B. A., & Nguyen, A. Q. (2010). Environmental assessment and modification as fall-prevention strategies for older adults. *Clinics in Geriatric Medicine, 26*(4), 633–644.

Randel, A. E., & Ranft, A. L. (2007). Motivations to maintain social ties with coworkers: The moderating role of turnover intentions on information exchange. *Group Organization Management, 32*(2), 25.

Rayton, B. A. (2006). Examining the interconnection of job satisfaction and organizational commitment: An application of the bivariate probit model. *International Journal of Human Resource Management, 17*(1), 139–154.

Rix, S. E. (2004). *Aging and work—A view from the United States.* Washington, DC: AARP Public Policy Institute.

Sandqvist, J., & Henriksson, C. (2004). Work functioning: A conceptual framework. *Work, 23*, 147–157.

Sanford, J. A. (2008, June). Future of workplace technology. Presentation at *InterGovernmental Committee on Disability Research State of the Science Conference on Employment of People with Disabilities.* Arlington, VA.

Sanford, J. A., & Milchus, K. L. (2006). Evidence-based practice in workplace accommodations. *Work: A Journal of Prevention, Assessment and Rehabilitation, 27*(4), 329–332.

Sanford, J. A. (2002). Time to get rid of those old gray grab bars and get yourself a shiny new pair. *Alzheimer's Care Quarterly, 3*(1), 26–31.

Sanford, J. A. (2004). In C. Siebert (Ed.), *Home modification practice guideline.* Bethesda, MD: American Occupational Therapy Association.

Sanford, J. A., Echt, K., & Malassigné, P. (1999). An E for *ADAAG*: The case for accessibility guidelines for the elderly based on three studies of toilet transfer. *Journal of Physical and Occupational Therapy in Geriatrics, 16*(3,4), 39–58.

Sanford, J. A., Griffiths, P. M., Richardson, P., Hargraves, K., Butterfield, T., & Hoenig, H. (2006). The effects of in-home rehabilitation on task self-efficacy in mobility impaired adults: A randomized clinical trial. *Journal of American Geriatrics Society, 54,* 1641–1648.

Sanford, J., & Hammel, J. (2006). *Impact of accessibility modifications to the home environment on community living and activity.* Gerontological Society of American Annual Conference, Dallas, TX.

Sanford, J. A., & Megrew, M. B. (1995). An evaluation of grab bars to meet the needs of elderly people. *Assistive Technology, 7*(1), 36–47.

Sanford, J. A., & Megrew, M. B. (1999). Using environmental simulation to measure accessibility for older people. In E. Steinfeld & S. Danford (Eds.), *Measuring enabling environments* (pp. 183–206). New York, NY: Plenum Press.

Schaie, K. W., Wahl, H.-W., Mollenkopf, H., & Oswald, F. (2003). *Aging independently: Living arrangements and mobility.* New York, NY: Springer Publishing.

Schartz, H. A., Hendricks, D. J., & Blanck, P. (2006). Workplace accommodations: Evidence based outcomes. *Work: A Journal of Prevention, Assessment and Rehabilitation, 27*(4), 345–354.

Scheschareg, R. (2005, May). *Gaining access to the $300 billion + consumer out-of-pocket spending market.* Advanced Home Healthcare Products and Services. Intuitive care advisors.

Scherich, D. L. (1996). Job accommodations in the workplace for persons who are deaf or hard of hearing: Current practices and recommendations. *The Journal of Rehabilitation, 62*(2), 27–35.

Schermerhorn, J. R. (2009). *Exploring management.* New York, NY: John Wiley & Sons.

Smith, S. K., Rayer, S., & Smith, E. A. (2008). Aging and disability: Implications for the housing industry and housing policy in the United States. *Journal of the American Planning Association, 74*(3), 289–306.

Shur, L., & Kruse, D. (2002). *Non-standard work arrangements and disability income* (p. 16). Champaign, IL: Disability Research Institute.

Schur, L., Kruse, D. L., Blasi, J. R., & Blanck, P. (2009). Disability disabling in all workplaces? Workplace disparities and corporate culture. *Industrial Relations, 48*(3), 30.

Spector, P. E. (1997). Job satisfaction: Application, assessment, cause and consequences. Thousand Oaks, CA: Sage.

Stoddard, S., Jans, L., Ripple, J., & Kraus, L. (1998). *Chartbook on work and disability in the United States.* An InfoUse Report. Washington, DC: U.S. National Institute on Disability and Rehabilitation Research.

Strong, S. (1998). Meaningful work in supportive environments: Experiences with the recovery process. *American Journal of Occupational Therapy, 52,* 31–38.

Strong, S., & Rebiero, K. (2003). Creating supportive work environments for people with mental illness. In L. Letts, P. Rigby, & D. Stewart (Eds.), *Using environments to enable occupational performance.* Thorofare, NJ: Slack.

Tinetti, M. E., Baker, D., Gallo, W. T., Nanda, A., Charpentier, P., & O'Leary, J. (2002). Evaluation of restorative care vs. usual care for older adults receiving an acute episode of home care. *Journal of the American Medical Association, 287,* 2098–2105.

Truesdale, S., & Steinfeld, E. (2002). *Visit-ability: An approach to universal design in housing.* Buffalo, NY: IDEA Center.

Unger, D., & Kregel, J. (2003). Employers' knowledge and utilization of accommodations. *Work, 21*(1), 5–15.

Uppal, S. (2005). Disability, workplace characteristics and job satisfaction. *International Journal of Manpower, 26*(4), 14.

Vebrugge, L., & Sevak, P. (2002). Use, type and efficacy of assistance for disability. *Journal of Gerontology. Series B. Psychological and Social Sciences, 57,* S366–S379.

Wahl, H. W., Fange, A., Oswald, F., Gitlin, L. N., & Iwarsson, S. (2009). The home environment and disability-related outcomes in aging individuals: What is the empirical evidence? *The Gerontologist, 49*(3), 355–367.

Waldrop, J., & Stern, S. (2003). *Disability status 2000—Census 2000 brief.* Washington, DC: U.S. Census Bureau.

Warr, P. (1999). Well-being and the workplace. In D. Kahneman, E. Deiner, & N. Schwarz (Eds.), *Well-being: The foundations of hedonic psychology* (pp. 392–412). New York, NY: Russell Sage.

Whittaker, S., Frohlich, D., & Daly-Jones, O. (1994). Informal workplace communication: What is it like and how might we support it? *Proceedings of the SIGCHI Conference on Human Factors in Computing Systems: Celebrating Interdependence.* Boston, MA: ACM.

Williams, M., Sabata, D., & Zolna, J. (2006). User needs evaluation of workplace accommodations. *Work: A Journal of Prevention, Assessment and Rehabilitation, 27*(4), 355–362.

Winter-Collins, A., & McDaniel, A. M. (2000). Sense of belonging and new graduate job satisfaction. *Journal of Nurses Staff Development, 16*(3), 103–111.

World Health Organization. (1991, June 9–15). *Action for public health: Sundsvall statement on supportive environments.* Sundsvall, Sweden: Author.

Wrzesniewski, A., McCauley, C., Rozin, P., & Schwartz, B. (1997). Jobs, careers, and callings: People's relations to their work. *Journal of Research in Personality, 31,* 21–33.

Wu, S., & Green A. (2000, October). *Projection of chronic illness prevalence and cost inflation.* Santa Monica, CA: RAND Corporation.

Wylde, M. (1997, May 7). Mod squad. *TeamRehab,* 28–31.

Yang, H., Harris, F., & Sanford, J. A. (2010a). Using research evidence to enhance workplace participation among people with disabilities: Implications for policies and practices. Presentation at *2010 National Association of Rehabilitation Research Training Centers Conference*, Alexandria, VA.

Yang, H., Harris, F., & Sanford, J. A. (2010b). Impact of job accommodations on the participation of employees in the workplace. In *International Conference on Ageing, Disability & Independence 2010*. Newcastle, UK: ICADI.

Yang, H., Harris, F., & Sanford, J. A. (2011). Workplace participation: Development of the Workplace Participation Survey (WPS) and its implications to OT practice. Presentation at the *AOTA 91st Annual Conference*, Philadelphia, PA.

Yeager, P., Kaye, H. S., Reed, M., & Doe, T. M. (2006). Workplace accommodations: Evidence based outcomes. *Work: A Journal of Prevention, Assessment and Rehabilitation, 27*(4), 355–362.

Yelin, E., & Trupin, L. (2003, May). Disability and the characteristics of employment. *Monthly Labor Review, 126*, 20–31.

Yelin, E., Sonneborn, D., & Trupin, L. (2000). The prevalence and impact of accommodations on the employment of persons 51–61 years of age with musculoskeletal conditions. *Arthritis Care Research, 13*(3), 168–176.

Zolna, J., Sabata, D., & Sanford, J. (2008). Accommodations for mobility in the workplace: A comparison of workers with and without wheeled mobility devices. In W. C. Mann (Ed.), *Aging disability and independence* (pp. 131–140). Gainesville, FL: College of Public Health.

Zolna, J. S., Sanford, J. A., Sabata, D., Williams, M., & Goldwaithe, J. (2007). Review of accommodation strategies in the workplace for persons with mobility and dexterity impairments: Application to criteria for universal design. *Technology and Disability, 19*(4), 189–198.

Zwerling, C., Whitten, P. S., Sprince, N., Davis, C. S., Wallace, R., Blanck, P. D., & Heeringa, S. G. (2003). Workplace accommodations for people with disabilities: National Health Interview Survey Disability Supplement, 1994–1995. *Journal of Occupational and Environmental Medicine, 45*(5), 517–525.

PART III

BREAKING DOWN BARRIERS:
ADOPTION OF UNIVERSAL DESIGN
AS A REHABILITATION INTERVENTION

EIGHT

Universal Design as a Rehabilitation Strategy

On the one hand, policy (at the reimbursement level), or lack of it (at the legislative level), bears considerable responsibility for spawning the current system of fragmented services. On the other hand, policy responses to support independent living and home health care, like the system itself, have been piecemeal and fragmented, leaving many people in homes that are unsupportive and in communities that offer them few housing options. This concern is particularly relevant in the current health policy context (Coyte & Young, 1997), where high-tech home care is increasingly seen as a quick solution to budgetary constraints and a growing elderly population.

To break down these barriers, universal design (UD) must be incentivized at all levels from public policy to provider practice and consumer confidence. To accomplish this, we must adopt an *International Classification of Functioning, Disability, and Health* (ICF) social model of disability; medicalize home and work environments; put health back in health, safety, and welfare; provide uniform certification across a variety of professions; and sensitize consumers.

ADOPTING AN ICF MODEL OF DISABILITY

Current U.S. policies reimburse for specialized assistive technology (AT) and accessible design (AD), which are expedient and may "fix" the problem. Yet, even when they have lower initial costs, AT and AD may have greater long-term costs and far less benefits to multiple individuals or society as a whole. To ensure that UD is a viable rehabilitation strategy for aging in place, health care policy needs to abandon outdated the 20th century medical model paradigm of health and activity and adopt a 21st century

ICF paradigm that supports health, activity, and participation as outcomes that are equally important but that have different rehabilitation intervention strategies. Such a paradigm shift will not only incentivize UD but also encourage rehabilitation strategies that provide the best fit for the situation, regardless of whether that is specialized or UD.

MEDICALIZING THE HOME AND WORK ENVIRONMENTS

Depending on the program and the needs, Medicare, Worker's Compensation, Vocational Rehabilitation, and other programs will cover costs for personal assistance, assistive devices, and medical technologies to improve an individual's ability to perform essential tasks in the home or workplace. However, they will not cover the cost of most UD solutions that benefit others or enhance the value of an individual's home, even if it would benefit the individual and save money in the long run. Nonetheless, although rehabilitation service providers strive to provide best-fit solutions for their clients, reimbursement policies that favor caregiver assistance and cookie-cutter AT solutions over universal interventions are restricting the playing field of best-fit solutions. Further, these policies fail to consider important situational and contextual factors, such as impact on the physical and social environment and effectiveness of intervention in the context, preferences, aesthetics, and stigma, that determine the best rehabilitation intervention possible.

Again, using the ICF as a relevant health paradigm, federal policy needs to recognize that the environment, whether it is the home or the workplace, is a health care setting and a legitimate target of rehabilitation interventions. In fact, home health care and short hospital stays in favor of discharge to the home implicitly recognize the home as a de facto health care setting. Unfortunately, there are no reimbursement programs for designing one's home for home health care and in-home rehabilitation that would provide the type of supportive environments that are found in institutional settings. Similarly, the National Institute on Occupational Safety and Health and the Occupational Safety and Health Administration clearly recognize the workplace as an important setting for employee safety and health. Federal policies that acknowledge the importance of supporting ICF constructs of health, activity, and participation in both home and work settings would serve to medicalize these environments and legitimize them as rehabilitation settings. This would not only reconcile policy and practice but would also help to rein in a housing market predicated on a

Peter Pan Policy where no one will ever grow up or ever grow old (Pynoos and Nishita, 2006).

For such a policy to succeed, the various professional organizations that represent physicians, occupational therapists, physical therapists, speech language pathologists, rehabilitation nurses, rehabilitation engineers, social workers, case managers, long-term care planners, and others in rehabilitation need to support and promote UD as a rehabilitation intervention. If, as the ICF suggests, the environment is important in both health treatment and prevention, then one should expect that the professionals responsible for our health and well-being would be aware of, if not somewhat knowledgeable about, these types of interventions. After all, preventative medicine and clinical intervention are dependent on a supportive environment. Although no one expects physicians to prescribe UD any more than they should expect a design expert to prescribe medications, they should at least be knowledgeable enough to recommend UD as a rehabilitation strategy and prescribe a consult with an expert in the area.

PUTTING HEALTH BACK INTO HEALTH, SAFETY, AND WELFARE

Despite the exclusion of UD strategies in local building ordinances, there is a growing movement in the United States and other countries to extend accessibility regulations to private housing. In the United States, there is a growing movement toward visitable housing, which, although still based on access rather than UD, is a step toward broader regulation of private housing.

Visitability has been extended in a number of municipalities in the United States to require or provide tax incentives for basic access for people with lower extremity limitations. Although basic access may enable an inhabitant to access the home and live on the first floor, it does not necessarily ensure that the environment will meet the health and activity needs of individuals who occupy the home. Similar policy changes that require or incentivize UD features, such as curbless showers, bathrooms with a 5-ft turning radius, and wider hallways, through tax breaks or fast-tracked approvals by municipal or state officials are needed to overcome the AD mentality.

CERTIFYING PROVIDERS

Professional organizations should focus on developing practitioner expertise by designing certification programs that promote uniform and accurate assessments, ensure appropriate intervention recommendations, and result in successful and efficacious interventions. However, educating the range of professionals involved in home and work rehabilitation interventions, including health care professionals, social service personnel, and workers in the building industry, will require changes not only at a level of the professional organizations but also at the regulatory level. At the organizational level, it will require a change in the laissez fare policy that acknowledges the need for, but does not proactively apply, a comprehensive program to ensure that professionals are adequately trained. At the regulatory level, it will require change in the way and to whom the Centers for Medicare and Medicaid Services (CMS) provides reimbursement. Although CMS already requires licensure/certification for some services (e.g. licensed occupational therapists can perform functional assessments and certified assistive technology professionals can perform AT assessments), certification for all of the various types of home intervention services (e.g., assessment, medical remodeling, training) need to be included. In addition, certification needs to be more stringent than those currently offered and needs to be designed specifically for the home environment (e.g., neither occupational therapy licensure nor assistive technology professional ensures a knowledge of either a client's housing needs or the home environment). Where CMS leads, private insurers will follow.

SENSITIZING CONSUMERS

When an individual is not familiar with the range of possible home modification solutions or has misperceptions about them, experience using the modifications is often the best way to educate the individual and determine the solution that best meets his or her needs. Although trying out potential solutions is common practice in purchasing most consumer items or even the provision of workplace accommodations for people with disabilities, home modification protocols do not use a similar approach. This finding is not surprising because workplace accommodations are typically small, portable devices (e.g., mouse or keyboard) or computer software (e.g., screen reader) that can easily be transported to and tried out at any worksite. In contrast, UD solutions are often large, not easily transported (e.g., cooktop), have to be installed (e.g., lever door handle), or built on site (e.g., curbless shower). As a result, it is difficult to try out or even see what the interventions will look like in one's home without actually modifying or installing them in the home, which can be a costly, time consuming or intrusive.

Alternatively, demonstration homes have proven to be a popular and effective means to display AT, AD, and UD interventions for the home. They also represent one of the few opportunities where people can actually learn by doing (Mills, Holm & Christenson, 2001). However, demonstration homes are geographically restricted and are typically sold to private individuals, limiting their exposure to a broad audience. In addition, cost and construction limit the scope and innovation of features, whereas liability concerns restrict the public's ability to try out new designs and supportive features. A more effective approach would be to have large home improvement retailers, such as Home Depot or Lowes, set up interactive displays at stores, where consumers could use and compare a variety of products, including those that are UD and those that are not. These displays might not only sensitize and create and awareness of UD among consumers but also create a market demand for it.

Consumer education also needs to demonstrate that UD has value added and produces cost savings. Value added resides in current and future ease of use and convenience, as well as the possible increased price of the residence or workplace at a later point in time. Cost savings will accrue because a household will spend fewer dollars on home modifications or institutionalization and moving to skilled nursing, hospital, or assisted living settings may be delayed or minimized. Similarly, an employer will spend less on accommodations and repeatedly adapting workstations to new employees. Financial savings can also accrue to insurers or government entities that fund or share funding for these health care and life care services.

A comprehensive assessment of affordability has to include a balance between initial costs and building life cycle costs, household lifetime costs, and cost savings, as well as the costs and benefits that are external to a particular circumscribed project. This becomes particularly relevant where project costs are immediately borne by one sector, such as home builders, and benefits are accrued by another or when those benefits are deferred until much later, such as home buyers who are able to age in place. The current lack of consumer demand for homes or work settings with UD features does not easily allow for higher prices that builders would like to charge for them. The builder would prefer that this long-term housing quality be priced into the home at the time of initial sale. That would mean that the universal home or workplace, when compared with homes that had otherwise equivalent but nonuniversal amenities, would command a higher price to the consumer. However, tepid market demand for UD suggests that consumers have not placed a higher value on long-term value of UD.

NINE

Whither Universal Design?

*T*here is a need for spaces, products, and technologies that work better for everyone, fit better in home and work environments and enable inclusion of all individuals. On the one hand, the basic universal design (UD) principles exist to enable better functionality of design in terms of both better activity performance (i.e., works better) and better participation (i.e., integrates better within the social and physical context). On the other hand, disability, health, and housing programs in the United States, operating independently of each other, have imposed a set of similar barriers that make it difficult for individuals with functional limitations to have access to rehabilitation interventions based on these principles.

For individuals with functional limitations and chronic conditions, health, housing, and work environments are inextricably intertwined, and with innovations in design and technology, are likely to become even more so. These interconnections are bolstered by the public health community itself, as embraced by the World Health Organization's *International Classification of Functioning, Disability, and Health* (ICF) model of health, in which the environment is seen as both a therapeutic health care milieu and a prosthetic health and rehabilitation intervention.

Although decisions about the most effective environmental intervention strategy (assistive technology, accessible design, or UD) are contextually determined, UD, which deliberately addresses both activity and participation as means to positive health outcomes, is the intervention that is most compatible with the ICF model. In addition, UD offers the promise of limiting the amount of specialized design that is ultimately needed or warranted. Unfortunately, a variety of interconnected barriers have limited the adoption of universally designed products, technologies, and spaces as environmental interventions. Limited information contributes to a lack of consumer demand; limited demand for services results in few experienced providers and remodelers; inexperienced providers and remodelers use ill-suited government guidelines and standards to produce less than desirable interventions; and small, scattered, little known, and underutilized funding sources produce a patchwork of public service programs and make it hard for low-income households to undertake projects. Consumers are often frustrated by the process of obtaining and making home modifications and discouraged by the results.

The most conspicuous barrier to adoption of UD as a rehabilitation strategy is our policy paradigm that awards specialized technology and personal assistance with limited and calculated benefits over everyday universal design that incorporates the prosthetic outcomes of specialized design, but has the potential for multiple and far-reaching benefits. Although the increased application of UD principles requires changes in consumer and provider behavior, it most glaringly requires fundamental changes in regulatory policy from building and zoning codes to health care reimbursement. This includes allowances in the codes to permit health-related environmental interventions that are necessary for people to age in place and the workplace, as well as changes in reimbursement that recognize and support environmental assessments and interventions as part of discharge planning and continue on an ongoing basis as conditions change and throughout our life span.

One drawback to the acceptance of UD is the lack of evidence of its effectiveness in promoting positive rehabilitation outcomes. In housing, demonstration programs such as the Money Follows the Person (MFP) can provide some of the needed evidence to validate the effectiveness of UD as a viable and valuable rehabilitation strategy. Rather than allocate resources to traditional health and rehabilitation models, the MFP program provides a mechanism for monies to follow the person into the community at levels equitable to those allocated for institutional/nursing home care. In addition, MFP necessitates the coordination of information, supports, services, and funding across systems and the need for consumer direction and control throughout the process.

Although the MFP is demonstrating that the home environment can function in lieu of institutional care, it does not specifically allocate funds for UD, nor does it designate the home as a health care setting. As a result, the MFP program is more of a paradigm adjustment rather than a fundamental change in thinking. As long as housing and health remain separate, decisions about the allocation of monies are driven by bureaucratic rules rather than by the needs individuals. Ultimately, the adoption of UD as a broad-based intervention strategy will require fundamental paradigm shifts in both housing and health that recognize the home environment and everything in it as an integral part of the medical milieu.

A second barrier to acceptance is the cost of UD. Today, UD products and environments are generally more expensive than other everyday consumer products. Typically, that is because universal designed products are designed better, are easier to use, and are more desirable than other products; and frankly, many people are willing to pay for better design. For example, a $300 iPhone is the most popular smart phone, even though many other phones are given away. However, the cost of specialized design for a few individuals is even more expensive. Going back to the case of Kara Lynn, the cost of the $300 iPhone compared to an $8,000 augmentative communication device that did not work as well demonstrates the potentially significant cost savings to both the individual and the American public

Taken to another level, the cost of new UD housing and workplaces or even retrofitting existing spaces with UD modifications that will benefit those who occupy the setting now and those in the future will be small compared with the costs of institutional care or having to repeatedly modify the same environment to meet the activity and/or health needs of each occupant over the life span of the residence or workplace. The question, therefore, is not are the costs of implementing UD as a rehabilitation intervention justified but what are the costs to the individual, the family, the organization, and society of not doing so?

The question is not about the cost of adopting UD as a rehabilitation strategy, but the cost of not doing so.

REFERENCES FOR PART III

Belser, S. H., & Weber, J. A. (1995). Home builders' attitudes and knowledge of aging: The relationship to design for independent living. *Journal of Housing for the Elderly, 11*(2), 123–137.

Coyte, P., & Young, W. (1997). Applied home care research. *International Journal of Health Care Quality Assurance, 10*(1), i–iv.

Davis, S. (1997). *The architecture of affordable housing.* Berkeley, CA: University of California Press.

Gilderbloom, J. L., & Markham, J. P. (1996). Housing modification needs of the disabled elderly: What really matters? *Environment and Behavior, 28*(4), 512–535.

Hyde, J., Talbert, R., & Grayson, P. J. (1997). Fostering adaptive housing: An overview of funding sources, laws and policies. In S. Lanspery & J. Hyde (Eds.), *Staying put: Adapting the places instead of the people* (pp. 223–236). Amityville, NY: Baywood Publishing.

Lau, D. T., Scandrett, K., Jarzebowski, M., Holman, K., & Emanuel, L. (2007). Health-related safety: A framework to address aging in place. *The Gerontologist, 47*(6), 830–837.

Mills, T., Holm, M. B., & Christenson, M. A. (2001). Public opinion of universal design in housing. *Proceedings of the Annual RESNA Conference.* Washington, DC: RESNA Press.

Pynoos, J. (1993, Fall). Toward a national policy on home modification. *Technology and Disability, 2*(4), 1–8.

Pynoos, J., Cohen, E., Davis, L., & Bernhardt, S. (1987). Home modifications: Improvements that extend independence. In V. Regnier & J. Pynoos (Eds.), *Housing the aged: Design directives and policy considerations* (pp. 277–303). New York, NY: Elsevier.

Pynoos, J., Liebig, P., Overton, J., & Calvert, E. (1997). The delivery of home modification and repair services. In S. Lanspery & J. Hyde (Eds.), *Staying put: Adapting the places instead of the people* (pp. 171–191). Amityville, NY: Baywood Publishing.

Pynoos, J., & Nishita, C. M. (2006). Elders and the right to housing. In R. Bratt, M. Stone, & C. Hartman (Eds.), *A right to housing: Foundation for a new social agenda.* Philadelphia, PA: Temple University Press.

Sanford, J. A., Griffiths, P. M., Richardson, P., Hargraves, K., Butterfield, T., & Hoenig, H. (2007). A comparison of televideo and traditional in-home rehabilitation in mobility impaired older adults. *Journal of Physical and Occupational Therapy in Geriatrics, 25*(3), 1–18.

Sohn, J. (1997). *Older consumers' pre- and post-trial perceptions of residential universal design features.* Kansas State University, Manhattan.

Vance, A. Insurers shun multitasking speech devices. *The New York Times,* September 15, 2009.

Wolford, N. (2000). *Universal design standards for single-family housing* (Unpublished doctoral dissertation). Oregon State University, Corvalis.

Index

(Page numbers followed by f and t indicate figures and tables, respectively.)